OPEN HIGHWAYS

BOOK 6

Helen M. Robinson
Marion Monroe
A. Sterl Artley
Charlotte S. Huck
William A. Jenkins
Ira E. Aaron

Linguistic Advisor, W. Cabell Greet

Gage Educational Publishing Limited
TORONTO

Contents

Section One

A Roadeo! What's That? 8

Truck Driver's Dictionary 14

Canadian Car Rallies 17

Chester's New Suit 19
by Eleanor Clymer

Code of Signals for Football Officials 32

An Interview with Russ Jackson 34

What's Going On Here? 42

Christopher Columbus 46
by Stephen Vincent Benét

The Story of Chocolate 48

Happy Election Day 52
by Ethelyn M. Parkinson

Chocolate Fudge 61

Adventures of Thomas O'Toole 63
by D. R. Kearns

The King and the Cats 70
Italian Folk Tale Retold by Nancy Ford

The Mysterious Cat 76
by Vachel Lindsay

Section Two

The Voyageurs.................................. 78
by Nathan Dreskin

The Great Canadian Canoe Race................. 83
by Nathan Dreskin

En roulant ma boule........................... 95

The King's Contest............................ 98
by James Holding

The Adventures of Suzy Sherlock................ 105
by Arlene Hale

How Good a Witness Would You Be?............ 113

The Mad Dog................................. 115
by Gay W. Holland

Louis Pasteur................................ 125

Cars of Yesterday............................. 130

Heroic Years of the Automobile................. 139
by Arthur R. Railton

First "Fill 'Er Up!" Stations..................... 146

Section Three

Bluey....................................... 150
by Irene Hilton

Locating Information.......................... 166

Animals of Australia.......................... 167

Christmas Day Weather........................ 170

Bottle Barometer............................. 173

The Blue Stone............................... 174
by Joy Cuffe

Space....................................... 183

Are There Men on Mars?...................... 188

Men in Space................................ 190

Orbiting English.............................. 193

More Orbiting English......................... 194

An Adventure with the Gods................... 195
by Catharine F. Sellew

Like Knights of Old........................... 210

Arthur Becomes King.......................... 212
    adapted by William Kottmeyer
Armor and Weapons of Long Ago................ 222

Section Four

Terry's Troubles.............................. 226
    by Joan M. Lexau
Something to Sing About....................... 242
    by Oscar Brand
The City Enforces............................ 254
    W. W. E. Ross
The Case of the Sensational Scent................ 256
    by Robert McCloskey
The Game of Seven Errors...................... 276
Really?....................................... 277
A Dream Come True.......................... 279
    by Kathryn Kilby Borland and Helen Ross Speicher
The RCMP.................................... 290
Why Fingerprint Identification?.................. 297
Fingerprint Yourself.......................... 297

Section Five

Twenty Minutes to Zero........................ 302
    by Leland G. Griffin
A Tool of Demolition........................... 313
Miracle over the Ruhr......................... 314
The Escape.................................... 320
    by Katherine B. Shippen
Dog Paratroopers.............................. 328
Dog Daze..................................... 334
Sidelights on Aviation......................... 335
    by Kevin V. Brown
What Makes a Jet Plane Work?.................. 336
A Spear for Omar.............................. 338
    by Heddy Rado
Adventuring Underwater....................... 350

Elephants!...................................... 357
  by Frank Buck
Animals Around the World...................... 374
Riddles Around the World...................... 376
  by Joseph Leeming

Burma Boy............................... 379
  by Willis Lindquist

Pronunciations................................ 382
Runaway Elephant............................. 383
Oo Yan's Plan................................ 388
Jungle Dawn.................................. 393
Charge of the Wounded Tiger.................. 399
Haji Meets the Great Elephant................ 404
Banished..................................... 412
A Warning from the North..................... 419
Secret of the Little Temple Bell.............. 424
Wild Elephant Raid........................... 434
Majda Koom's Battle with Haji................ 443

Answers................................. 450

Glossary................................. 454

Section One

A Roadeo! What's That?

By the end of this article you will be able to tell how a Roadeo got its name.

Here are men who will try their skill at a Roadeo.

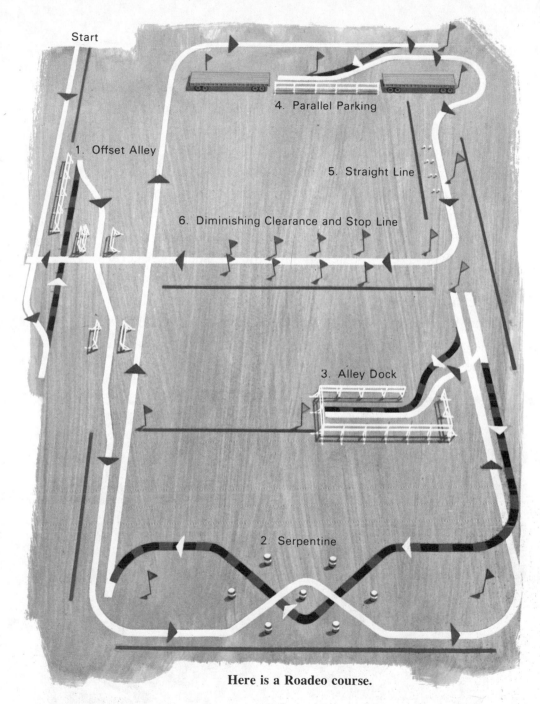

Start

1. Offset Alley

4. Parallel Parking

5. Straight Line

6. Diminishing Clearance and Stop Line

3. Alley Dock

2. Serpentine

Here is a Roadeo course.

Men who take part in Roadeos are truck drivers. They drive many different kinds of trucks. A winner is chosen for each kind. Drivers handle trucks with as much skill as cowboys handle horses.

A truck driver cannot be in a Roadeo if he has had an accident during the past year. This is true even if the only accident he had was not his fault.

Drivers first show that they can check a truck to see that it is in good, safe running condition. Each driver is given a truck he has never seen. Several things have been done to the truck to put it out of perfect running order. Maybe a tail light is out. Maybe the horn won't work. Maybe the rear-view mirrors have been moved. A driver must find the things that need to be fixed.

Drivers do an offset alley test. They guide trucks through tight places without stopping or backing up.

For the serpentine test they wind in and out between barrels. They go through frontward. Later they back through.

In another test a driver must back his truck up to an alley dock. He can use only rear-view mirrors in guiding the truck. He must stop with the tail gate of the truck not more than six inches from the loading platform. But the truck must not touch the dock.

Parking a truck at a curb between two other trucks is not easy. The right wheels must be six inches or less from the curb. The driver loses all the points for this test if he touches the curb. He also loses the points if he touches either of the other trucks.

For the straight line test, two rows of rubber balls on tees are set up. A driver must guide the wheels of his truck between the rows without touching the balls. The rows are so close together that there are only two inches to spare. The balls bounce away at the slightest touch.

Roadeos are held every year in many cities of the United States and Canada. Maybe you will see one someday.

Truck Drivers' Dictionary

Soon after 1900, people began to travel in "horse-less carriages." About 1910 someone got the idea of making "horseless wagons," or trucks, to haul things.

Over the years words have been borrowed or made up to mean special things about trucks and trucking. One driver in the picture below is talking to the other.

There we were. One fellow bareback. One dusting along with a load of post holes. I was last with a yard mule. We saw some bolognas a fellow had dropped. So we put a circle of pots around them.

The man and woman do not know what the driver means. Do you?

These six definitions and pictures show what the
truck driver who is talking on the opposite page
really means.

bareback: tractor without its semitrailer.

yard mule: small tractor used to move
semitrailers around at a truck terminal yard.

bolognas: tires.

load of post holes: empty truck.

dusting: car or truck moving with one
wheel off the pavement and throwing up a
cloud of dust.

pots: flares placed on a highway to warn
other motorists of danger.

On the next page there are four more definitions
that might be in a truck drivers' dictionary.

Can you match each of the terms below with two different pictures? One picture will show what a term means to truck drivers. The other picture will show what the term might mean to someone else.

the Hound: Greyhound bus.

peanut wagon: small tractor pulling a large trailer.

push water: gasoline.

peach picker: a very high cab-over-engine tractor.

Have you heard?

Q. If a policeman saw a truck driver go down a one-way street the wrong way and stop beside a fire hydrant, why didn't the policeman give the driver a ticket?

A. Because the truck driver was walking.

16

Canadian Car Rallies

Car rallies have been popular in
Europe for a long time. About 1954
they became popular in Canada.
Any person who is a good driver can
take part. The driver must be willing
to follow the rules of the rally. Each
rally has a definite route that cars
must follow. Some routes are very
long, for example, the 4000-mile
route from Montreal to Toronto.
Some are shorter but more dangerous, for example, the winding route
through the Caribou mountains.
Every route challenges car and
driver.

Before the rally starts, the driver
gets a sheet of instructions. This
tells him the time he is to be at the
starting point. It tells him how fast
he is to travel. It tells him when
and where he can stop to sleep. It
also tells him he must carry emergency supplies such as a first-aid
kit, a fire extinguisher, flares, and a
tow rope.

Luckily, the driver does not have
to handle emergencies by himself.
He is allowed to take a navigator

with him. The navigator might be his best friend, his wife, or even his grandmother. The navigator is expected to check the road maps, the road signs, and the speed. He has a compass, a stop watch, and other instruments to help him. He also looks for bears and moose that might block the road. He may even have to sing to keep the driver awake. In some rallies the driver has to drive for as long as twenty-two hours without stopping.

To make sure the driver follows instructions there are check points all along the route. The driver is expected to pass each check point at the exact time stated on his instruction sheet. If he arrives a minute early or late, he loses points. More points are lost for each additional minute of error. Imagine what a blizzard or flat tire might do to his score! There were 61 check points in the 1970 International Canadian Winter Rally. The cars went 1117.17 miles around Ontario and Quebec. One driver lost 7659 points. Three tied for first place. They didn't lose a *single point!*

Chester's New Suit

by ELEANOR CLYMER

Shopping Is Not Bad

It was Saturday, and it was a beautiful fall day. Chester Basset woke up early and looked outside.

"Boy, oh, boy!" he said to himself. "Football weather!"

Chester was very fond of football. He wasn't so good at it because he hadn't had much practice. A football was a hard thing to catch because of its funny shape. If you dropped it, it didn't roll. Instead, it went bounding away in some strange direction unless you threw yourself down on it and stopped it.

Chester practised as much as he could. He practised with his friend Joe Burton, who lived across the street, and with his friend Sam Cole, who lived next door. They did a lot of passing and kicking and running with the ball.

19

Reprinted by permission of Dodd, Mead & Company from *Chester* by Eleanor Clymer. Copyright 1954 by Eleanor Clymer.

But today Chester and Joe and Sam were going to be in a real game with some other boys who were pretty good players. Chester hoped he would do so well that he would be asked to play often.

He had thought for a long while that if he had a football uniform, or at least a helmet, he would play better. He had asked his mother plenty of times, but she always said they couldn't afford it.

Now he pulled on his oldest jeans and sweat shirt. He looked at himself in the mirror and thought how handsome he would be in a uniform, or at least a helmet. Then he ran downstairs.

His mother and his big sister were in the kitchen.

"May I have my breakfast early?" Chester asked. "I have to play football."

"Breakfast is ready," said his mother. "But you can't play football. We're going downtown to shop. Penelope needs a new dress. You need a new suit."

"Suit! Can I have a football suit?" said Chester.

"No, dear," said his mother. "You need a good suit to wear when we go visiting."

Chester didn't want a good suit, and he didn't want to visit.

"I don't need a suit," he said.

"Yes, you do," said his sister Penelope. "You look terrible in those jeans."

"If I had a football uniform, I would look better," said Chester.

"I can't afford a football suit," said his mother. "We've talked about that before. Remember?"

"Can I at least have a helmet?" Chester asked.

"No, dear," said his mother.

"Well, will we get back home so that I can play in the football game today?" asked Chester.

"I don't know," said his mother. "We'll do the best we can. But I can't promise."

Soon after breakfast they set out for the stores. First there was a long bus ride. If Chester hadn't wanted to play football, he wouldn't have minded that part at all. His mother had let him buy two chocolate bars and a comic book.

When they got to the store, they went to the boys' department, where they found a dark-blue suit that Chester's mother liked. Chester didn't care how it looked. If his mother was pleased, he was satisfied.

Right in the middle of the floor was a figure of a boy in a gorgeous red-and-blue football uniform with a helmet to match. Chester wished that his mother would see how handsome the outfit looked. But she didn't even glance at it. She paid for his suit, and the man wrapped it and handed Chester the package.

"Here you are, son," he said.

Chester didn't know why strangers always called him son. But if they wanted to, it was OK with him.

Up to now, he thought, shopping hadn't been bad. Maybe he'd get home in time to play in the game.

They got on the escalator and went up a couple of floors to the high-school girls' department.

On the way they passed a display of games and toys. Chester would have liked to stop and look.

"Can't I wait for you here?" he asked.

"No, you come along. I don't want to lose you," said his mother.

So they went to get Penelope's dress. Penelope cared very much how her dress looked. It seemed as if she had to try on every dress in the store. She even had to try on the ones she didn't like, to be sure she didn't like them.

"Aw, hurry up," Chester muttered. "Let's get out of here."

Penelope said, "Mother! Make him behave!"

It Gets Worse

There was a customer not far from them, a stout lady with a fur coat and a little bit of a dog on a leash. She was buying a dress for her granddaughter, and she didn't know what size to get.

She made the saleslady get out every dress, and she held each one up and said, "I think she is bigger than this." Or she said, "No, she's smaller."

Finally she said, "That boy is just her size." And she came over to Chester and held the dress up against him.

Chester was horrified. Nobody had ever done such a thing to him before.

"No, this is too big," said the lady. "Wait here, young man, till I get a smaller size."

Chester wasn't going to wait. He was going to get out of there before she came back. The next thing he knew she would make him put the dress on!

His mother and Penelope had gone into a dressing room. He couldn't go in after them, and he couldn't yell. He looked around to see where he could hide. Over at the side of the room he saw some racks of dresses. They were evening dresses or something. Anyway, they were pretty long. Chester hurried over and got down on his knees and crawled underneath. He was hidden. He sat there with the dresses hanging over his head. He pulled out his comic book and read it and chewed a chocolate bar. He was safe.

He must have been sitting there for ten minutes when he saw something moving among the dresses. He was scared. Maybe a clerk had seen him and would pull him out and take him to the store manager for eating chocolate there. But no! The dresses parted, and he saw the stout lady's dog.

"Oh!" Chester whispered. "So you got away from her, too!"

The little dog sat beside Chester. The dog had something in his mouth. It looked like an old piece of leather. He put it down and chewed it. Then he picked it up and shook it. He was having lots of fun. Chester would have liked to play with the dog, but he thought it would make too much noise. So he went on reading.

Pretty soon there *was* a noise. Across the floor someone was yelling, "My money is gone! Someone has taken my purse! Where is it?"

Another voice said, "Don't get excited, madam. You must have dropped it. We'll find it."

"No, we won't," yelled the first voice. It was the stout lady. "Somebody must have taken it. My bag was open, and it was taken out."

Then a man's voice asked, "How much money was in your purse?"

"Over fifty dollars!" screamed the lady.

Everybody was getting very much excited. Chester peeped out. More people were coming. They were crawling around on the floor, looking. The manager was very upset. Chester didn't know it, but the lady was the mother of the store's owner.

Suddenly Chester looked at the little dog. He was sitting there with the old piece of leather between his paws.

"Why, that's a purse you've got," said Chester. "Is that what all the yelling is about?"

Chester reached out to take the purse away, but the dog growled. Chester didn't know what to do. He ought to ask the lady if that was her purse. But if he came out, she might try more dresses on him. And if he took the wallet away, the dog might bite him. Still, it wouldn't be right to sit and do nothing. He jumped up, knocking several dresses off the rack. He grabbed the dog's leash and dragged him toward the lady. The dog held on to the wallet.

"Is this it?" Chester asked.

Everybody turned and stared at him. The lady was very angry. "Young man!" she said. "What are you doing with my dog?"

"I was hiding," said Chester. "The dog found me. He was chewing on this wallet. Is it yours?"

The lady got even madder. "Of course it is," she cried. "How did it get there? Who took it? I'll call the police!"

"Excuse me, ma'am," said the manager. "But it seems your own dog took it. It must have fallen out of your bag. Why were you hiding, boy?"

Chester's face got very red. "I—I didn't want her to try dresses on me," he mumbled. Everybody laughed, and he got even redder.

The lady picked up the dog. She put the purse in her bag and snapped it shut. Then she walked out.

Chester's mother and Penelope had arrived by now with Penelope's new dress.

"Chester! What have you been up to?" demanded his mother.

"Nothing," said Chester. "I was hiding under those dresses——"

"Under the dresses!" his mother said. "I do hope you haven't spoiled any of them."

"Excuse me," said the manager. "Please don't scold him. He did us a big favor. The lady was quite excited because she thought her wallet had been stolen. This boy deserves a reward. Just what would you like to have, young fellow?"

"Me? A reward?" said Chester. "Oh, boy! Could I—— Do you think I could have a football helmet?" He thought it was OK to ask for that.

"A helmet! You may have a whole uniform!" said the manager. "Come with me."

He led the way to the boys' department. Chester's mother and sister came along, carrying the packages.

"See that this boy gets a football uniform that fits him," he told the clerk. "It is a gift from the store. What color would you like to have, young man?"

Chester said, "A red-and-blue one like that."

The clerk brought out a uniform.

"Boy, oh, boy!" Chester whispered as he tried it on. He could hardly believe his luck. He looked in the mirror. He wouldn't have known himself.

For once his sister Penelope had nothing to say. She just stared at him.

"Now," said the manager, "is there anything else you would like, young man?"

"Yes," said Chester. He looked at the big clock on the wall. It was one o'clock.

"What is it?" asked the man.

"I wish that we could go home right away," said Chester. "Then I could get into the game."

The man turned to Chester's mother. "Madam," he said, "this is the first time I have ever asked a customer to go home. But could you see that this boy gets to the game?"

Chester's mother laughed. "I guess I can," she said. "Now that he has the suit, he really ought to get some use out of it."

Cartoon adapted from *Action Time* magazine, 1963, Vol. 2, No. 2. By permission of Edwards & Deutsch Lithographing Company.

Books to Read

CHRISTOPHER, MATT. *Break for the Basket.*
Little, 1960.

Story of a shy boy who finds it very hard to make friends. This is also the story of fast basketball.

NEIGOFF, MIKE. *Nine Make the Team.*
Whitman, A., 1963.

Boys who have been Little League stars sign up for the Junior High team. They find out baseball is different under tough Coach Harris. In a practice game the catcher calls for a fast ball, but the pitcher throws a curve. The coach suspends him. Is this fair?

NEIGOFF, MIKE. *Smiley Sherman, Substitute.*
Whitman, A., 1964.

When Smiley went out for the freshman football team, he was faced with a question and a mystery. Question: Can an athlete be a good winner and a good loser at the same time? Mystery: Why had his father never told him he was an all-American?

PHILLIPS, MAURICE. *Lightning on Ice.*
Doubleday, 1963. (Signal Book)

Kim Morgan was a sophomore and a runt, but he made the high-school hockey team. He thought his troubles were over, but they were just beginning.

Code of Signals for Football Officials

At major Canadian football games there are five field officials and five side-line officials. The field officials are the Referee, Line Umpire, Back Umpire, Head Linesman, and Field Judge. The side-line officials are the Downsman, two Yardsmen, the Timekeeper, and the Scorer. The signals shown on these two pages are used by the officials.

FIRST DOWN
Arms at right angles.

SECOND DOWN
Hands upright at shoulder level.

THIRD DOWN
Arms crossed at chin level.

TOUCHDOWN OR FIELD GOAL
Both arms extended above head.

SAFETY TOUCH
Hands together above head.

SINGLE POINT
One arm extended above head.

Notice that some of the signals look pretty much alike. For example, the signal for a "First Down" and the signal for a "Single Point" might be mixed up by someone who was not watching carefully.

OFFSIDE
Hands on hips.

NO YARDS ON KICK
Arms folded.

INTERFERENCE
Pushing forward from shoulders.

ROUGH PLAY
Either arm extended sideways.

BLOCKING FROM REAR
Striking back of knee.

CONTACTING KICKER
Raising and touching lower leg.

INCOMPLETE PASS
Shifting arms in horizontal plane.

PENALTY DECLINED
Shifting arms at knee level.

REQUEST FOR MEASURE
Underhand lifting motion.

If you do not know what all the football terms on these pages mean, you can find out by looking in a football rule book. Or you might ask a football coach or player to tell you what they mean.

An Interview with Russ Jackson

For a number of years, Russ Jackson played the first string, or regular, quarterback with the Ottawa Rough Riders football team. Many sports writers consider Russ, who was born in Hamilton, Ontario, to be the finest player who has ever played Canadian football. By the time he retired at the end of 1969, he had won an unprecedented number of major awards for his ability in football.

In 1963, 1966, and 1969, Russ won the major Schenley Award, which is given to the most outstanding player in Canadian football. Four times, between 1959 and 1969, he won the second Schenley Award, which is given to the most outstanding Canadian player in Canadian football. In his final year of football Russ was named Canadian Athlete of the Year, and also won the Lou Marsh Trophy, the Ontario Jaycee Award, and a medal of service of the Order of Canada. In his final football game, the 1969 Grey Cup game, he was named the most outstanding athlete and the most valuable player on the Ottawa team.

Along with his professional football career, Russ worked at an equally demanding second career, that of teaching. In his third year as a mathematics teacher at Ottawa's Rideau High School, he was made head of the department. In 1966 he became vice-principal of Sir John A. Macdonald High School, the position which he held when he retired from football in 1969.

In the following interview, Russ tells how he got started on his two careers, and explains why he was a success at both of them.

34

Have you always been interested in athletics, Russ?

Since I was eight or nine, I've taken part in every sport I could. In high school, I played football, basketball, hockey, and baseball. I used to prefer baseball to football. In fact I wanted to be a baseball pro. When I was sixteen, I even had a tryout with a New York Yankees farm team.

What made you decide against pro baseball?

There were two reasons. One, I would have had to give up my education in order to play baseball, and I liked school too much to do that. And two, the American boys were twice as good as I was.

So you began to play more football?

Yes. In my fourth year at high school, I joined the junior team and became quarterback. That was the first time I'd played organized football. Before that I had just played with the other guys in pick-up games after school.

Russ Jackson with the Schenley Award given to the most outstanding player in Canadian football. Russ won this award in 1963, 1966, and 1969.

Do you think that playing pick-up football, without a coach, helps a boy to become a better player?

Yes, I do. In preparing for a football career — or any career as a professional athlete — a young guy has to work out a lot on his own. Coaches just don't have time to develop every player individually. Besides, no one can tell you how to throw a ball. Everybody throws it differently. To learn to do it well, you have to get out and practise on your own.

Were you big and hefty as a teenager?

No. Until the summer I was sixteen, I was quite short, about five three. I was very broad through the chest and shoulders, though. Then suddenly I grew six or seven inches. Before that my parents were afraid I'd get hurt if I played on a football team. But after I'd grown, they figured I could take care of myself. When I decided to join the team, they didn't object very much.

Is there any place for small players in football?

Definitely, and especially in high school and college ball. The game is changing, with more emphasis on skill. As it changes, it means that brains become more important to the game than heavy muscles. There are quite a few light-weight players in Canadian ball today.

So you don't think a kid who really wants to play football, but isn't big or strong, should give up?

Of course not. Will power and hard work have a lot to do with someone's success. It's really wanting something that makes the difference — that's true off the football field as well as on it.

Were there any big thrills when you played high-school ball?

Because of my age, I was placed in the junior team during the regular season, but when the playoffs and the Red Feather game (a charity game which has the top eight school teams in Ontario competing) arrived, I was shifted to the senior team. I felt really great about being good enough to make the playoffs.

When you graduated from high school, you went on to play football in university?

Yes.

Did you have much trouble with your school work when you took part in so many sports?

I had no trouble at all. I think playing at a sport motivates you to get high marks. You have to work harder at your schoolwork if you are participating in a sport. Your time is more valuable to you, and you use it more wisely. Both the studying and the playing seem to mean more, somchow.

You went to McMaster University in your home town of Hamilton, Ontario. Why didn't you go to a university that had a better-known football team?

Lack of money was the main reason. I had none, and my folks weren't well off. If I had gone to an out-of-town university, I'd have ended up owing between $5000 and $10,000 when I graduated. I didn't want that. As it was, I lived three blocks from the university. Besides, McMaster had an excellent Maths and Physics course, and Math was my great interest next to football.

You got A's in your courses all the way through university and graduated with an Honors Bachelor of Science degree. You could easily have continued on to get other degrees. Why didn't you?

I had to make a choice — either to stay in university and forget about football or have a football career and use my math training somewhere else. Teaching was the answer — I could teach mathematics in high school and still play professional football. I've no regrets about my choice. I've had the best of both worlds.

How did you get into professional football?

Well, the scouts for the professional football teams attend university games to find out who are the good players. They sign up the players that are any good. I nearly went to Vancouver, but at the last minute they took another player, and Ottawa took me.

Were you glad to join the Ottawa Rough Riders?

I thought I wanted to go with the Hamilton Tiger Cats, but Ottawa was the team that had taken me. So that was that. As it turned out, it was for the best, anyway. I might have been warming a bench with Hamilton, the way home-town players often do.

Did you find it difficult combining two careers, one as a teacher and another as a football player?

Not at all. Surprising as it seems, football took me away from the school very little. Most games were on weekends; practices were after school hours. I lost a few days a season when we were playing out west. I was very well organized so that I didn't waste any time. I guess that was easy for me because of my mathematical mind.

Russ Jackson carries the ball for Ottawa Rough Riders.

Does coming into the classroom as a well-known public figure present any problem?

In the football world, I was Russ Jackson the football player, but in the school, I was Mr. Jackson the mathematics teacher. I never discussed football in the classroom, or even in the staff room, any more than I talked about teaching while on a football assignment. They were separate parts of my life.

Were the kids fans of Russ Jackson the football player?

I don't really know. As I say, there was very little reference to football in school. But I do know that each time we played in the Grey Cup, the school sent me a good-luck telegram with the name of nearly every kid in the school attached. I was very touched by this.

What are some other highlights of your football career?

Well, the biggest thrill surely has to be three times winning two Schenley Awards in one year. It happened in 1963, in 1966, and again in 1969. Those years I got both the award for being the most outstanding player in Canadian football and for being the best Canadian player. I was really surprised to get them more than once. Getting the Canadian Athlete of the Year Award in 1969 was a thrill, too.

How much did your training in mathematics help when you were on the field?

Not any more than training in other subjects. It helped me to pick out weaknesses in the opposing team's defence, and to figure out strategy to break their defence down.

Why do you think you were such a good quarterback?

A quarterback has to be a good leader. Basically, he must be able to establish authority over the other players. I've seen good quarterbacks who had great ability as players but who weren't sure of themselves as leaders. The other players sensed this. I think my voice helped me. I've got a good commanding voice. When I gave a player an instruction, he followed it.

Do you use the authoritative voice in the classroom as well?

As a matter of fact, yes. I have a no-nonsense style of teaching. I find it's the most effective way for me.

Would you ever like to coach a team?

Never. You'd think a quarterback would be the most logical one to go on to coaching. After all, he has to know more than any other player about football and football strategy. But coaching is above all a teaching job, and I already have a full-time job doing that. *Playing* football gave me a challenge and a different second career. Coaching would be too much like what I'm already doing all week long. Besides, my real interest in football was playing the game. When I decided to stop playing pro ball, I was willing to leave the game.

What about teaching? Will you continue on there?

One way or another, I'll always be involved in education. Even if I leave teaching and go into, say, politics, my concern will be with education. That is the most challenging field of all.

Thank you Russ, for taking time to talk with us. Best wishes for your future career, wherever it leads you.

Students and staff express approval of teacher Russ Jackson's accomplishments in football.

What's Going On Here?

On the next three pages are ten pictures that have appeared in the sports sections of newspapers. As you look at each picture, try to name the sport that is shown.

A

B

C

Photographs A, D, E, G, H, I, and J from Associated Press, photographs B and F from Wheeler Newspaper Syndicate, and photograph C from United Press International.

D

E

F

G

43

H

I

J

On page 45 are parts of ten different news stories that have appeared in the sports sections of papers. Read each item. Look for a word clue to tell you what sport the item is about.

1. He took a healthy cut at the ball, but missed.

2. A pair of baskets gave North a 6-5 lead.

3. Sweden's entry sent his serves sizzling over the net.

4. AUSTRALIAN CRAWL 100 Yards in 1 Minute and .4 Seconds

5. Arizona State College coed watches her par putt roll toward the cup.

6. Player follows through with his approach and watches the ball roll on its way down the alley.

7. Big Eight Meet 300-Yard High Hurdles

8. Australia's champion shot six arrows into a six-inch circle from a distance of 90 feet, using a bow of 28-pound strength.

9. The Danish entry breezed along the waters of Tampa Bay in the World Flying Dutchman Championship race.

10. LEAFS WON 2-1 Defensive Goalie Tries to Knock Puck Out of Way

Now can you match each item above with a picture on page 42, 43, or 44? Match the numeral before the item with the letter by the picture. For example, 1 and D are the same sport—baseball. The words *healthy cut* might tell you that the sport is baseball. The numeral 7 and the letter A are the same sport—track. The words *high hurdles* tell you for sure that the sport is track.

Write all your answers on a piece of paper. Be sure to name each sport and clue you found.

Christopher Columbus
1446?-1506
by STEPHEN VINCENT BENÉT

There are lots of queer things that discoverers do
But his was the queerest, I swear.
He discovered our country in One Four Nine Two
By thinking it couldn't be there.

It wasn't his folly, it wasn't his fault,
For the very best maps of the day
Showed nothing but water, extensive and salt,
On the West, between Spain and Bombay.

There were monsters, of course, every watery mile,
Great krakens with blubbery lips
And sea-serpents smiling a crocodile-smile
As they waited for poor little ships.

There were whirlpools and maelstroms, without any doubt
And tornadoes of lava and ink.
(Which, as nobody yet had been there to find out,
Seems a little bit odd, don't you think?)

But Columbus was bold and Columbus set sail
(Thanks to Queen Isabella, her pelf),
For he said "Though there may be both monster and gale,
I'd like to find out for myself."

46

From *A Book of Americans* by Rosemary and Stephen Vincent Benét. Holt, Rinehart and Winston, Inc. Copyright 1933 by Stephen Vincent Benét. Copyright renewed 1961 by Rosemary Carr Benét. Reprinted by permission of Brandt & Brandt.

And he sailed and he sailed and he *sailed* and he SAILED,
Though his crew would have gladly turned round
And, morning and evening, distressfully wailed
"This is running things into the ground!"

But he paid no attention to protest or squall,
This obstinate son of the mast,
And so, in the end, he discovered us all,
Remarking, "Here's India, at last!"

He didn't intend it, he meant to heave to
At Calcutta, Rangoon or Shanghai,
There are many queer things that discoverers do.
But his was the queerest. Oh my!

The Story of Chocolate

WHEN Columbus returned to Spain after discovering America, he brought back many treasures to the king. Among them were some dried-up, brown beans.

What strange beans! Surely, they are not worth much. The gold and jewels are more valuable to Spain.

IN 1519 Hernando Cortés was in Mexico. The Aztec Indians treated him like a god. He was often served a "drink of the gods," called chocolatl.

This drink is cold and bitter. If it were heated and had sugar in it, I might like it.

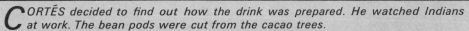

ORTÉS decided to find out how the drink was prepared. He watched Indians at work. The bean pods were cut from the cacao trees.

THEN the beans were taken from the pods, washed, and roasted. The roasted beans were ground together with herbs and spices. And then water was added to make a paste.

THE Spaniards planted the beans, and for 100 years they alone knew the secret of growing cacao and making the chocolate drink that everyone liked. THE new drink was mixed with milk and cinnamon and served hot. It became a favorite all over Europe.

SOMETIME in the 1600's, Chocolate Houses opened in England. They became meeting places for famous and wealthy people.

IN 1876 a Swiss named Daniel Peter mixed milk with chocolate powder and let it get hard.

This is something new. I'll call it milk chocolate.

HE also made the smooth cream fondant chocolate that is used in candy today.

This chocolate is good enough to eat!

WHAT was once a drink only for gods is now one of the most popular foods in America. In fact, chocolate is eaten and used in cooking all over the world today. Many things have been made from chocolate.

WHATEVER is done with chocolate in the years to come, the special taste will remain—the taste that won the name "drink of the gods."

51

Happy Election Day

by ETHELYN M. PARKINSON

Mrs. Parkinson has written this story in the first person. You will soon find out whether she wrote about something that happened to her or whether she is pretending to be someone else.

Monday

In Miss Coppersmith's sixth-grade room we have class officers. Sixteen girls and fifteen boys were present when we voted.

Florence Importance Whipp is President. I, Jeffrey J. Thorne, am Vice-President. Florence says she voted for me so that she could give me orders.

Julie Hubbard is Secretary, which is OK. Boys do not care to write dear little thank-you letters.

Bruce Hubbard was elected Sergeant-at-Arms. He is Julie Hubbard's cousin, so some girls voted for him.

Today Miss Coppersmith made an announcement. "Boys and girls, Bruce moved out of town Saturday. We are very sorry to lose our Sergeant-at-Arms, and of course, we must elect a new one."

I am a fast thinker. I jumped up. I said, "I wish to nominate Joybells Walker. I mean my good friend, Honest Hugo Walker."

"I second the nomination!" said Charlie Cinnamon. "All in favor——"

"Wait, wait!" Miss Coppersmith said. She was laughing. "Not so fast, boys! Sergeant-at-Arms is a very important office!"

53

That is true. The Sergeant-at-Arms is like a base-ball umpire. He decides when the rules are broken. Sometimes, for punishment, we have to stay in at recess. Sometimes we do extra lessons. For very bad things we have to go to the office. The Sergeant-at-Arms goes along to tell the principal what we did.

Miss Coppersmith said, "Let's think this over for a while and nominate two candidates. Then we will have a campaign. The candidates will tell what they will do, if elected. Everyone will decide which candidate to vote for. Thursday will be election day."

So at recess Freddie Fountain said, "The girls will nominate Gorgeous Gloria Jones. If she is elected, she will tell on the boys. If a girl breaks a rule, Gloria will be looking the other way."

"Boys are better," Charlie said. "Bruce was a good Sergeant-at-Arms. We will elect Joybells, but we have lots of time. Let's play ball."

Monday is the older boys' day to have the football end of the playground. So we played baseball.

"We need another man," Freddie said. "Hey, Petrina! Petrina Bronson!"

When we need another man, we get Petrina. She is a good player for a girl. When she is not playing ball, she helps the first-graders play games. Our gym teacher, Mr. Dollman, says she is his right-hand man.

"Come on, Petrina!" Freddie called. "You are on my team!"

"I'll be there in time to bat!" Petrina yelled. She hates to leave the first-graders by themselves.

Charlie struck Freddie out. Then I batted next. When Petrina came to play, Joybells was yelling, "Strike three! You're out, Jeff!"

"Cheat! Cheat!" I yelled. "That was no strike!"

Joybells howled, "You're out!"

"That was no strike!" Freddie yelled.

"Wait a minute!" Petrina said. She walked up to me and smiled. "Jeffrey!" she said. "I saw that. It was a strike. You're out."

"A fine thing!" Freddie yelled. "A fine thing, Petrina! You're on my team! I let you make eight home runs last week. And now you turn against us!"

"It was a strike, wasn't it, Jeffrey?" Petrina said.

Well, I am a very honest guy. "OK." I said. "I do not like fights with girls. I am out." So no one was mad, and it was a very good game.

Tuesday

Tuesday morning Joybells said, "The girls are campaigning for Gloria Jones." Joybells put a big piece of fudge in his mouth.

"Where did you get the fudge?" I said.

Joybells said, "It is campaign fudge." He took another piece out of his pocket. "Gloria made it."

"Hey! That is dishonest," I said. "Is it good?"

Joybells said, "I haven't decided." He unwrapped another piece.

"We will help you decide," said Charlie. "Hold him, guys."

So we held Hugo's hands and feet, and Charlie took the fudge out of his pocket.

"You didn't have to work so hard," Joybells said. "It was yours, anyway. Gloria sent it to you."

"It has a dishonest taste," I said.

That morning Gloria played a piano solo. There was a poster on the bulletin board: Vote for Gloria— The Best Piano Player! So the fellows did not clap.

After school we were worried. "Gloria will win," I said, "unless we think up something good to say about Joybells."

"I gave you some fudge," said Joybells. "I am unselfish. And I am kind to my rabbit. I give him lots of clover."

"We are not rabbits," said Freddie. "We do not eat clover. It's no use. Sixteen is more than fourteen, and we are defeated."

"That is so," Joybells said. "Sixteen girls will vote for Gloria. Fourteen boys will vote for me."

So I went home feeling very worried.

Mom was at the telephone, and I heard her say, "I've had a terrible day, Carrie. I'm going to take a long, warm bath and do some thinking. There's no place to think like the bathtub! I relax. And the answers to my problems just come to me."

If it worked for Mom, it might for me. I hurried upstairs, ran some water in the tub, and hopped in.

In a minute Mom called, "I must be dreaming! It isn't Saturday. I didn't drag you here. Are you sick?"

I called to her, "I am thinking! I am just trying to figure out how to make fourteen more than sixteen."

Mom said, "Any woman who thinks she knows what a boy will do is living dangerously!"

That was when the big idea struck me. "You are right!" I said. "And you know who is living dangerously? All the girls in our room!"

That night we had a meeting at Charlie's house. Very secret.

Wednesday

The next afternoon Florence called our class to order to nominate candidates.

Julie stood. She said, "I wish to nominate my charming friend, Gloria Jones."

Two girls said, "I second the nomination!"

I stood up. Florence gave me a sweet smile. She was sure I would nominate Joybells, and Gloria would beat him. But the girls were living dangerously.

I said, "I nominate Petrina Bronson!"

"I second the nomination!" yelled the guys.

Poor Florence! Her ears almost fell off.

The other girls were busy almost fainting, so the nominations closed.

"Now," Miss Coppersmith said, "we will have one day for campaigning. Ready for recess! Jeffrey, please remain."

So I remained. I did not feel alone. I could hear the guys breathing in the hall.

So could Miss Coppersmith. "Well, come on in, gentlemen," she said.

The fellows came in. She said, "What happened? Monday, you tried to nominate Hugo."

"Well," I said, "sixteen is more than fourteen, so Hugo could not win. But some girls like Petrina better than Gloria. And all the boys will vote for Petrina. We made some posters, too."

We showed our posters to Miss Coppersmith. She read them.

"H'm!" Miss Coppersmith said. "Would Petrina make a good Sergeant-at-Arms?"

"Well," I said, "we did not think about that. But Petrina is good at managing people. She manages the little kids' games."

Charlie said, "She likes boys as well as girls."

Miss Coppersmith nodded. "When there are so many good things to say for your candidate, why don't you say them? Then you will not need to say anything against the other candidate. If we do this right, then—no matter who wins—our sixteen girls and fourteen boys will be thirty friends."

"That figures!" we said, and tore up our posters.

Thursday

Thursday, Freddie and Charlie made speeches for Petrina. Petrina made a speech, too. She said, "If I am elected, I will work hard for good order in our room. If I am defeated, I will still help keep order."

Gloria made a speech, and then we had election.

Petrina was elected 17-13.

Gloria was first to congratulate her, and no one was mad. And it was a happy election day because seventeen and thirteen makes thirty friends.

Chocolate Fudge

You will need:

large mixing bowl
mixing spoon
measuring cup

measuring spoons
metal spatula or knife
pan measuring 9×9×2 inches
   or 8×8×2 inches

two 3-ounce packages cream cheese
1 pound confectioners' sugar
four 1-ounce envelopes unsweetened
   chocolate-flavored product*

1/2 teaspoon vanilla
2/3 cup chopped nuts
pat of butter

*This product may be found next to the baking choco-
late in the grocery store. If you cannot find it, use
four 1-ounce squares of unsweetened baking chocolate,
instead. However, you must melt the baking chocolate.

How to make the fudge:

1. Put the cheese in the bowl and let it warm to room temperature.

2. When the cheese is warm, start adding half the sugar gradually. Each time you add sugar, stir the mixture before adding more.

3. Open the chocolate envelopes at the top and squeeze the chocolate into the fudge mixture.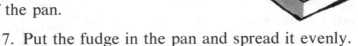

4. Now add the rest of the sugar gradually.

5. Stir in the nuts and vanilla.

6. Butter the pan. Use a piece of wax paper to spread butter over the inside of the pan.

7. Put the fudge in the pan and spread it evenly.

8. Now comes the hardest part! Chill the fudge for two hours or longer. Use a refrigerator or set the pan outside your classroom window if the weather is cool.

9. Wash the bowl, spoon, and other tools you used.

10. When the fudge is firm, cut it into squares. If you make 5 cuts across the pan each way, you will have 36 pieces of fudge.

Adventures of Thomas O'Toole

by D. R. KEARNS

The author of this story says, "Most people believe Columbus discovered America. That may be because most people never heard of Thomas Phineas O'Toole. Here is the story of O'Toole as I heard it. You may believe it or not."

O'Toole Discovers America

Thomas Phineas O'Toole first heard of Columbus in the year 1490. Now T. P. (that was what T. P.'s friends called him) was no sailor. He was just an old storyteller who lived in Ireland.

"People and their newfangled ideas!" he said to Gabby Donovan, his lifelong friend. "Begorra!" he said. "If that fellow Columbus finds there is no edge to the world and no sea serpents to gobble up people that come too near the edge, I'll have no one listening to me spin yarns!"

It was a problem, indeed, for old T. P. And he decided to do something about it. "Well, if the world is round, bedad, it will be this Irishman who first finds it out!"

Gabby stared. "You mean—" he said. "Do you mean that *you*, Thomas Phineas O'Toole, are going to find out?"

"How right you be!" T. P. said. "That is, if you will join me, Gabby, me friend."

Gabby was no seafaring gentleman, either. But he was game. "For friendship's sake, I'll do it!" he said.

They bought a small ship for the voyage. They named her *Shamrock* for good luck. Then they stocked the hold with provisions and headed out to sea.

For the first week, T. P. just soaked up the sun and looked for sea monsters. Gabby did most of the work. One day Gabby shouted from the crow's-nest, "Ahoy! Sea serpent to the starboard!"

Old T. P. didn't know what starboard meant. He was sure Gabby didn't, either. So he just looked where his friend's finger was pointing.

T. P.'s eyes almost jumped out of his head. "It's a dragon!" he yelled. "No! It's five dragons!"

"And they're breathing fire and water!" screamed Gabby.

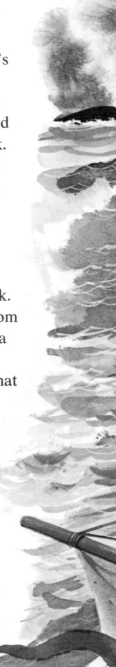

T. P. was so excited that he scurried up the mast and hid in the crow's-nest with Gabby.

After a while T. P. said, "Take a look, Gabby."

Gabby shook his head. "No, you look," he said.

Finally both of them peeked down at the water.

"Why, you blundering 'fraidy cat!" laughed T. P. "It's only a school of whales!"

Gabby looked, then laughed, too. "I was sure I saw them shooting off geysers of fire," he said.

"That was the sun shining on the water they were spouting," T. P. explained.

Things quieted down again after that. Four, six, eight weeks went by. They saw no serpents and no edge of the world.

"Maybe you've been wrong," said Gabby. "Maybe the world *is* round."

"If so," said T. P., "I'll be the first storyteller in Ireland to tell the tale."

On the second day of the ninth week, Gabby shouted, "Land ahoy!"

T. P. jumped from his bunk and looked. Sure enough, in the distance rose a mound of green-covered earth.

Gabby slid down the mast. He hurried to T. P.'s side. "Well, what do you know!" he said. "The world *is* round! Do you figure that's India?"

Old T. P. wasn't sure of anything right then. But he wouldn't let Gabby know it. So he said, "Of course. Of course it's India, Gabby Donovan. And them that lives there be Indians!"

T. P. and Gabby stayed in the new land for about a year. They taught the natives many things. Then they went back to Ireland. Back home T. P. told many a fancy tale about his adventures.

Here are some of them.

The Indians Get Tomahawks

During his stay with the Indians, old T. P. always carried a hatchet by his side. One day he saw a great bird swoop down on the village.

That bird was just about to sink its talons into a tame deer when old T. P. let his hatchet fly.

It caught the bird between the eyes. Gabby ran and held up the bird and hatchet.

"Look, Tom!" he said. (At times Gabby called his friend *Tom*.) "Look, Tom! A hawk!"

The Indians thought Gabby was trying to teach them the name of the weapon. They thought he said, "Look! Tomahawk!"

After that they made and used hatchets. But they called them tomahawks.

The Indians Learn a Dance

One time old T. P. stubbed his big toe on a rock. He was in such pain that he went stamping and yelling around in a circle.

T. P. clapped his hand over his mouth several times and yelled at the top of his lungs. Oh, how he whooped and hollered!

The Indians didn't know that he had stubbed his toe. They thought he was teaching them a dance.

After that when the Indians danced, they danced in a circle. And they whooped and clapped their hands over their mouths.

The Indians Paint Their Faces

T. P. got himself a bad case of sunburn one day. He had some bright-yellow salve that he hoped would soothe the sting. He put the yellow salve all over his red, sunburned face.

Then he went to find a shady spot. He sat down near a blueberry patch. Soon he began nibbling berries.

When he went back to the village, he had a pretty colorful face. It was all red and yellow and blue.

After that the Indians put paint on their faces, too.

The Indians Wear Feathers

An Indian squaw caught old T. P. taking corn-meal cookies one time. She threw her cookie batter at him. The batter landed in his hair. Try as he might, he could not wash the sticky batter out of his hair.

That same day T. P. got a turkey. While he was plucking the bird, a big wind came up.

When the wind died down, T. P.'s head was covered with feathers. They were stuck fast to his hair.

The Indians liked T. P.'s feather headdress. So they started to wear feathers in their hair.

The Indians Name Their Homes

At last it was time for T. P. to go back to Ireland. The Indians had learned to love their Irish friends. They wanted to do something to honor them.

The Indians said they would name their country O'Tooleland or Gabbyland. But T. P. wouldn't hear of it and neither would Gabby.

So the Indians did the next best thing. They named their homes after the one who had taught them so much. They called the tent that each Indian lived in a tepee after T. P. O'Toole.

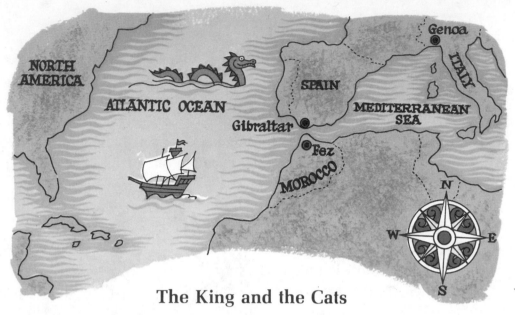

The King and the Cats

ITALIAN FOLK TALE RETOLD BY NANCY FORD

A long time ago in Genoa, Italy, there lived a man whose name was Ansaldo degli Ormani. He had a ship of his own and went on trading expeditions.

One day he set out to sail across the Mediterranean Sea. The hold of his ship was filled with silk, wine, ivory, and silver.

Westward he sailed, and farther westward, though the seas in that direction were little known. Some folk said he would meet sea monsters and other frightening things. But Ansaldo was not afraid.

At first the trip was pleasant. But when the ship reached the great ocean beyond Gibraltar, a storm arose. Huge waves broke over the decks of the ship.

Ansaldo and his sailors thought that the ship would surely go under. But at last the sun broke through the clouds, and they sighted an island in the distance.

Ansaldo ordered the ship steered toward the unknown land. Soon he stepped ashore and found that the people of the island were friendly. Ansaldo was welcomed by messengers from the king of the island. Then Ansaldo and his men were invited to a banquet at the royal palace.

When they arrived at the palace, the king led them into a banquet hall. The table was set with gold and glass as fine as anything Ansaldo had seen in his own country.

But there was something he had *not* seen at home. And it puzzled him greatly. Standing along the walls of the banquet hall were dozens of servant girls. Each held a long willow switch.

What possible use, Ansaldo wondered, can there be for switches in a banquet hall?

He took his place at the table beside the king, and began to tell some of his adventures.

Then the food was carried in. No sooner had it been put on the table than hordes of mice rushed in. At once they scratched their way up the table legs to grab the food. The servant girls shook their willow switches wildly to chase the mice away.

Ansaldo begged the king's permission to leave for a short time and hurried to his ship.

When he returned, he brought two of the crew's pets, a pair of fine cats.

It was now the king's turn to be surprised. Never before had he seen animals like these. As soon as Ansaldo freed the cats, they leaped on the mice. What a hurrying and scurrying there was then! Before the king could blink twice, the mice had run for shelter.

Ansaldo and his men stayed at the island several weeks. They traded with the people of the island. The cats, of course, continued their war on the mice.

Finally as meal after meal was served and no mice came to the banquet hall, the king realized that the bother of mice at the table had ended. He could not thank his visitor enough. Nor could he give enough praise to the two cats.

When Ansaldo was ready to sail home, the king walked with him to the ship. Servants went along carrying gold, silver, rubies, diamonds, and pearls. All these treasures were from the royal storehouses.

The king said, "Please accept these as tokens of my gratitude. Thank you for your wonderful gift to us."

Fair westerly winds carried Ansaldo home. News of Ansaldo's adventure soon spread through his town.

There was one man, Giocondo dei Fifante, who heard only part of the story. "Have you heard," said a friend, "about Ansaldo degli Ormani's good luck? The king of some western island has heaped riches on Ansaldo in exchange for two cats."

When Giocondo heard this tale, he burned with envy. "I shall visit that island," he decided. "I shall take much finer gifts than two cats. I shall take valuable goods to that king. In return he is sure to give me riches even greater than those he gave to Ansaldo."

Giocondo talked to Ansaldo's sailors to find out the way to the western island. Next he sold everything he owned. With the money he got, he bought leather belts, lace, paintings, and fine clothing. And then he hired a ship and crew and set sail for the island.

Giocondo was impatient during the long voyage. But at last he found the island and sailed into port. He went at once to the palace with many gifts for the king. The king received this new visitor with pleasure. He was delighted when he heard that Giocondo was from the same country—even the same city—as Ansaldo.

The king was at a loss to know just how to thank Giocondo for his many gifts. What could the king do to show his appreciation? Of course, he could give a banquet for the visitor, as he had for Ansaldo. But he must also think of a better way to reward this merchant who had come to trade and had brought many presents as well.

So the king consulted his royal advisors. "How can we return this visitor's kindness?" the king asked. "Think of the most valuable thing we have on the island. We will share it with him."

Many suggestions were offered. For a long time the king shook his head at each one. "Not good enough," he said. But at last someone had an idea that pleased the king. "The very thing!" he exclaimed. "The very finest thing on our island!"

On the day that Giocondo left, the king followed Giocondo to his ship. The king made a grand speech. Then he presented the greedy merchant with two fine kittens. They had been born of the cats that had been given to the king by Ansaldo degli Ormani!

The Mysterious Cat

by VACHEL LINDSAY

I saw a proud, mysterious cat,
I saw a proud, mysterious cat
Too proud to catch a mouse or rat—
Mew, mew, mew.

But catnip she would eat, and purr,
But catnip she would eat, and purr.
And goldfish she did much prefer—
Mew, mew, mew.

I saw a cat—'twas but a dream,
I saw a cat—'twas but a dream,
Who scorned the slave that brought her cream—
Mew, mew, mew.

Unless the slave were dressed in style,
Unless the slave were dressed in style
And knelt before her all the while—
Mew, mew, mew.

Did you ever hear of a thing like that?
Did you ever hear of a thing like that?
Did you ever hear of a thing like that?
Oh, what a *proud* mysterious cat.
Oh, what a proud *mysterious* cat.
Oh, what a proud mysterious *cat*.
Mew . . . Mew . . . Mew.

Reprinted with permission of The Macmillan Company from *The Congo and Other Poems* by Vachel Lindsay. Copyright 1914 by The Macmillan Company. Renewed 1942 by Elizabeth C. Lindsay.

Section Two

"Shooting the Rapids" by Mrs. F. A. Hopkins, from an oil painting in the Public Archives of Canada.

The Voyageurs

by NATHAN DRESKIN

The story of the *voyageurs*, the famous French Canadian canoemen, is almost as old as the story of Canada.

In the 1600's, the voyageurs went out from the settlements of Montreal and Quebec to meet the Indians in their own lands and trade for their furs. The voyageurs paddled the canoes used by the explorers and by the great fur-trading companies of North America. In particular, the voyageurs were responsible for the success of the North West Company of Montreal.

The North West Company was formed in Montreal in 1783. And Montreal was a long way from the far northwest where the Indians had the richest furs. But the men of the North West Company knew the voyageurs. They knew how well they could handle the great canoes. They knew that they could depend on the voyageurs to transport men and supplies and trading goods from Montreal to the trading posts far to the west. They knew that they could depend on them to bring back to Montreal the rich furs that would be shipped to Europe.

The voyageurs wore red woollen caps, colorful sashes, and deerskin leggings and moccasins. Every spring they gathered on Montreal Island above the Lachine Rapids. There they loaded the *canots du maître* or Montreal canoes. These magnificent birch-bark canoes were thirty to forty feet long. They carried several tons of freight wrapped in ninety-pound packages. In them, the fur-trading parties travelled to the head of the Great Lakes.

Before departure, the canoes were blessed. Farewells were said, and last-minute instructions given. The voyageurs pushed off amid a chorus of good wishes for a *bon voyage*. As they paddled up the St. Lawrence, the sound of their gay singing floated back to shore.

The number of paddlers in each crew varied from seven to fifteen. The number depended on how much space was needed for cargo and passengers, and on the difficulty of the route. There are records of one Montreal canoe that had a crew of seventeen paddlers and a steersman.

In a canoe crowded with people and supplies there was no room for tall, long-legged men. The voyageurs were usually of average height — about five feet, six or seven inches. They were sturdily built, with broad backs, strong arms and legs. They moved quickly and gracefully, whether they were paddling, carrying canoes and supplies over a trail or *portage*, or setting up camp. They were proud of their canoes and took great care of them. They were always eager to prove their paddling skill in a good race. They attacked dangerous rapids with zest and courage. They boasted of their ability to carry not just one, but two, or even three or four, ninety-pound packs over difficult portages.

An astonished traveller wrote this about the crew of one Montreal canoe:

> *I could hardly believe my eyes. They took their canoe out of the water, unloaded it, made a campfire, mended a break in the canoe with heated pine gum, reloaded the canoe, cooked a meal, shaved, washed, and re-embarked — all in under one hour!*

When they were relaxing, the voyageurs smoked their pipes, sang and joked, and sometimes grumbled. There were dances and joyful reunions when the crews from Montreal met the crews from the northwest at the main trading posts at the western end of Lake Superior.

At these forts, the cargoes from the big Montreal canoes were unloaded and re-distributed in the *canots du nord*. These smaller, twenty-five foot "canoes of the north" carried men and supplies to the trading posts in the far northwest. And the precious furs that the northern canoes had brought out from these trading posts were put into the Montreal canoes for the trip to the east.

"Voyageurs at Dawn, 1871" by Mrs. F. A. Hopkins, from an oil painting in the Public Archives of Canada.

After the reloading, some of the voyageurs again manned the great Montreal canoes and returned to Montreal and home. On the return journey, their load of furs was light and their pace was swift.

The remaining voyageurs paddled the northern canoes far into the Canadian Northwest. These were the true *hommes du nord* — the men of the north who shared in the life of the trading posts. These voyageurs were traders as well as canoemen. They traded to the Indians the blankets, cloth, pins, jewellery, flour, and other items that they had brought from Montreal.

In spite of the voyageurs' skilful paddling, the heavily loaded birch-bark canoes were frequently upset. Wooden crosses on the canoe routes marked the spots where men had drowned when a boat had overturned or been wrecked by hidden rocks.

The voyageurs wore their hair long to protect themselves from black flies and mosquitoes. But long hair was poor protection against the swarms of these insects that attacked the paddlers as they carried their back-breaking loads over long and difficult portages.

The voyageurs' food consisted mainly of thick pea or corn soup with pork or bacon in it. The men used wooden spoons, and usually all ate from the same pot. But the canoemen also caught and ate wild game and fish whenever it was available, and they picked fresh berries. When they headed inland to the north and west of the Great Lakes, pemmican became their basic food.

The voyageurs' journeys were always races. They had to travel as fast as possible and in every kind of weather. They began the long journey from Montreal in the spring, and often they had to race to reach Montreal or the forts before the rivers froze. They paddled or walked from dawn to dusk except for brief rests. Under favorable conditions, a good canoe could cover seventy miles a day. An express canoe, travelling light, and with no more than six paddlers, could cover as many as seventy-five or even eighty miles a day. But forty or fifty miles was the average daily distance covered by a fur-trade canoe.

From the Indian, the white man received the gift of the birch-bark canoe. Without this marvellous canoe and the men to paddle it, the fur trade could not have been so successful. And the men with the skill to handle the fur-trade canoes were the voyageurs — men of courage, skill, and good humor.

Public Archives of Canada photo

May 24, 1967—they're off! The paddlers race to their canoes at Rocky Mountain House, Alberta, to begin their journey to Expo '67 in Montreal.

The Great Canadian Canoe Race

by NATHAN DRESKIN

By the early afternoon of May 24, 1967, some 5000 spectators had gathered in the town of Rocky Mountain House in western Alberta. They were there to watch the start of the Centennial Voyageur Canoe Race. This was to be the longest, wettest, riproaringest race in Canadian history: ninety men would paddle ten canoes over 3200 miles to Montreal. It would take them 104 days.

A jet plane could have taken them that distance in four and a half hours. But Canada was celebrating its one-

83

The canoes set off from Rocky Mountain House.

hundredth birthday. What better way to celebrate than to bring back, for a short time, the famous voyageurs of Canada's past. And that's what led to the great Canadian canoe race.

Eight provinces, the Yukon, and the Northwest Territories entered their canoes in this race. They named their canoes after explorers who were linked with their own early history: Nova Scotia, *John Cabot*; New Brunswick, *Samuel de Champlain*; Quebec, *La Verendrye*; Ontario, *William McGillivray*; Manitoba, *Radisson*; Saskatchewan, *Henry Kelsey*; Alberta, *David Thompson*; British Columbia, *Simon Fraser*; Yukon, *Robert Campbell*; Northwest Territories, *Sir Alexander MacKenzie*.

To develop their muscles and skill, the canoeists trained for a year. In the summer of 1966 they held two trial runs. The first was a 600-mile trip in British Columbia from Fort St. James to Prince George, then down the Fraser River to Vancouver. The second was a seven-day race from Montreal to New York City through Lake Champlain and the Hudson River. When winter came, the canoeists kept in condition by running, weight-lifting, and exercising in gymnasiums. They even put their canoes into indoor swimming pools, with the bows against a wall, and paddled hard for hours!

The canoes in the 1967 race resembled the *canots du nord*, the northern canoes used by the voyageurs. But for safety, lightness, and strength they were constructed of fibre glass, not birch-bark. Each canoe weighed 260 pounds and was twenty-five feet long, four feet wide, and eighteen inches deep.

The teams finally chosen for the big race included doctors, lawyers, teachers, students, fishermen, businessmen, trappers, miners, clerks. The youngest canoeist was a seventeen-year-old Ontario school boy, Geoffrey Peruniak; the oldest team member was a forty-nine-year-old New Brunswick forest ranger, Henry Lounden.

Chief Voyageur Bill Matthews of Ottawa organized the event, and each team had a chief voyageur, as follows: Nova Scotia, J. Bothwell; New Brunswick, J.-C. Richard; Quebec, R. Bellemare; Ontario, J. Mitchell; Manitoba, J. Rheaume; Saskatchewan, P. Whitehead; Alberta, J. Nickel; British Columbia, W. Blackburn; Yukon, W. Sinclair; Northwest Territories, J. W. Eades.

Each team consisted of nine paddlers, three of whom were spares. At any one time, six men actually manned the canoe while the others went ahead by road to set up camp at the next stop. Saving time this way was important. First prize was to be awarded to the team with the lowest total travelling time.

And so the race began, that afternoon of May 24, in a cold rain, after several days of celebrations that had included street dancing, a giant barbecue, and a parade. After the launching ceremony, the paddlers raced to the edge of the North Saskatchewan River. In the first 1000 yards of the course, they paddled their bucking, pitching canoes through the foaming white water of two sets of rapids. It was a fitting beginning for a trip halfway across a continent.

In the days that followed, the teams faced drenching rains, hot sun, thunderstorms, black flies, mosquitoes, and many treacherous rapids. They had to carry their canoes and supplies across seventy back-breaking portages, a total of sixty miles.

Their course: along the North Saskatchewan River to The Pas, then south through Lakes Winnipegosis and Manitoba to the Assiniboine River and the Red River; from there to Lake Winnipeg and the Winnipeg River; into Lake of the Woods and Rainy River; across the big waters of Lake Superior and Lake Huron to the French River, Lake Nipissing, Trout Lake, and the Mattawa River; down the Ottawa River to the St. Lawrence and Montreal and — the final goal — the island site of Expo 67.

The crew from the Northwest Territories carries the *Sir Alexander MacKenzie* over a portage.

Those who watched the brigades sweeping down the rivers of Canada felt as if history had come alive before their eyes. At first, British Columbia took the lead. Then Manitoba.

Racing eastward, the 1967 canoeists found that the constant paddling hardened their muscles. Exposure to sun and water browned their skin. And always they had to keep paddling in the exact beat called by the captain.

Often they would get the signal from the captain: "One, two, three . . . *slide!*" At this command, the paddlers would slide across their seats and paddle from the other side of the canoe so that one arm would not become overtired. The men had to scrape along on their knees and bottoms to make the shift without tipping the canoe. One canoeist figured that during the journey he slid some thirty-eight miles on the seat of his pants! The paddlers wore out many pairs of pants and developed calluses on their knees.

The canoemen averaged thirty to thirty-five miles a day. They stroked sixty to sixty-five strokes a minute, a gruelling pace to keep up. To save time, they ate concentrated food from tubes while they paddled.

Food, in fact, is one example of the differences between the journeys of the voyageurs and the Centennial canoe race. The voyageurs existed largely on pea soup and pemmican and whatever game and fish and berries they could obtain. Nothing like this fare for our Centennial canoeists! Here is what they ate on their journey eastward: 30,000 eggs; 2½ tons of bacon; 60,000 pancakes; 10,000 quarts of milk; one half ton of honey; 6 tons of steak; 2½ tons of potatoes; 5000 loaves of bread; and 1½ tons of butter.

While the voyageurs of yesteryear had to depend on their long hair to keep the swarms of flies and mosquitoes from their faces and necks, the 1967 canoeists were much better off — they used up 200,000 ounces of insect repellent!

The crew and passengers in the fur-trading canoes were alone against the wilderness; the Centennial canoeists had some protection. They had safety boats along; helicopters were on call; and about twenty-five trucks equipped with radios followed the crews to ensure the safety and well-being of the men.

The Ontario crew in the *William McGillivray* heads into choppy water near Britannia (Ottawa).

89

Clothing and blankets are aired and a paddler relaxes in a woodland campsite.

In total overall time, the 1967 journey was slow by voyageur standards. But it wasn't the lack of speed or the sixty miles of portaging that slowed the modern canoeists. No, it was having to stop at some ninety communities along the way to join the Centennial celebrations. After a hard day's paddling, the 1967 voyageurs often put on exhibition races before thousands of spectators.

Here is an interesting comparison. The Centennial canoeists did the seventy-nine-mile lap from Portage La Prairie to Winnipeg in nine hours and thirty-eight minutes, a back-breaking clip! And 150 years ago, a passenger in a voyageur forty-foot freighter-canoe recorded: "They paddled from sun-up to sunset and covered seventy-nine miles. And they were still fresh! No humans except French-Canadians could have done this. They slept a few hours under their overturned canoes, were up at the first call in the morning."

Our Centennial canoeists covered 409 miles with nine stops in Alberta; in Saskatchewan, 574 miles and ten stops; Manitoba, 682 miles and twenty-one stops; Ontario and Quebec, 1621 miles with forty-seven stops in Ontario and six in Quebec. In all, 3286 miles and ninety-three stops. Vast crowds turned out all along the way to greet the paddlers and welcome them to their local celebrations. There was no end to the barbecues and cook-outs of beef, moose, and buffalo. At one stop, improperly prepared moosemeat gave the paddlers upset stomachs for two days!

The Centennial voyageurs were in Winnipeg for the Dominion Day festivities on July 1, 1967. There they

Crowds welcome the canoeists at Britannia (Ottawa).

had a welcome change from western beef — the New Brunswick crew had a special shipment of lobsters brought in by plane.

The first major delay, of five hours, happened on Lake of the Woods when twelve-foot waves forced the teams to take shelter. Then at Emo, Ontario, the New Brunswick crew had — of all things — its canoe stolen while the men slept. But the police quickly recaptured it.

The paddlers were lucky on Lake Superior, one of the world's roughest inland waterways. The crossing, with stopovers, took from July 24 to August 11, and it was the first time in fifteen years, according to the local residents, that the lake was calm enough for such a trip.

Meanwhile, Manitoba, which had taken the lead from British Columbia early in the race, grimly held it. British Columbia and Alberta were close behind.

The brigade of canoes reached Ottawa on August 30. They were entertained at Government House. That night, on Parliament Hill, there was a two-hour centennial show: broad-axe dancers, tap, square, and Indian dancing, accordion playing, fiddling and street dancing. The canoeists forgot their aching muscles and danced too.

After Ottawa, the paddlers still had to overcome their most dangerous obstacle, the Lachine Rapids. Not all of them managed to do it. These rapids had challenged the most skilful paddlers among the early voyageurs, and the dangers had not lessened in 200 years. The rapids tipped the Yukon crew into their raging waters and swamped the Alberta canoeists.

But, finally, on September 4, after fifteen weeks of paddling from the foothills of the Rockies, the brigade reached Ile Sainte-Hélène at Expo 67. It was a lovely

Malak Studio

The Alberta crew's *David Thompson* shoots the Lachine Rapids near Montreal.

The canoes arrive at Ile Ste-Hélène, the island site of Expo '67.

balmy afternoon when the canoeists stroked their way into Regatta Lake to the cheers of thousands. Their arrival marked the end of a long, hard race.

Manitoba won the Canoe Race with a total travelling time of 531 hours, 6 minutes, and 15.5 seconds. British Columbia came second, and Alberta, third. They were followed by Ontario, New Brunswick, Saskatchewan, Quebec, Northwest Territories, Yukon Territory, and Nova Scotia. Each member of the winning crew received $2500; members of the second-place crew, $2000 each, and of the third-place crew, $1500. Members of all the remaining crews received $1000 each. And each of the modern voyageurs received a watch from Expo 67.

The Chief Voyageur of the winning *Radisson,* Jim Rheaume, called the course "An unbelievable endurance test for any athlete. No athlete in any sport," he continued, "is ever required to give all he's got for so long a time. And brother, did all of them come through beautifully!"

The winning Manitoba crew consisted of: Jim Rheaume 37, chartered accountant, Flin Flon (Chief Voyageur); Norman Crerar, ski instructor, Flin Flon (Captain); Joe Michelle, 32, trapper, Sturgeon Landing; Joseph Carrière, 37, railwayman, Cranberry Portage; John Norman, 31, miner, Creighton; David Wells, 19, miner, Flin Flon; Blair Harvey, 24, social worker, Winnipeg; Donald Starkell, 34, railwayman, Winnipeg; Wayne Soltys, 25, miner, Flin Flon; Gib McEachern, 27, ski instructor, Flin Flon.

John Fisher, Centennial Commissioner, said of the early voyageurs that if it had not been for the birch-bark canoe and the rhythm of the paddles, the West would have developed much more slowly. To the 1967 voyageurs he said, "You have stirred the hearts of all Canadians. You are the heroes of our Centennial year."

And they surely were.

En roulant ma boule

The voyageurs constantly sang as they paddled. Most of their songs were ballads they had learned in Europe that told of the adventures of brave knights and fair princesses. "En roulant ma boule" (while rolling my ball) is the tale of a young prince who takes his shining gun and shoots at "three beautiful ducks." This was probably the most popular of all voyageur songs, and it was sung in many forms. Its gay tune was also heard as a dance song in the lonely trading posts.

In the French verses for this song, many lines are repeated. Eight verses are given here, together with the corresponding English words. The music includes the chords for guitar playing. Perhaps you know someone who can play the song for you and help you to learn the French words.

Gaily
Refrain

English words by Edith Fowke

En rou-lant ma bou-le rou-lant, En rou-lant ma bou - le.

En rou-lant ma bou-le rou-lant, En rou-lant ma bou - le 1. Der-
1. Be-

rièr' chez nous, y'a- t'un é - tang, En rou-lant ma bou - le, Trois
hind our house we have a pond, Where

DC al Fine

beaux ca - nards s'en vont bai-gnant, Rou-li, rou-lant, ma bou-le rou-lant.
three fine ducks swim round and round.

96

1. Behind our house we have a pond,
   En roulant ma boule,
   Where three fine ducks swim
       'round and 'round,
   Rouli, roulant, ma boule roulant.

1. Derrièr'chez nous y'a-t'un étang,
   En roulant ma boule,
   Trois beaux canards s'en
       vont baignant,
   Rouli, roulant, ma boule roulant

Refrain: En roulant ma boule roulant,
         En roulant ma boule.

2. To hunt them comes the young king's son,
   En roulant ma boule,
   With him he brings his shining gun.
   Rouli, roulant, ma boule roulant.

2. Le fils du roi s'en va chassant,
   En roulant ma boule,
   Avec son grand fusil d'argent.
   Rouli, roulant, ma boule roulant.

3. He aims it at the black for fun
   But then he hits the whitest one.

3. Visa le noir, tua le blanc,
   O fils de roi, tu es méchant!

4. "Oh, prince, now see what you have done!
   You've killed my duck, the whitest one!"

4. O fils du roi, tu es méchant!
   D'avoir tué mon canard blanc.

5. From his bright eyes two di'monds fall,
   And from his bill drops gold for all.

5. Par dessous l'aile il perd son sang,
   Par les yeux lui sort'nt des diamants.

6. Out from his wing the red drops pour,
   And on the wind his feathers soar.

6. Et par le bec l'or et l'argent,
   Toutes ses plum's s'en vont au vent.

7. Three maidens fair his feathers take,
   A bed for weary men they make.

7. Trois dam's s'en vont les ramassant,
   C'est pour en faire un lit de camp.

8. C'est pour en faire un lit de camp,
   Pour y coucher tous les passants.

The King's Contest

by JAMES HOLDING

Once upon a time when the city of Fez was still new, it was ruled by a king named Moulay. The king loved his city. He was proud of it. But many a time he lay awake at night, worrying about it.

"Fez is indeed a fine city," he often said to his wife. "It has everything to make it beautiful and famous. It has mosques with extra-tall towers. It has wonderful palaces like mine. It lies in the middle of a

98

dry and barren land, but magic springs of water flow out of the ground in Fez. These springs give us plenty of water to drink and gardens of sweet-smelling flowers. All the same, I worry about Fez."

"Why do you worry about it?" his wife would ask.

"Well, after all," the king would say, "Fez is very far away from other places. The paths that lead to it are few and narrow. Indeed, the world hardly knows that Fez is here. I'm afraid that in a few years its name will disappear from men's minds. Then the city will die and be forgotten. Don't you think that would be a shame?"

"Yes, I do," the king's wife would say. "It would be a shame if the city of Fez died and was forgotten. But I am not going to worry my head about it."

"I shall go on worrying, if you don't mind," the king would say. And he went on worrying.

Then a wonderful idea occurred to him one day.

There is no reason why I should worry about Fez all by myself, he thought. I shall get all my people to help me worry.

So he had a contest announced to the people of Fez. Whoever thought of the best way to make the name of Fez so famous in the world that it would be remembered forever would receive three bags of gold and the Royal Order of the Lion.

Everybody in Fez began to think very hard about how to win the three bags of gold. They didn't much care whether they won the Royal Order of the Lion or not. It was just a yellow ribbon to wear across the chest. And it was not worth three pennies.

Soon the king began to get hundreds of answers to his contest. Some of the ideas were good. Some of them were bad. And a lot of them were just plain silly.

One man came to the king and said, "King Solomon had six hundred wives. This made him so famous that he and his city of Jerusalem have never been forgotten. Why don't you marry *seven* hundred wives? Then you will be more famous than Solomon. And the city of Fez will be remembered forever. I offer my own daughter as the first of your new wives."

The king said, "I can't marry seven hundred wives. It is quite impossible. My wife would not like it."

Another man came to the king one day. He said, "O King! What we need in Fez is a senate to help you rule the city. We need a senate made up of a few of the smartest men in Fez, such as me. The city of Rome had such a senate long ago. And Rome became famous and has never been forgotten."

The king said, "I do not need help to *rule* my city, thank you. I just need help to make the city famous."

And so things went on. Many ideas were brought to the king. But none of them suited him.

Then one day a servant told the king that a young boy named Abou wanted to see him.

"Bring him in!" cried the king. "Maybe this boy will win the three bags of gold and the Royal Order of the Lion. Oh, I hope so!"

He was disappointed when he saw the boy. Abou was thin, dirty, and ragged. He kept one hand behind his back. But his large dark eyes looked at the king without fear. The king liked that.

"What is your idea," the king asked, "for making Fez famous and remembered forever?"

Abou brought his hand from behind his back.

"This is it, Sire," he said. And he held out a hat. Nothing else. Just a hat. A round, flat-topped hat made of felt. It was bright red and had a black tassel on it.

"What a peculiar-looking hat!" the king said. "Are you joking with me, boy?"

"No, Sire. This hat can make Fez famous and remembered forever."

"How?" asked the king.

"If you wear it instead of your turban," said Abou, "all the men in Fez will then want to wear one like it. They all like to wear what the king wears."

"Yes," said the king. "But how would that help?"

"Why, the caravan men who come to Fez would see these red hats being worn by the men of Fez. Then *they* would want to wear them, too. The men of the desert like to copy the men of the cities."

"True," said the king. "But how would that help?"

"The caravan men would go to other cities, wearing the red hats," the boy said. "And the men in *those* cities would want red hats, too."

"Oh, no!" said the king. "I don't think so. City men do not copy men of the desert. It's the other way about. You just said so."

The boy said, "Pardon me, Sire, but men of other cities would want to wear my hat because it's so very comfortable. Put it on, Sire. Feel how light it is. It protects you from the sun. But it's cooler than a turban, and it has a tassel on it for brushing away flies."

The king tried on the hat. "It's not bad," he said. "It feels good." He looked in a mirror and said, "It looks good, too. But even if all the men in Morocco wear hats like this, how will it help my city of Fez to become famous and be remembered forever?"

"Every time a man mentions his hat," said Abou, "he will say the name of your city."

"How's that?" asked the king.

"Because it's the name of the hat. I call it a fez."

The king said, "Abou, I believe you have won the bags of gold and the Royal Order of the Lion. I'll give them to you presently, but answer one question. Why cannot another fellow make these hats and call them something else?"

Abou said, "The berries I used to dye the hat that special red grow nowhere else but in Fez. So only someone who lives in Fez can make a true fez hat."

The king leaped up. "I shall wear your hat in the streets today! All men who see it and want to buy one shall be sent to you, Abou."

"Then," said Abou, "I won't need the bags of gold."

The king was astonished. "Why not?"

Abou said, "Because I'll get rich making thousands of fezzes. I'll be the richest hatmaker in Morocco! And our city will be remembered forever."

"Won't you even take the Order of the Lion?" the king asked wistfully.

"Certainly, Sire," said Abou. "And I shall wear it as a token of respect to you and our city."

Many hundreds of years have passed since then. But the city of Fez still flourishes, and its name is not forgotten. One reason is that, wherever a person looks in North Africa today, he sees men wearing the round, flat-topped, red hat that Abou called a fez. Perhaps you have seen one, too.

The Adventures of Suzy Sherlock

by ARLENE HALE

My brother Bobby came tearing around the corner of the house. "Hey, I got it!" he yelled. "I got it!"

"Got what?" I asked, as if I didn't know. We had been hearing about just one thing for the past week at our house.

"My driver's licence!" Bobby said. "Come on out front. I'll take you for a spin if Dad says it's OK."

"So who wants to go for a ride?" I asked. "Do you think you're the only boy who ever got a licence?"

"OK!" Bobby said angrily. "OK, Suzy! It will be a long time before I ask you to go for a drive again."

I yawned. Bobby went tramping into the house.

105

Reprinted from *Calling All Girls Magazine*, copyright © 1965 by The Better Reading Foundation, Inc.

Then old Mr. Winters spoke. He asked, "Do you mean to say that boy has been given the right to drive? A young scamp like him?"

"He has his driver's licence," I said. "He's old enough. And he's passed all the tests."

"Good heavens!" said Mr. Winters. "Tell him to keep out of *my* driveway. I won't have him running over *my* flower beds or crashing into *my* car. Do you understand?"

After that, I went into our house. Bobby was going out the front door. He was driving to the market to get groceries for mother.

"That Mr. Winters!" I said to Mom. "He hates young people! What's the matter with him?"

"I don't know, Suzy," said Mother. "But I feel sorry for him. He must be lonely living in that big house all by himself. Just try not to bother him."

For the next few days all we heard about at our house was Bobby's driving. Finally at dinner one night, Dad said, "I'm glad you passed the test, Bob. But be sure you always drive carefully. Remember the rules. And if you get into any trouble, there will be no more driving for six months."

"Gee whiz, Dad!" Bobby said. "You talk like I'm a ten-year-old!"

I said, "Maybe it's because you act like one."

Bobby glared at me. He knows my weakness. He knows I want to be a detective when I grow up, and he thinks that's silly.

"Suzy Sherlock, the famous detective!" he jeered. "Suzy Sherlock Holmes! You wouldn't know an air rifle from a pistol."

My brother makes me so mad! I just boil inside. I keep hoping I can solve a really big case and get my name in the paper. But being a detective when you're only twelve years old is not easy. I've made such a pest of myself at the police station that the officers all run and hide when they see me coming.

"Just you wait!" I said. "Just you wait!"

"I'll wait," said Bobby. "But you'll never solve a case. Not even a little one. Now take me, I get things done. I even got a driver's licence."

Not long after that, Bobby came home looking pale. A tail light on the car had been smashed.

"I don't know how it happened," he told me. "I was parked downtown, and when I came back——"

"A likely story!" I said. "But I'll help prove your innocence. If you really are innocent."

"Honest! Someone hit me when I was parked!"

Bobby was so upset he didn't realize I had offered to help him. I was a little surprised myself. But I felt sorry for him. He'd be sick if he couldn't drive for six months. And to pay for the repairs would take his allowance for weeks!

"Listen, Bobby!" I said. "We have to be logical. Did you notice the car that was parked back of you?"

"No, I didn't," he said. "No car was there when I parked. Nor when I went to get the car, either."

"Oh, great!" I said. "Was anyone around? Did you try to find someone who had seen the accident?"

"No. I was too upset to think straight," said Bobby.

Just then Dad marched in. "Bob!" he roared. "How could you have done a thing like that?"

Bobby gulped. "How did you know?" he said.

"How did I know?" yelled Dad. "Mr. Winters was waiting to jump on me the minute I got home."

"What's he got to do with it?" I asked.

"Haven't you looked at his fender?" asked Dad. "Haven't you seen what Bob did to his car? There's tail-light glass all over Mr. Winters' driveway!"

"But, Dad!" said Bobby. "I didn't hit Mr. Winters' car. Somebody downtown banged into our car. I can show you the exact spot where it happened. Honest! I didn't hit Mr. Winters' car!"

Dad sighed and said, "I believe you, Son. We'll go tell Mr. Winters. I'm sure he can be reasoned with."

"I'm not sure he can," I said.

I was right. Mr. Winters thought that Dad, Bobby, and I were making up the whole story.

"I've reported it to the police," he said. "And I intend to sue. My lawyer will see you tomorrow."

The three of us went home. I've never seen our family so low. Dad and Mom just sat. Bobby went to his room and shut the door. It was clear that it was up to me to prove Bobby hadn't hit Mr. Winters' car.

I went to the police station that evening. When I came in, the policemen started to run. But I grabbed a sleeve and held on, talking fast. Finally, to get rid of me, the officer agreed to do something to help me.

By now it was dark. I marched home. I went into our house and got an empty envelope, a small brush, and a flashlight. Then I went outside again.

I crossed over to Mr. Winters' driveway, staying in the shadows the best I could. When I came to

Mr. Winters' car, I knelt down. I flipped on my flashlight for a moment and swept bits of glass into the
envelope. Then I ran.

But Mr. Winters had seen me! He began to yell
and run after me. Just as I reached my own porch,
he caught up with me. "Now, what were you up to?"
he roared.

My family heard all the noise. Dad and Mother
and Bobby came running out.

"What's going on?" Dad asked.

"It's your daughter now!" roared Mr. Winters. "I caught her fooling with my car!"

I waved the envelope at him. "I have proof here that Bobby didn't hit your car, Mr. Winters!" I said. "Come to the police station with me. I dare you to come, Mr. Winters."

"I'll come," said Mr. Winters. "But you will be sorry I did, young lady."

All five of us went to the police station. It took the policemen a good ten minutes to get around to my business. An officer finally took my envelope and went away with it. While he was gone, I died a thousand deaths. My whole career as a detective might hinge on what happened next.

Finally the officer came back. I was almost afraid to hear what he had to say.

"Mr. Winters," he said, "the car that struck yours earlier today was a 1965 sedan."

"How can you know that?" Mr. Winters asked.

A '65 sedan! I nearly fainted. Our car is a 1968 station wagon. I had proved that Bobby had not hit Mr. Winters' car!

The policeman held up a tiny piece of glass. He said, "You can tell from a sample of glass what kind and model of car the glass came from. It's too bad, Mr. Winters, we couldn't do that years ago when your wife was killed by that young hit-and-run driver. If we'd had today's knowledge then, we might have been able to track him down."

I gasped. A hit-and-run driver! Mr. Winters' wife! Now I understood why he was so cranky.

"I'd rather not discuss that," said Mr. Winters. "But you are sure about this '65 sedan?"

"Yes," said the officer. "There's no doubt at all."

Mr. Winters sighed. "I owe this family an apology. You especially, Bob," he said.

"It's OK," Bobby said.

My, but I was proud of my brother!

Dad said, "We could all use a cup of coffee. Why not come home with us, Mr. Winters? My wife baked a cake today."

Mr. Winters blinked. Then he smiled. He looked like an entirely different man. "I'd like that," he said. "I get mighty tired of my own company."

We all tramped out of the station. I was still shaking. It could have been someone else's '68 wagon that hit Mr. Winters' car. Then where would I have been?

Bobby was staring at me. "You did it, Sherlock! You really did it!" he said. "You saved me!"

"Oh," I said airily, "I know how to get a few things done, too."

How Good a Detective Are You?

How many problems were in this story?

Were all of them solved?

Which ones were not solved?

You may need to reread the story to answer these questions.

How Good a Witness Would You Be?

You are crossing the street when a thief runs from a jewellery store window and jumps into a waiting car. It is driven away quickly. Later you are called as a witness. You are asked to tell what you saw.

Take a good look at the picture above. Then turn the page. See how many of the questions on page 114 you can answer without looking back at this picture.

Adapted from *Reader's Digest Treasury for Young Readers* (1961). Published by the Reader's Digest Association.

Down the side of a sheet of paper write the numerals from 1 through 11. Write answers for as many of the questions below as you can.

1. What time was it?
2. How was the thief dressed?
3. Did he seem to have an injury?
4. If so, how do you think the injury was caused?
5. What did he probably use to break the window?
6. What was he carrying in his left hand?
7. What color was the car that was waiting for him?
8. What was the licence number of the car?
9. Do you think he was going to drive the car himself?
10. Were there any witnesses besides yourself?
11. Did anyone nearby seem to be acting suspiciously?

If you could not answer all the questions, look again at the picture on page 113. Write the rest of your answers and change any others that you wish.

Now turn to page 450 and check your answers.

A Book to Read

Cases of Sherlock Holmes, adapted by WILLIAM KOTTMEYER. McGraw-Hill, 1947. (Webster Every-reader)

Four short stories about crimes Sherlock Holmes solved. These stories show how the great detective solved mysteries from very small clues. The book also has a chapter about the author, Sir Arthur Conan Doyle, and some real crimes he solved.

The Mad Dog

by GAY W. HOLLAND

Enemies

Dan knelt beside the dog. She was shaggy, small, and sick. She was gasping for breath. Grandpa had found her lying on the pine needles in the woods this afternoon. To Dan she looked like the mad dog that had come out of the night two months ago and bitten Major. To Dan she looked like that killer.

Adapted from *Twelve/Fifteen*, February 14, 1965. Copyright © 1964 Graded Press. Published by Graded Press.

Major had been Dan's best friend, and friends are hard to find in the hills near the Wyoming mountains. Major had been a German shepherd puppy.

Dan remembered the night when his puppy had been attacked. A sharp cry had rung through the air. Dan had run out of the house and had seen the pup limping toward him. Another dog was moving toward the woods. It moved with a queer, sideways gait. Major had got rabies from the bite of that mad dog. Dan had tried to forget the awful last days of Major's life. But he couldn't.

Dan studied the dog by the stove. He wasn't sure she was Major's killer. She looked like the same dog. But even if she wasn't, he didn't want her around.

"Do we have to keep her, Grandpa?" asked Dan. "She's no bigger than a half-growed cat. And she's too sick and old to hunt with."

"Well, Dan," said Grandpa, "she needs a friend. Just like your Major did."

"This one's a good-for-nothin' she-dog," said Dan. "Major was the greatest. I bet there never was another dog like him."

"Now, Dan, don't go comparin' this here dog to Major," said Grandpa.

Dan didn't speak. Grandpa leaned forward. "Boy, you ain't listenin'!"

"I am so."

"Then how come you was starin' at the ceiling like a teakettle about to scream? Thought I learned you to speak your piece."

Dan looked at his grandfather, then at the dog. He had no proof that she was the killer.

"I just don't like her, that's all. Major was the best ever." Dan's voice shook on the word *Major*.

"Well, she's goin' to be around a spell," Grandpa said. "Have you come up with a name yet?"

"No," Dan mumbled. Major was the only name he could think of.

After a moment of silence, Grandpa said, "Reckon we'll call her Tag-end."

He moved over to kneel beside the dog. She lay on her side with her legs held stiffly away from her body. Her chest moved slowly and unevenly.

Grandpa patted her head. "She's too blamed hot," he said.

Dan said, "Maybe by morning she'll be OK. Good enough to leave, even."

Grandpa frowned. "You best get goin' to bed, boy," he said.

Dan went into his bedroom. The wind whispering through cracks in the wall helped him go to sleep.

The next morning Dan was finishing breakfast as the sun slanted through the pine trees and into the house. He watched Grandpa lean over Tag-end.

"A mite better. But still too warm," said Grandpa as he patted the dog. Tag-end's nose pushed into Grandpa's hand. Her tongue touched his fingers. "Friendlier, too. That's a mighty good sign."

Grandpa pulled on his jacket. "Old girl needs more sleep," he said. "And it's time we got workin', Dan."

Dan and his grandfather felt a chill in the air as they walked outside. The stream nearby was racing downhill over the rocks. The spring run-off had begun, and the water was already above its usual high mark. It was almost up to the wooden bridge that crossed the creek fifty feet from the house.

"Just give the dog a chance, boy," Grandpa said.

Dan looked at the shape that the toe of his shoe was making in the dirt. It was the outline of a German shepherd.

"Good-for-nothing she-dog," he muttered.

"What's that?"

"Oh, nothin'."

Grandpa walked over to the tractor. He hooked the tractor to the plow. Then he filed a few patches of rust from the metal of the plow.

Dan chopped wood for the stove. Chips went flying in all directions as he cut a log into chunks. Then he split each chunk into four pieces. Time after time his axe sank deeply into the wood. Dan did not know that anything was wrong until he heard his grandfather yell.

The yell came so unexpectedly that Dan jerked away from the chopping block and dropped the axe.

Grandpa wasn't beside the tractor. The yell came from the creek. Suddenly Dan saw him. He was standing knee-deep in the swift water of the stream. His hands were clutching a dark shape that floundered in the current. It was Tag-end!

Dan rushed to the edge of the stream. As he ran in, the force of the water tore at him. He reached for his grandfather. But the rushing water pushed Tag-end against Grandpa's legs and knocked the old man off balance. Dan grabbed his grandfather's jacket and took a firm hold on it.

The cold water shook Dan and jarred his teeth. It roared in his ears. The chill numbed his feet and legs. He grabbed for Tag-end with his free hand. He couldn't let go of Grandpa. But he couldn't let Tag-end drown, either.

The boy's hand touched the dog's cold body. But Tag-end slid past his fingers. She was being swept away by the current.

Grandpa tore loose from Dan and plunged toward
the dog. He caught hold of Tag-end's hind leg and
pulled her to him. Dan managed to grab the dog and
raise her above the water.

Together, the old man and the boy scrambled to
dry land. It was Dan who was holding the wet dog.
Her tail was thumping against his chest.

Dan placed the dog on the ground and sat down beside her. Tag-end coughed and stood up. She shook herself, sending cold water in all directions. Dan laughed. She was dumb, all right. Not many dogs would wander into a stream and nearly drown. But dumb or not, she was alive. And Dan was glad.

Suddenly Tag-end trotted away. She headed for the pine woods, barking at a bird.

Dan whistled and started after her. Then he stopped. She was the one! Her trot was crooked. She had the same jerky, sideways gait he had seen the night Major was attacked. She *had* to be the killer!

Friends

"Look at her light out! All perked up!" Grandpa said as Tag-end disappeared among the pine trees.

Dan didn't answer. He stared at the trees. His thoughts raced in circles. Tag-end is Major's killer. But she's sick and needs help. But she's the one——

"Well, get after her, Dan! Reckon she'll lose herself." Grandpa moved around to look at Dan's face. "What's the matter, boy? You gone loco?"

After a second, Dan spoke. "I can't go after her, Grandpa. I just plain *won't!*"

"But I figured you was——"

"She just causes trouble," Dan said. He couldn't give the real reason. He knew Grandpa would say it was just a crazy idea. The way Grandpa felt about Tag-end, he would never believe it.

"What's got into you? You're the changingest boy I ever did see!" shouted Grandpa.

"I won't! I won't! She's not worth it!" cried Dan.

"Ain't worth what?" said Grandpa. "Ain't worth goin' into the woods for?"

"Not anything! She's scrawny and dumb——"

"You best come up with a better reason than that," interrupted Grandpa. "Get it out, boy!"

The old man looked sternly at Dan.

Dan said, "She's the one, Grandpa. I know she is."

"The one what?"

"The stray. The one that bit Major. And gave him rabies." Dan's words came slowly.

Grandpa said, "That's plumb crazy. Tag-end don't have rabies."

"But she had when she bit Major," Dan insisted.

Grandpa touched Dan's shoulder. "So that's what got you riled up. Look, Dan, she can't be the killer. A dog goes mad, it don't last a week. You know that."

Dan said, "How come she trots like that dog did?"

"Lots of dogs trot that way," Grandpa answered. "There's no gettin' round it. The mad dog's dead."

Dan felt a shock. Tag-end not the killer! Just a helpless stray!

Grandpa waited a minute. Then he started to the house. "Reckon I best get dry clothes," he said.

Dan ran. He ran toward the woods. Somewhere in there Tag-end might be lost and cold and wet. Dan knew the woods well. He and Major had often explored the thickets, clearings, and tall trees. But the boy had no idea where Tag-end might have gone.

He followed a deer trail. Surely Tag-end would have stuck to a path until it ended in a tangle of fallen branches and weeds.

After a bit Dan stopped to rest. He tried to picture Tag-end. She must be tired. Maybe she was lying somewhere, wondering why no one came for her.

He jumped up and began fighting through a tangle of dead trees and berry bushes again. Long whips of wiry wood snapped at his face and legs. His hands were caked with sticky pine sap and were sore from many scratches. He tried to run. But it was more like leaping out of one tangle and into another.

Suddenly the sun shone round the boy as he stepped into a clearing. He whistled. It didn't matter what whistle. Just anything. Tag-end might bark if she heard him. But everything was still.

He crossed the clearing. Where could he go from here? He stopped before entering the woods again and whistled once more.

What was that? A whimper? It came from the far edge of the clearing. He ran until he reached the dog lying in the grass.

Tag-end gave a short, happy bark as she stood up. She wasn't hurt, just tired and scared and lost. She was nothing like Major. But she didn't have to be. Dan loved her, anyway.

"Everything is OK now, girl," Dan whispered. He picked her up and hugged her. Her heart beat loudly against his chest. "Everything is OK now," he said again softly.

Louis Pasteur

A Scientist Is Born

In the mountains in the eastern part of France there is a town named Dôle. In one of the tall, narrow houses on the Street of the Tanners in this town, Louis Pasteur was born on December 27, 1822.

Tanning hides to make leather had been the trade of the Pasteur family for many years. Louis' father had learned the trade from Louis' great-grandfather. But Louis did not become a tanner when he grew up. He became a scientist who was known all over the world.

Louis Pasteur's name is said or seen every day in the word *pasteurize*. Almost everyone uses pasteurized milk because such milk has been treated to kill germs and keep it safe for drinking.

Louis Pasteur discovered the process called pasteurization. But he was searching for a way to keep wine from spoiling when he did. The farmers in his part of France made a living by growing grapes and making wines to sell. Sometimes the wines spoiled before they were sold. Pasteur felt he must find a way to help his neighbors, and he did.

In his long life Louis Pasteur discovered other things that helped many people. His last great scientific adventure began when he was sixty years old.

Pasteur remembered from his childhood the terrible disease called rabies. He wanted very much to do something about it.

He knew that a virus in the saliva of a mad dog or other mad animal caused the disease. He knew that often a person who had been bitten by a mad animal did not get sick until many days afterward.

He decided that maybe the sickness developed slowly because the virus that caused it attacked the brain. It would take a long time for the virus to travel from a bite on a person's arm or leg to his brain.

To test his theory, Pasteur decided to inject saliva from a mad animal into the brain of a dog. He did this, and the dog became mad. He tried the same thing with other dogs. All the dogs became mad. At last Pasteur was satisfied that his theory had been proved.

The next step was to make a vaccine to protect animals from the disease. Louis Pasteur finally made the vaccine from dried spinal cords of animals that had died of rabies. He used the vaccine with great success on animals that had been bitten by mad animals. But it was some time before he dared to try it on a person.

One day in 1885 a woman and her son appeared at Pasteur's door. The woman explained that her nine-year-old son had been bitten by a mad dog, and she begged Pasteur to save the boy.

Louis Pasteur wanted to help Joseph Meister, but he was almost afraid to try. Besides, he was not a doctor. He went to talk to two doctors about the boy. They said Pasteur should give the vaccine to Joseph.

Each day for twelve days, Pasteur injected Joseph with the vaccine. Joseph did not like the jab of the needle, but he liked being at Pasteur's laboratory. He had fun, day after day, watching Pasteur's animals. Louis Pasteur, however, became more and more worried as the days went by.

On the evening of the twelfth day, Joseph was not sick. He went to sleep peacefully. But Pasteur spent a bad night. During the long, dark hours, he feared the boy would die. The next morning Joseph was still not sick. And as time went on, he remained well.

It has been more than eighty years since the first person, a boy in France, was saved from rabies. Today people and animals all over the world are saved from the disease, thanks to Louis Pasteur.

Arbois, ce 19 Sept. 1885

Mon cher petit Joseph,
J'ai bien reçu ta lettre du 17 Septembre et suis heureux des bonnes nouvelles que tu me donnes de ta santé.
Mme Pasteur désire avoir ta photographie avec le petit costume que tu avais à Paris quand ta mère t'amenait au laboratoire de la rue d'Ulm. Envoies-en 3 ou 4 exemplaires.
Voici de quoi la faire faire et payer tes timbres-poste.
Conduis-toi bien, travaille avec suite et application et continue de te bien porter.
Présente à ta mère tous mes souhaits pour elle et sa petite famille.
L. Pasteur

Louis Pasteur sent this letter to Joseph Meister later in the same year that Joseph was saved from rabies.

Arbois, September 19, 1885

My dear little Joseph,

I have received your letter of September 17 and am happy about the good news that you give of your health.

Madame Pasteur wishes to have your photograph with the little suit that you had at Paris when your mother used to bring you to the laboratory on the street of Ulm. Send 3 or 4 copies.

Here is something to have the photograph made and to pay for the postage.

Behave yourself, work with perseverance and application and continue to stay in good health.

Give your mother all my good wishes for her and her little family.

L. Pasteur

Here is a translation of Pasteur's letter.

128

Letter courtesy of the Pasteur Institute, Paris.

More about Joseph Meister

By 1888 many people were going to Louis Pasteur to be saved from rabies. Money had been gathered for the Pasteur Institute, and it had been built in Paris.

When Joseph Meister grew up, he became a guard at the gate of the institute. He is shown below standing beside the statue that reminds people of Pasteur's battle against rabies.

129

Photograph courtesy of the New York Academy of Medicine Library.

Cars of Yesterday

In Canada and the United States there are museums in which old cars are on display. Bellm's "Cars of Yesterday" museum in Sarasota, Florida, has over a hundred antique cars. Some of these cars, and Canada's first car, are described on these pages. Notice that the number of cylinders, the horse power (hp), and the miles per hour (mph) increased quite a bit from 1897 to 1930.

1897 DURYEA—2 cylinder, air-cooled engine.

1899 LOCOMOBILE STEAMER—2 cylinder, 5½ hp at 300 pounds steam pressure. The engine and boiler are under the seat.

1901 OLDSMOBILE 1 cylinder, 4½ hp. This curved-dash model was America's first mass-produced car.

1902 STANLEY STEAMER—2 cylinder, 5½ hp. This car was nicknamed "Teakettle on Wheels." It took seven minutes to build up enough steam to get it to go.

1904 RAMBLER—1 cylinder, 8 hp. The ring under the steering wheel is the accelerator.

1898 WINTON
The second "gasoline automobile" sold in North America. Bought for $1000 by Mr. John Moodie of Hamilton, Ont., in April, 1898. The car could go 15 miles on a gallon of gasoline and do 25 to 35 mph. Note the row of nails to discourage riding on the rear deck.

1898 WINTON—Canada's first car after it was remodelled in the winter of 1898. Mr. Moodie had the style of his car changed to include a backing seat and a railing so that he could take his family driving.

Photos from the June, 1926 issue of *Canadian Motorist*. Reprinted by permission of the Ontario Motor League.

133

1908 NATIONAL—4 cylinder, 50 hp, aluminum body. This was a famous racing car. It sold for $4000.

1910 FORD
4 cylinder, 18.5 hp. This Model-T Torpedo was Ford's first sports car.

1911 STAVER SPECIAL
4 cylinder, 65 mph in
second gear. This early
hot rod is the only car
of its kind ever built.

**1911 WAVERLEY
ELECTRIC**
The batteries operating
this car were under the
front and back hoods.
They needed to be charged
every 60 to 80 miles, or
about every four hours.

1914 OVERLAND
4 cylinder. This is one
of the first cars with
electric lights and a starter.

135

1914 WOODS MOBILETTE—4 cylinder, 12 hp, up to 45 miles on a gallon of gas. This car was very lightweight and economical.

1923 Chevrolet—4 cylinder, first foot accelerator. This car sold for $525.

1930 DUESENBERG—straight 8 engine, 265 hp, guaranteed to do 115 mph. Some Duesenbergs cost as much as $30,000. Every Duesenberg was custom-built.

Something to Do

Make a table showing the information in the article. Your table will begin like this:

DATE	NAME	CYLINDERS	HP	POWER	MPH	PRICE
1897	Duryea	2	---	---	---	---
1899	Locomobile Steamer	2	5½	Steam	---	---

You will not find in the article all seven things about each car, but you may know some of the things that are missing. If so, put them in your table.

Heroic Years of the Automobile

by Arthur R. Railton

First Auto Race

The first auto race of all time took place in France in 1895.

Emile Levassor won the race with a car he had designed. He drove the whole distance—732 miles—himself. It took him 48 hours and 48 minutes to drive from Paris to Bordeaux and back. The relief driver never touched the tiller.

Levassor's car had a gasoline engine. Some cars in the race were powered by steam or by electricity.

The picture shows Levassor reaching the finish line in Paris.

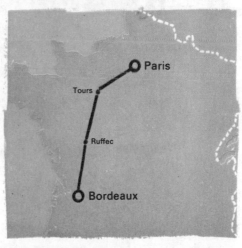

139

Text and pictures adapted from *Popular Mechanics* (January 1959). Published by Popular Mechanics Company.

Coast-to-Coast in the U.S.A.

Two men and a dog made the first coast-to-coast trip in 1903.

Doctor H. Nelson Jackson and a mechanic, Sewall K. Crocker, left San Francisco on May 23 to drive to New York. Their car was a 1903 Winton. It had an extra gas tank and was loaded with camping equipment.

When the party crossed the desert, even the dog wore goggles. They reached New York 64 days after the start.

The picture shows Doctor Jackson driving across canvas spread over a soft spot in the sand.

Across Two Continents

On June 10, 1907, five autos left Peking, China, to race 9000 miles to Paris. No one had done this before. No one was sure what lay ahead.

Owner and driver of one car, the Itala, was an Italian prince, Scipione Borghese.

The Itala won the race. It got to Paris 61 days after the start.

The picture shows Borghese in his car being pulled up over a mountain pass in China.

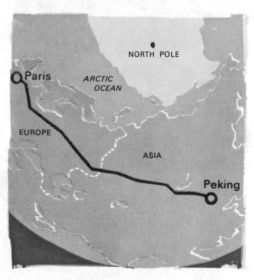

143

Race Around the World

Six cars left New York City on February 12, 1908, to go by land all the way to Paris. The cars were to cross the Bering Straits on ice. The drivers found they could not make the trip on land.

Months later three of the cars did get to Paris. They had followed the route shown on the map below.

The picture shows one of the cars stuck in the mud in Indiana, early in the race.

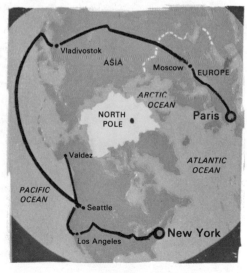

145

First "Fill 'Er Up!" Stations

When automobiles first coughed their way down the streets of North America, horses and people were scared. The horses neighed, and the people ran for cover.

In spite of the fright that those first automobiles caused, they soon became popular in the United States and Canada. The two countries were on their way to becoming nations on wheels.

Text and illustration adapted from *Action Time Magazine* (1962, Vol. 1, No. 1). By permission of Edwards and Deutsch Lithographing Company.

People who drove automobiles had to have fuel to put in them. In 1900, gasoline was sold in few places. Drivers sometimes had to settle for a can of benzine bought at a drugstore.

Canada's first filling station, in Vancouver, was a tiny iron shed. A small garden hose, without a nozzle, brought the gasoline to the cars from a kitchen "hot-water" tank.

Canada's pioneer gasoline station was set up at the corner of Cambie and Smythe streets in Vancouver in 1908. It was probably the first gasoline station in North America. In the early "filling stations," gasoline was stored inside a shack. One five-gallon can of gasoline at a time was brought from the shack to a

147

Photograph from the February, 1939 issue of *Canadian Motorist*. Reprinted courtesy of the Ontario Motor League.

curbside pump. Sometimes the gasoline was poured through a chamois to strain it. But many times in those days the gasoline was not strained. Often it had dirt and sometimes even bits of grass in it. A filling station man had to have a measuring can and a funnel to measure and pour the gasoline he sold.

As automobiles and filling stations became more common, free services began to be offered. The first were free air and free water.

It is not known who built the first actual "service station." It is known that the first ones were smaller than hot dog stands. But Canada never could have become a nation on wheels without them.

"If I had wanted the car washed, I would have said so."

Section Three

Bluey

by IRENE HILTON

Jacaranda Cottage

It was almost Christmas Day in Sydney, Australia. Bluey and Stan were watering flowers in Stan's back yard. Now and then they would turn the hose on each other. But they still felt as hot as boiled lobsters.

"Stan! Bluey!" Stan's mother called from the house. She was waving a letter at them.

They dropped the hose and went over to hear what she had to say.

"It's a letter from Grandpa," Mrs. Green told the boys. "He says to bring Bluey when we visit him and Grandma for the holidays. Bluey, would you like to go with us for Christmas and Boxing Day?"

"Wowser! Would I just!" Bluey said eagerly.

Bluey's name was Cecil Bishop. But everyone called him Bluey. He liked the name because almost every redhead in Australia was called "Bluey."

At four o'clock on Christmas Eve, Bluey went to Stan's house. There was much scurrying to the car and back as the Green family and Bluey loaded the car with luggage and Christmas presents. It looked as if they were leaving town for a year instead of two days.

The older children in the Green family, Stan, Sonny, and Eve, squeezed into the back seat along with Bluey. Then Mr. and Mrs. Green piled packages on their knees until there was a mound of parcels topped by a

151

line of children's heads. Kookie, Bluey's kookaburra bird, was in the back seat, too. The littlest Green girl, Dawn, sat in the front with her parents. She would have been buried in the back.

The five children began singing at the tops of their voices as soon as the car was on its way.

The more the car swerved and swayed on the twisty road, the more the children enjoyed it. They were too busy singing to admire the beautiful scenery as the road wound over the hills. They were too busy to be scared by the bare remains of trees burned black by bush fires of summers past.

Whenever the car swished by a pale golden beach, the children cheered.

At last the car pulled up at Grandpa Green's house.

"We're here, Grandpa! We're here, Grandma!" the children shouted. And they fell into the arms of their grandparents.

Bluey waited quietly until this noisy greeting was over. The little wooden house with its wide veranda looked cool and friendly. Across the road the giant gum trees of the Australian bushland were asking to be climbed. Behind the house, the beach and the sea spread to right and left. Bluey sighed contentedly. He was glad his mother had thought he should spend Christmas at this new place.

"Welcome to Jacaranda Cottage, Bluey," called Stan's grandfather over the heads of his grandchildren. "Time for a quick swim before tea."

Bluey thought that spending Christmas with a big family was wonderful. Kookie seemed to like it at Jacaranda Cottage, too. He perched on the roof or in a tree and gave his gurgling, laughing call. *Hoowah-hoowah-hee-hee-hee-ee-ee-ee!*

On Christmas Eve the Greens and Bluey sang all the carols they could think of. They finished with "Good King Wenceslas." No one thought it funny that on a blistering hot night they should think and sing only about the coldest things.

> Good King Wenceslas looked out
> > On the Feast of Stephen,
> Where the snow lay round about,
> > Deep and crisp and even;
> Brightly shone the moon that night,
> > Though the frost was cruel,
> When a poor man came in sight,
> > Gathering winter fuel.

On Christmas Day, Bluey looked at the thermometer hanging on the wall. "Grandpa Green," he said, "it's a hundred and ten in the shade."

"This weather's a fair scorcher," said Grandpa.

That night the heat was so stifling that Bluey and all of Stan's family stayed on the beach till long after bedtime.

"Where's our nice cool breeze tonight?" Grandma complained as she wiped her face.

Bluey shrugged. "It just gets hotter and hotter," he said, pouring water over himself and Stan.

The next day, Boxing Day, was even hotter. The whole family spent the morning on the beach. In the distance Jacaranda Cottage seemed to float and dance in the heat.

Stan's father said, "I'm certainly pleased there's no work today. Let's hope that the weather breaks by tomorrow."

But as the midday sun blazed down, there was no sign of any break in the weather.

After lunch the grown-ups tried to cool the house a little by hanging wet towels and blankets over the doors and windows.

The children were too hot to play. Bluey lay by the water's edge. Every few minutes the surf would come hissing over him. Then it would roll, hissing, back again. It was the only way to keep cool. He was drowsy and content.

Hoowah-hoowah-hoowah-hee-hee-hee-ee-ee-ee.

It sounded like Kookie in the distance. Nearer came the cry, and still nearer. Bluey sat up. That cry is too high, too sharp, Bluey thought. Something is wrong.

Again the kookaburra called. It was more like a scream than a laugh. It held a note of terror that made Bluey's blood run cold. Kookie burst through the trees, circling wildly. Then he screamed again and crashed into the roof of Jacaranda Cottage.

"Kookie!" Bluey cried. He jumped to his feet and ran toward his pet. The bird slithered down the roof and fell onto the stone path with a sickening thud.

"Kookie," Bluey said again as he gathered his pet into his arms. "You're hurt!"

Kookie's eyes were closed. Bluey placed one finger gently under the left wing. He thought he could feel the beating of a tiny heart. He smoothed Kookie's wings. What had terrified the bird so? He felt the legs and back. There were no broken bones.

He could hear more birds squawking in the distance. A flock of galahs, kookaburras, hawks, and sparrows flew screaming out of the bushland. Over the cottage roof they flew. Then they wheeled round and followed the coastline until they were out of sight.

Bluey's fingers touched something hard and scratchy.

What's that on your wings, Kookie? he wondered. He sniffed a couple of times.

Bush Fire

"I smell burning," Bluey said. "Your wings are burned, Kookie," he added in alarm. He sniffed again. No doubt about the smell of burning.

"There's a fire," he whispered hoarsely. Then at the top of his voice he cried, "Fire, everyone! Fire! Fire!"

Kookie lifted his head and made feeble movements with his wings.

"Easy there, Kookie," Bluey said as he laid the bird gently in the shade of a bush. Bluey ran to the jacaranda tree that grew by the house. He crouched under a thick branch. Then, flinging his hands high over his head, Bluey sprang upward. His fingers curled themselves round the branch. For a moment he hung there, swinging back and forth. Then with a mighty heave, he swung himself up. Up and up he went to the top of the tree like a young monkey, sending a shower of blue flowers to the ground.

Near the top he found a fork in the branch, where he sat, hanging on with both hands. The branches were thin and bouncy at this height.

A sudden movement could fling him into the air like a stone from a slingshot. So he sat quietly.

He stared out across the treetops. Thousands of birds were now flying wildly from the bushlands. Billowing black clouds arose in the distance.

"Smoke!" Bluey gasped. "The whole bushland is on fire. Where is everybody?" he groaned.

"Grandpa Green! Grandpa Green!" Bluey shouted at the top of his voice. "Bush fire! Come quick!"

Long tongues of flame zigzagged across the treetops in the distance.

"Bush fire! Bush fire!" Bluey shouted again. Had they all fallen asleep? His eyes followed the road to a point where it left the seashore and wound over the hill through the trees. Both sides of the road were already alight.

Rats, opossums, and rabbits, their fur flaming, were running for their lives along the road. A hawk swooped down out of the sky, grabbed a rabbit in its claws, and continued on its flight. The other animals sped on, terrified.

Bluey could hear the roar of a car speeding along the road, its horn blaring. Through the fire it sped, and blazing twigs bounced from its roof in a shower of sparks. As it roared past Jacaranda Cottage, Bluey waved at the soot-blackened men in it, letting them know he had heard their warning horn.

The four grown-ups came into the yard at last.

"Stay up there in the tree, Bluey," Grandpa Green shouted. "Keep your eyes on the flames as they come this way."

Stan and the other children came racing from the beach.

"Break off branches and dip them in the rain barrel," their father shouted to them.

Eve, Sonny, and Stan tore frantically at whatever bushes were nearest.

The children soaked the branches and threw them in a heap. The branches would be ready to use to beat out flames, if needed. The grown-ups threw blankets on the ground and soaked them with the hose.

Bluey turned his attention back to the fire. Spurts of flame were leaping from tree to tree. The fire was halfway along the stretch of road now.

"It's coming nearer," he called out.

Grandpa Green nodded to show he had heard.

"Take branches and spread out round the house," Grandpa Green ordered. The rest of his remarks were drowned by the roar of flames and the crackle of dry, burning timber. Showers of sparks were shooting through the air like a fireworks display.

As Bluey watched, he saw a tongue of fire lick the treetops on the other side of the road. Suddenly the trees burst into flames. From his perch high up in the jacaranda tree, Bluey could feel waves of heat blowing over him. It made him dizzy, so he tightened his grip on the branch.

Suddenly a blazing log broke free. It bounced into the middle of the road, sending sparks in all directions. Horrified, Bluey watched as the log rolled across the road and onto the lawn of the cottage.

"Fire, Grandpa, fire!" he shouted, pointing to the log. But his voice was drowned in the noise from the fire and the orders the two men were shouting.

Faster rolled the log and still faster. It smacked heavily against a wooden support of the front veranda and became wedged. It was still burning.

Bluey came down the tree as if it were a greased pole. Flames were spurting from the veranda. Bluey dashed up to Grandpa, snatched his wet blanket, and threw it on the flames. They sizzled and were gone.

Grandpa Green rushed to help Bluey. They rolled the burning log in the blanket. Then they rolled the whole bundle away from the house.

"Good work, Bluey," Grandpa Green panted. He picked up a stick and beat a loud tattoo on the drainpipe. Everyone came running.

"It's too dangerous for you children now," Grandpa warned them.

"But we want to help," the children insisted.

"Too dangerous," Grandpa Green panted. "The house has been on fire once. It could happen again. It could go up like a tinderbox. All of you go and sit in the water among the rocks. It's the only safe place."

"We're not afraid. Let us help," Bluey insisted.

"We can see you're not afraid," Stan's father said. "But it won't be much help if one of you gets hurt."

"Dad's right," Stan said.

"I suppose so," Bluey agreed.

"The way you can help best, Bluey, is to lead the way to the beach and get in the water. Now hurry!" said Mr. Green. "Stan, you go last. Make sure the others get there safely."

The grown-ups took positions in front of the house. Mr. Green picked up the hose and sprayed the blankets again. Then he sprayed the wooden porch and front of the house.

Storm

Bluey picked up Kookie. Then slowly, unwillingly, he led the way toward the ocean. The other children followed. Bluey started across the beach. Then he halted uncertainly. He lifted his face high. He licked a finger and held it up.

"The wind! The wind!" Bluey shouted as the other children eyed him curiously.

Before he could say more, a great gust swirled across the beach and slapped against their chests.

Bluey spun round and raced back to the house.

"A real southerly buster! Feel it!" he shouted to the grown-ups.

The little house shook and rattled. Dry branches scraped against one another. Flames and billowing smoke rolled back over the wild bushland.

The wind roared in from the ocean. There was a blinding flash of lightning. Thunder growled from behind the little group standing before Jacaranda Cottage. Their faces were hit by big raindrops.

"Look at that storm!" Bluey shouted, pointing to the sea. Inky black clouds were rolling in. Suddenly a lightning flash seemed to tear the clouds wide open. Bluey felt as though a bucket of cold water had been emptied on him.

"Look at the rain!" he cried.

Everyone stood staring as rain doused the flames. The burning trees sizzled when the water hit them. Steam and smoke swirled up toward the sky.

It was very dark now. The blanket of storm clouds had blotted the sunlight out entirely. Rain beat down on the roof like a drummer in a band.

The more rain that fell, the more excited they all became.

"It saved us! It saved us!" Bluey sang at the top of his voice. He danced a jig and waved his arms in the air. The others joined in, even the grown-ups. They were all dancing, with the rain streaming down their faces.

The storm stopped as suddenly as it began.

Back to Sydney

After supper Mr. Green drove his family and Bluey home. Kookie rode in the back seat with the children, as before. Everyone could see treetops shining like glowworms in the night as the wind whipped the smoldering branches. Sometimes a crash and a shower of sparks showed where a tree fell. Everyone was glad to get back to the city, safe from bushland fires.

Locating Information

The story "Bluey" told two things about Boxing Day. If you do not remember what they were, skim pages 151, 154, and 155 to find out.

If you look in a dictionary, you will find this:

> **box ing** (bok′sing), the sport of fighting with the fists. *n.*
> **Boxing Day,** December 26, a legal holiday in several provinces.

In an encyclopedia you will find this:

> **BOXING DAY** is a holiday that is celebrated in Great Britain and in some Canadian provinces on the first weekday after Christmas. It may have originated in the custom of giving Christmas boxes to tradesmen, servants, and minor public officials, such as postmen and lamplighters. Many families now give small amounts of money instead of boxes, and Boxing Day is now observed as part of the legal Christmas holidays. The day, also known as St. Stephen's Day, is traditionally the time for a kind of theatrical called a Christmas pantomime.
> RAYMOND HOYT JAHN

If you do not know the words *traditionally, theatrical,* and *pantomime,* you will want to look them up.

Would you look in a dictionary or an encyclopedia to find out how to pronounce the words? to find out what the words mean?

Where in this book would you look to find out how to pronounce the words and what they mean?

Does a dictionary or an encyclopedia tell you more about a subject? What did you learn about Boxing Day from the encyclopedia that was not in the dictionary?

Animals of Australia

The kookaburra belongs to the kingfisher family. It is one of the best-known birds of Australia. It eats snakes, frogs, insects, and lizards. The kookaburra begins its song at dawn. The song is loud screams mixed with braying laughter. Is it any wonder that sleepy Australians call this bird the "bushman's clock" or "laughing jackass"?

The koala or Australian bear looks very much like a teddy bear. It is about 2 feet long with gray, woolly fur. The koala lives in eucalyptus trees and eats the leaves and buds of the trees. It feeds at night and sleeps during the day. A koala baby is about an inch long at birth. It lives in its mother's pouch for six months. Then the baby rides piggyback on its mother's back until almost fully grown.

The cuscus is another pouched animal. It lives in trees in the rain forests of Australia. Thick, woolly fur protects it from the rain. It eats fruit, small birds, and insects. The cuscus usually moves only at night, and then very slowly. It uses its long tail to grab branches as it moves.

The kangaroo has a small head, short front legs, and long, powerful hind legs and tail. The tail helps the animal sit up. Kangaroo babies are about an inch long when they are born. They stay in the mother's pouch until they are big enough to hop around. Full-grown kangaroos have been known to hop as fast as 30 miles an hour and as high as 30 feet in the air. They eat grasses and herbs.

The platypus is one of the two egg-laying mammals in the world. It has webbed feet with claws, and a bill like a duck's. It lives near rivers and streams and eats the shellfish, worms, and insects it finds in the water and mud. The platypus is about 18 inches long. It is hard to get a good look at this animal because it is very shy. A platypus spends most of its time in its burrow on a riverbank.

The echidna is sometimes called the porcupine anteater, spiny anteater, or Australian porcupine. It is the only egg-laying mammal besides the platypus, but it does not look like the platypus. It is a land animal and eats ant larvae. The eggs of the echidna are carried in its pouch. When the young hatch, they live in the pouch for several weeks.

Christmas Day Weather

This weather map appeared in the *Sydney Morning Herald* of December 26, 1964.

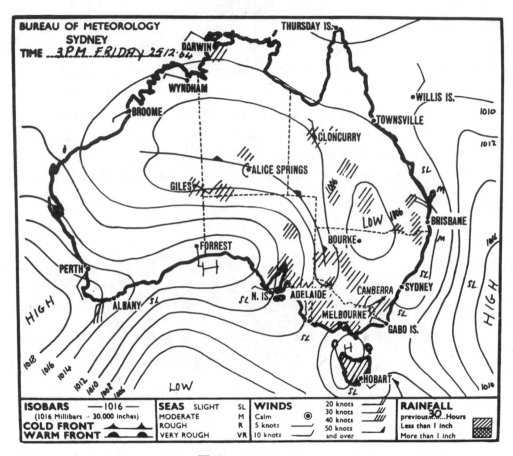

Temperatures

	Maximum	Minimum		Maximum	Minimum
Melbourne	78	59	Hobart	63	55
Brisbane	83	71	Adelaide	70	62
Sydney	80	69	Perth	74	58
Canberra	77	58	Darwin	89	74

This weather map was prepared by the Vancouver Weather Office, December 26, 1964.

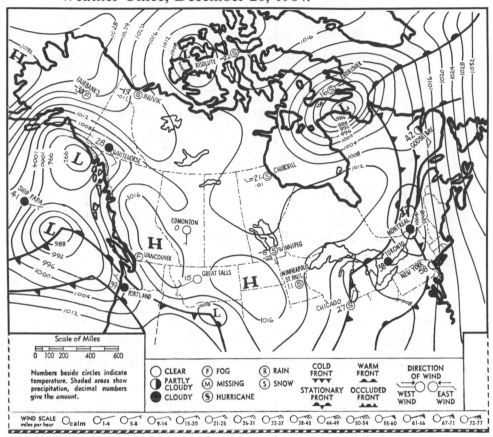

Temperatures

	Maximum	Minimum		Maximum	Minimum		Maximum	Minimum
Baker Lake	—41	—46	Lethbridge	23	—25	St. John's	44	28
Calgary	18	—16	Montreal	53	41	Saskatoon	—10	—34
Charlottetown	51	43	Moosonee	14	—2	Sydney	45	37
Churchill	—20	—28	North Bay	40	24	The Pas	—13	—22
Edmonton	8	—24	Ottawa	49	35	Toronto	51	35
Fort William	9	—10	Peace River	8	—22	Uranium City	—22	—38
Fredericton	49	39	Penticton	17	5	Vancouver	29	10
Frobisher	18	—18	Prince George	—7	—26	Victoria	34	30
Gander	41	29	Prince Rupert	26	0	Whitehorse	0	—10
Goose Bay	45	20	Quebec City	47	34	Windsor	42	36
Halifax	51	46	Regina	—10	—31	Winnipeg	—5	—26
Inuvik	—13	—25	Resolute	—1	—25	Yellowknife	—36	—42

Write answers to these questions on a piece of paper. Be ready to discuss your answers.

Are the temperatures shown on pages 170 and 171 for Christmas Day or for Boxing Day? How do you know?

What temperature is shown on page 170 for Bluey's hometown? If you do not remember the name of his hometown, reread page 151.

What would Irene Hilton, the author of "Bluey," have had to change in the story if she had written about Christmas and Boxing Day of 1964? Rereading pages 154 and 155 will give you a clue.

The word *isobar* appears underneath the Australian weather map. Look this word up in the glossary. Then study the Australian weather map and the weather map of Canada. Are there isobars shown on the map of Canada?

Information about wind appears below both weather maps. Find the information and decide what word is used on the Australian map instead of the term "miles per hour."

Find the word in the glossary. What does it mean?

On page 171 find the maximum temperature of a city near your home. Was it colder, warmer, or about the same temperature as in Sydney, Australia?

Bottle Barometer

This bottle barometer is a good weather forecaster.

● Partly fill a wide-mouthed bottle with water.

● Place a saucer over the mouth of the bottle so that the underside of the saucer is on top. Now turn the whole thing upside down, holding the saucer tightly against the bottle. Put a little water in the saucer.

● Make a scale for the outside of the bottle. Use a ruler to mark inches and half inches on a strip of paper. Paste this scale on the bottle.

As the atmospheric pressure rises and falls, the water will rise and fall inside the bottle.

When a high-pressure area, or good weather, is approaching, the water will rise on the scale.

When rain, or a low-pressure area, is approaching, the water will fall.

173

"Bottle Barometer" from *Kitchen Table Fun* by Avery Nagle and Joseph Leeming. Copyright © 1961 by Avery Leeming Nagle. Published by J.B. Lippincott Company.

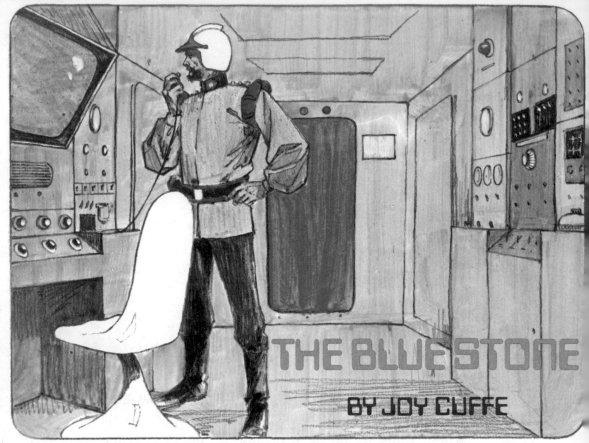

THE BLUE STONE

BY JOY CUFFE

CHARACTERS

CAPTAIN ROACH	NUMBER FIVE
NUMBER TWO	CASRA
NUMBER THREE	VOICE
NUMBER FOUR	

(The time is the future, the scene is the control room of a moon Sub-Station. There are three doors [Centre, Right, Left]. Right and left doors lead to living quarters. Centre door guards two locked chambers through which entrance must be made to the Sub-Station. The locks are controlled by turning Wheels 1, 2, and 3 on the instrument panel [Stage Right]. The panel also has a dial to control the supply of oxygen [Dial 0]. There is a red warning light above the panel.

Curtain rises on an empty stage. Strange music is heard. The television is not on; but from a radio transmitter and receiver [Stage Left] a message is coming through.)

Adapted from the June, 1966 edition of *School Magazine*, Volume 51, number 5, published by the New South Wales Department of Education. Copyright, 1965, by Joie Elsa Cuffe (Joy Cuffe) and reprinted by her permission.

VOICE (*amplified*): Earth calling Lunar Sub-Station. Come in, Lunar. . . . (CAPTAIN ROACH *enters, Stage Right, and hurries across to radio set.*) Earth calling Lunar Sub-Station. Come in, Lunar. . . . Come in, Lunar. . . .

ROACH (*on microphone*): Lunar receiving Earth. Captain Roach reporting. Come in, Earth. Over.

VOICE: Captain, is all in order there? Over.

ROACH: Yes, all in order. The expedition went out two weeks ago. They have just contacted me. We are expecting them to return fifteen-thirty hours today. Over.

VOICE: Have they located the Blue Stone? Over.

ROACH: Yes. They are bringing in a sample. Over to you.

VOICE: Who are the explorers? Over.

ROACH: Number Three and Number Five. Two and Four are here. Over.

(*There is static interruption. The voice which continues is that of* CASRA.)

CASRA: Here are further orders, Captain Roach. When the explorers return, contact Earth immediately. Over.

ROACH (*unconcerned about change of voice, speaks wearily*): Orders understood. Over and out (*replaces microphone*).

TWO (*entering, yawning, Stage Left*): What time is it?

ROACH: Fifteen hundred hours. Is Number Four awake?

TWO: Yes. He's coming.

(*Enter* NUMBER FOUR, *Stage Left.*)

ROACH: Earth made contact while you slept. They must still be having trouble with transmission. They even switched operators during the message.

TWO: Are they worried that the others won't find the Blue Stone?

ROACH: Three and Five also radioed while you slept. They have found the Blue Stone!

TWO: At last! Where did they find it?

ROACH: Eighteen miles from the Island Crater.

TWO: Then they're on the way back?

ROACH: Yes. They should be here fifteen-thirty hours.

FOUR: Imagine finding the Blue Stone that has far more radioactive power than any material on Earth.

TWO: Imagine the problems of mining it!

FOUR: When will we be going home to Mother Earth?

ROACH: Not yet, Number Four. Orders are to contact Base as soon as we have a sample of the Stone. (*Red warning light flashes at three-second intervals. On. Off. On. Off.*)

TWO: Captain!

FOUR: The light! They're here! They're outside!

ROACH: They're early! Get to the radio, Number Four. (*Local inter-communication. Simple switch control.*)

FOUR (*microphone*): Lunar to Three. Come in, Three and Five.

THREE (*voice through amplifier*): Open up and let us in!

ROACH (*takes microphone*): Captain Roach here, Number Three. Is the Stone enclosed in a radiation-proof bag?

THREE (*amplifier*): Yes, sir. Everything's under control.

ROACH: Right! We'll open up. (*He motions to* NUMBER TWO, *who takes wheel control, Stage Right.*) Open lock, Number Two.

TWO: Open lock. (*turns Wheel 1*) Right, sir.

FOUR (*on microphone*): Lunar to Three. Air lock opening. (*Pause*)

THREE (*amplifier*): O.K. We're in.

ROACH: Close lock!

TWO: Close lock. (*reverses Wheel 1*) It's tight, sir.

ROACH: Leave the Blue Stone in the outer chamber. Repeat that order.

THREE (amplifier): Order understood. I repeat: leave the Blue Stone in the outer chamber. We're ready for second lock.

ROACH: Right, Number Two, open lock!

TWO: Open lock. (*turns Wheel 2*)

FOUR (*on microphone*): Air lock open. Safe to proceed into second chamber, Three and Five.

THREE (*amplifier*): Moving in now. (*Pause*) We're in!

ROACH: Close lock, Number Two!

TWO: Close lock. (*reverses Wheel 2*)

ROACH: Increase the supply of oxygen!

TWO: Increasing oxygen. (*turns Dial 0*)

176

FOUR (*on microphone*): O.K., Three and Five. Remove space suits.

TWO: I'm glad they're back! They've been gone for fourteen days.

ROACH: Yes, fourteen days out there! It's as much as a man can stand. Fourteen days . . . fierce, naked light. No winds to stir the dust, no waters to moisten it. No cloud in the airless sky. No movement. No life . . . .

(*Buzzer, on amplifier*)

FOUR: There's the buzz! They're ready to come in.

ROACH: Right, Number Two. Open up!

TWO: Opening, sir. (*turns Wheel 3*)
(*Centre door to give appearance of automatic opening. Red light ceases. Enter* NUMBER THREE *and* NUMBER FIVE.)

ROACH: Welcome home!

FIVE: Thanks, sir. Whew! What a trip!

THREE: How about something to eat?

FOUR: I'll get a meal. Real food! On the double! (*Exit, Stage Right*)

ROACH: Did the food capsules last?

THREE: Well enough. During the intense heat we weren't very hungry. It's good to be back!

ROACH: We'd better contact Earth, Number Two. (NUMBER TWO *goes to radio, turns a complex system of dials, and sets transmitter.*)

TWO (*on microphone*): Lunar Sub-Station to Earth. Come in, Earth. Lunar Sub-Station to Earth . . .

VOICE (*amplifier*): Earth to Lunar. Earth to Lunar . . . (*There is static, as before.* ROACH *moves to radio.*)

ROACH (*on microphone*): Lunar reporting. Come in, Earth. Over.

CASRA (*amplifier*): Earth to Lunar Sub-Station. Are you receiving, Captain Roach? Over.

ROACH (*on microphone*): Roach reporting. Receiving loud and clear. Explorers have returned with a sample of the Blue Stone. Awaiting further orders. Over.

CASRA (*amplifier*): Listen carefully, Captain Roach! We have learned that the rays in the Blue Stone are capable of piercing the radiation-proof bag. If this happens, the rays can easily penetrate the door between the outer and inner chamber. If they combine with the oxygen in the inner chamber, an explosion will destroy everything. Can you remove the Blue Stone from the Sub-Station at once? Over.

ROACH (*microphone*): Lunar to Earth! . . . Message received. There is no way we can do it in a hurry. The men are out of their space suits. What do you advise? Lunar to Earth . . . Lunar to Earth . . . . I can't make contact! It's dead!

THREE: The Blue Stone! Why didn't they warn us before?

ROACH: I don't know. But . . . if those blue rays pierce the sealing door, we're dead men!

THREE: But, sir, our ship's out there! We could escape!

ROACH: And how do we reach it without using the air lock?

TWO: But we can't just sit here and do nothing! Any moment now those blue rays will pierce the protective bag!
(*Red warning light flashes at three-second intervals. On. Off. On. Off.*)

FIVE: The radar, sir!

ROACH: What? . . . Something's out there! Switch on the televiewer!

TWO (*at screen, Right*): Televiewer on, sir.
(*They group in front of the screen, obscuring audience view.*
NUMBER FOUR *enters, Stage Right.*)

FOUR: What is it? What's the matter?

THREE: Look!

FIVE: What are they?

ROACH: A fleet of ships!

TWO: Round, like saucers!

THREE: Look at them glow! Like lamps in the dark . . .

FIVE: They're so still!

ROACH: How many are there? One, two, three, four . . .

THREE: Five, six, seven . . .

ROACH: They're not ours. So whose ships are they?
(*They stand watching the red light as it flashes. On. Off. On. Off.*)

TWO: Captain! The viewer! (*They stand back.*) It's blank! (*checks the radio*) It's not an instrument problem. What happened?

ROACH (*looking again at flashing light*): I . . . don't know . . .

CASRA (*amplifier*): Captain Roach!

THREE: Listen!

ROACH: It's Earth! They've made contact! (*goes to radio*)

CASRA (*amplifier*): No, Captain Roach. I am not from your Earth. I am Commander of the ships that landed.

ROACH (*on microphone*): Captain Roach here. Who are you?

CASRA (*amplifier*): Open the air lock, Captain Roach!

ROACH (*on microphone*): Who are you? Why have you come here?

CASRA (*amplifier*): You are in great danger, Captain Roach. I have come to control the destructive rays of the Blue Stone. Open the air lock!

ROACH (*on microphone*): Whoever you are, it's too late! To enter the lock means death!

CASRA (*amplifier*): Captain Roach, the Blue Stone has no effect upon me. Open the air lock!

THREE: At least it's better than doing *nothing*, sir!

ROACH (*considers for a moment*): Open the lock, Number Two!

TWO: Yes sir. Open lock. (*turns Wheel 1 in firm grip*)
(*Strange music is heard all the time* CASRA *is on the Sub-Station.*)

CASRA (*amplifier*): I am in. Close the lock now, Captain Roach.

ROACH: Close lock!

TWO: Close lock. (*reverses Wheel 1*) It's tight, Captain.

ROACH: Well, he's in. Now, we wait! (*Pause. Silence. Light continues to flash On, Off, On, Off, until* CASRA *comes on stage.*)

TWO: It seems forever.

CASRA (*amplifier*): I have finished. Please open the second lock, Captain Roach.

ROACH: Is the Blue Stone under complete control?

CASRA: It is perfectly safe now.

ROACH: Open lock, Number Two!

TWO: Lock open, sir. (*turns Wheel 2*)

CASRA: I'm in, Captain Roach.

ROACH: Close second lock!

TWO: Lock closed, sir. (*reverses Wheel 2*)

ROACH: Increase oxygen, Number Four.

FOUR: Increasing oxygen, sir. (*turns Dial 0*)

CASRA (*amplifier*): It is safe to open the emergency doors now, Captain.

ROACH (*hesitantly*):
Number Two, open
the third lock . . .

TWO: Yes, sir. Third
lock open! (*turns Wheel 3*)

ROACH: Be on guard!

(*Centre door opens slowly.
Red light ceases flashing.*)

(CASRA *stands, as door
opens and remains open.
The form is clad in
space-protective material,
unburdened, and of such
utter simplicity that the
beauty of the personality
is dominant. The face and
hair are blue, and about
the whole form lies the
suggestion of this one
color, even to the silicate
dust on the shoulders.*)

CASRA: I am Casra.

ROACH: Where are you from?

CASRA: I am from another
Solar System.

ROACH: Then you travel
millions of miles in those
ships!

TWO: How long does it take
you to reach this Moon?

CASRA (*stepping forward as
centre door closes*):
We travel
beyond the speed of light.

ROACH: I didn't think
it possible . . .

CASRA: There are many things the Earthmen have yet to learn, Captain Roach. The Blue Stone has shown you that. You wanted its power, yet you did not understand that power.

ROACH: What does the Stone mean to you?

CASRA: It has been used by our people for a long time.

ROACH: Have you always found it here, on our Moon?

CASRA: Yes. On each trip we usually collect sufficient Stone to last a hundred of your years. There were no Earthmen on the Moon when we were last here.

ROACH: How do you use the Blue Stone? What power does it have?

CASRA: Exactly the power that your scientists believe it has. Amazing radioactive power . . . . Did you not say so, only half an hour ago, Captain Roach?

ROACH: How . . . ?

CASRA: My friend, I have been aware, for some time, of all you have said and of all you have tried to do.

ROACH: Your voice . . . it's familiar . . . the radio!

TWO: The warning! The static interruption!

CASRA: Your radio methods are simple, Captain Roach. To intercept is easy. I pretended to be an Earthman to help you. I did not think you would believe Casra . . .

TWO: But why help us?

CASRA: I was here. . . . It was no bother. There is plenty of room in the universe for all creatures. Earthmen are welcome. It is good to know you are learning.

ROACH: We all thank you!

THREE: Are there many on your planet?

CASRA: There are many.

FIVE: Do you travel far?

CASRA: We travel the universe.

ROACH: Tell us, is there an end to the universe?

CASRA (*studies him before answering*): We have not found it. (*Pause*) Now, Earthmen, I must go.

ROACH: So soon? But you've only—

CASRA: I must go. Open the lock, Captain Roach.

181

ROACH: We can't let you go, just like that! There's so much . . .

CASRA: The time has come for me to go. I have enclosed the Blue Stone in a bag of the same special material that I am wearing. The blue rays cannot penetrate it. Guard the stone well. It holds many secrets.

ROACH: Will we see you again?

CASRA: You have seen me once. In your imagination you will see me again. (*Raises his hand, signalling for closing of door.*)

ROACH: Close the door, Number Two.

TWO: Door closing.

(TWO *takes Wheel 3. Door closes. The backs of the players are to the audience, as the crew stands, shoulders square, intent upon the departure of* CASRA.)

CASRA (*amplifier*): I am ready for the next lock, Captain Roach.

ROACH: Open second lock!

TWO: Open lock. (*turns Wheel 2*)

CASRA (*amplifier*): I am in the first chamber.

ROACH: Close lock.

TWO: Close lock. (*reverses Wheel 2*)

CASRA (*amplifier*): I am ready to leave.

ROACH: Open first lock.

TWO: First lock open. (*turns Wheel 1*)

ROACH (*amplifier*): Are you there, Casra? . . . Are you there? . . . (*Red light flashes: On; Off; On; Off. Men concentrate on light. Music fades.*)

ROACH (*when flashing stops*): He's gone . . . . Close lock.

TWO: Lock closing. (*reverses Wheel 1*) Right, sir.

(*They all turn, puzzled, and gaze at one another.*)

THREE: What did he mean . . . in our imagination we'll see him again?

ROACH (*stands, not answering for a moment, then speaks thoughtfully, slowly, to his crew*): Perhaps we have hit upon something so far ahead of us in Time that we're not quite sure what was real and what was not. . . . (*Walks slowly downstage.*) Perhaps what has just occurred was nothing more than a product of our imaginations . . . (*Faces audience. Pause. Speaks directly to them.*) After all, what you have just seen . . . hasn't happened. . . . Yet!

(*Music surges. Curtain.*)

Space

What is space? It is the lonely, airless region that lies outside the earth's atmosphere.

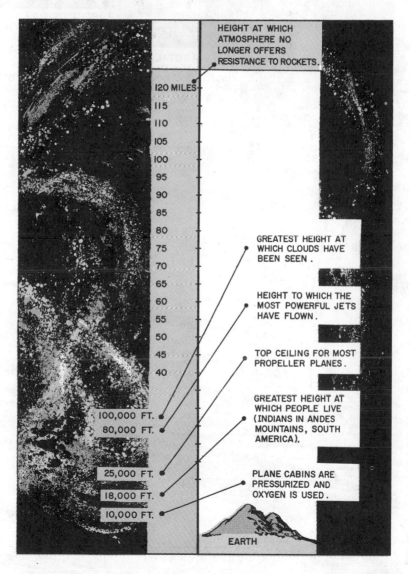

HEIGHT AT WHICH ATMOSPHERE NO LONGER OFFERS RESISTANCE TO ROCKETS.

120 MILES
115
110
105
100
95
90
85
80
75
70
65
60
55
50
45
40

GREATEST HEIGHT AT WHICH CLOUDS HAVE BEEN SEEN.

HEIGHT TO WHICH THE MOST POWERFUL JETS HAVE FLOWN.

TOP CEILING FOR MOST PROPELLER PLANES.

GREATEST HEIGHT AT WHICH PEOPLE LIVE (INDIANS IN ANDES MOUNTAINS, SOUTH AMERICA).

100,000 FT.
80,000 FT.

PLANE CABINS ARE PRESSURIZED AND OXYGEN IS USED.

25,000 FT.
18,000 FT.
10,000 FT.

EARTH

Text and pictures from *The Illustrated Story of Space* appearing in *Classics Illustrated* from *The World Around Us* series, January 1959. Published by Gilberton Company, Inc.

184

185

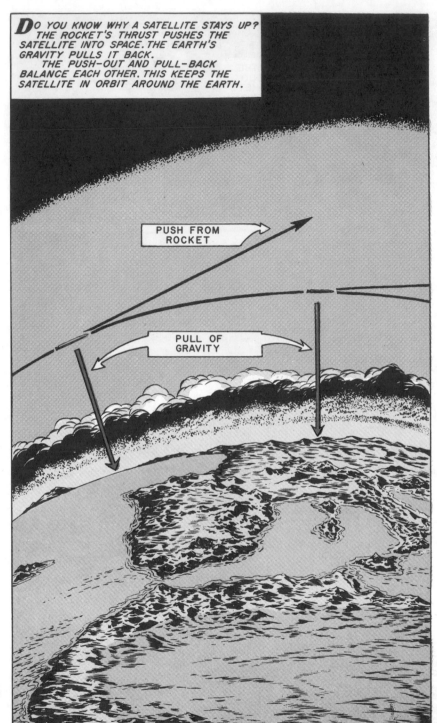

186

The answers to the following questions are in this book. Write your answers on a piece of paper. Write, also, where you found each answer.

When was the picture article on pages 183-186 written?

What is the greatest height at which clouds have been seen?

Where is Cape Kennedy?

What does the word *satellite* mean in this article?

What else can it mean?

What does NASA stand for?

Do you think this cartoon is funny? If not, maybe the information given on page 183 will help you see the joke.

187

Are There Men on Mars?

Debate began in the 1870's about life—even men—on the planet Mars.

It was 1877 when Giovanni Schiaparelli, an Italian astronomer, told about seeing crisscross lines on Mars. He called them *canali,* which means "channels." But people began using the English word *canals* for the lines. The canals, people said, were 1000 miles long. Earthmen had just spent ten years making the Suez Canal. It was only 100 miles long. Surely the 1000-mile canals must have been made by supermen!

Those canals caused writers to make up science-fiction stories about life on Mars and men from Mars.

In November 1964 the United States sent up the Mariner 4. It travelled 228 days, 325 million miles. Then in July 1965 its camera took pictures of Mars.

Photograph from NASA. (National Aeronautics and Space Administration, U.S.A.)

```
851089838102111580803400808190109529032010
   51031232257423
552502090314402006359221113011935580322253
871252818080809782308028908020948080928220
85008983810823158888087508080501095880321017
55553109121647200635342112251193558032250
871252048080831150308028988020972680048233
```

What the Mariner 4 camera saw came back to the earth in the form of numerals. Computers turned the numerals into pictures. When the Mariner 4 pictures had been printed, what did people learn about Mars?

They learned that Mars is more like the moon than like the earth. The part of Mars photographed seems never to have had oceans, lakes, rivers, or canals. Without water, intelligent life as we know it cannot exist. Are there men on Mars? Why does it seem unlikely?

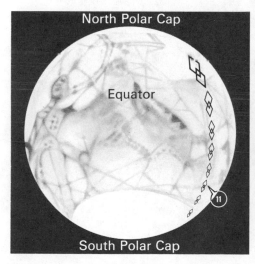

Area of Mars Photographed

Photograph Number 11

189

Diagram by Van Dyke. Used by permission of *Newsweek*. Photographs of coded telemetry message and Mars from NASA.

Men in Space

This cartoon was in a newspaper on March 24, 1965.

LADDER

These headlines and this table were in newspapers on June 3, 1965.

In the table find the names printed in the cartoon on page 190. Which name in the table is the real name of the "Molly Brown"? How did you decide?

4-DAY GEMINI SPACE TRIP AWAITS 9 A.M. BLAST-OFF
Gemini 4 Ready
McDivitt and White Ready
Aimed for a Space First

Other Manned Space Flights

CAPE KENNEDY (UPI) — Manned space flights to date:

Mission	Nation	Date	Crew	Flight	Spacecraft Weight
Vostok 1	USSR	4/12/61	Gagarin	1 Orbit	10,417 Lbs.
Freedom 7	US	5/5/61	Shepard	Sub-Orbital	3,000 Lbs.
Liberty Bell 7	US	7/21/61	Grissom	Sub-Orbital	3,000 Lbs.
Vostok 2	USSR	8/6-7/61	Titov	17 Orbits	10,430 Lbs.
Friendship 7	US	2/20/62	Glenn	3 Orbits	2,987 Lbs.
Aurora 7	US	5/24/62	Carpenter	3 Orbits	2,975 Lbs.
Vostok 3	USSR	8/11-15/62	Nikolayev	64 Orbits	10,428 Lbs.
Vostok 4	USSR	8/12-15/62	Popovich	48 Orbits	10,428 Lbs.
Sigma 7	US	10/3/62	Schirra	6 Orbits	3,030 Lbs.
Faith 7	US	5/15-16/63	Cooper	22.9 Orbits	3,000 Lbs.
Vostok 5	USSR	6/14-19/63	Bykovsky	81 Orbits	10,441 Lbs.
Vostok 6	USSR	6/16-19/63	Tereshkova	48 Orbits	10,428 Lbs.
Voskhod 1	USSR	10/12/64	Komarov Feoktistov Yegorov	16 Orbits	11,700 Lbs.
Voskhod 2	USSR	3/18/65	Belyayev Leonov	17 Orbits	11,700 Lbs.
Gemini 3	US	3/23/65	Grissom Young	3 Orbits	7,000 Lbs.

191

Table reprinted from the *Chicago Daily News*, June 3, 1965. Copyright © 1965 by United Press International.

Pictures like this one of Edward H. White II taking a walk in space appeared in news magazines in June 1965.

Photograph by James A. McDivitt, NASA.

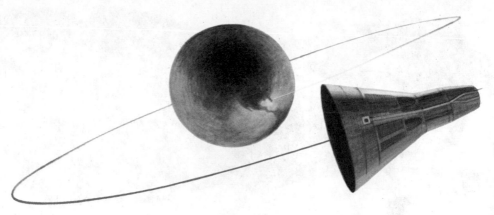

Orbiting English

Some space terms are very new. We know that *A-OK* means that everything is fine. But we do not know who first used the term. We may never know.

Space-age slang is used and understood by people at Cape Kennedy and by others who know a lot about space exploration. The terms printed in italic type in the following paragraph are space-age slang.

The *bird watchers* stared at *Big Joe* in disbelief. The call to *clear the pad* had already been sounded, and the *beast* was ready for *blast-off.* Unless a *bug* appeared to halt the countdown and cause a *scrub,* the *lox* would soon go to work and the rocket would *shed her skirt.* With the *go juice* ready and the *hot rock* inside the *greenhouse* in *go condition,* the *lift-off* was *in the green.*

Write in your own words what the last paragraph means. You may need to reread the paragraph before you write. If you do not know the meaning of a term printed in italics, you can find it on page 451.

Reprinted and adapted by permission from *Junior Scholastic,* © 1965 by Scholastic Magazines, Inc.

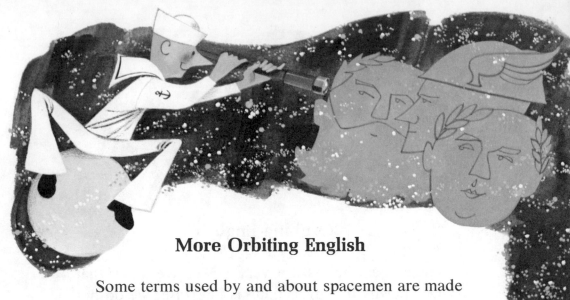

More Orbiting English

Some terms used by and about spacemen are made up of words that are very old.

The word *astronaut* comes from two Greek words. In Greek the word *astron* meant "star." And the word *nautes* meant "sailor."

"How lovely!" we say when we think of today's astronauts as "starsailors."

Parts of other space terms, like *Project Mercury, Saturn Booster,* and *Jupiter Missile,* also come from an ancient language, Latin. It was spoken by people in ancient Rome.

Mercury, Saturn, and Jupiter were names of Roman gods. Later these names were given to planets.

Have you heard?

BOB: If an athlete gets athlete's foot, what does an astronaut get?

JUDY: Don't ask me.

BOB: Missile toe!

Reprinted and adapted by permission from *Junior Scholastic,* © 1965 by Scholastic Magazines, Inc.

An Adventure with the Gods

by CATHARINE F. SELLEW

Preface

This story that I have written is not really my story. It is much older than I am. It is much older than your mother and father, or your grandmother and grandfather, or your grandfather's grandfather. It is so old that it was told thousands of years before America was discovered!

There weren't any books in those long-ago days. And in the ancient lands of Greece and Rome, the only stories people knew were told to them by men who went from town to town, singing of brave heroes, beautiful maidens, and terrible dragons. These men came to great feasts and sang to the guests about all the things they had seen and heard in other lands.

The people wondered about strange things in the sky and on the earth. They wondered why the plants and animals lived and grew and died. The singers at the feasts sang stories that gave answers to these questions.

People in those days didn't think of God as we do. So the singers sang about many powerful gods and goddesses who, they believed, made and ruled the earth. They sang of how these gods and goddesses helped as well as punished the people on earth.

This story is one of the songs that were sung at those feasts. Today we call them myths.

195

Adapted from *Adventures with the Gods* by Catharine F. Sellew, by permission of Little, Brown and Company. Copyright 1945, by Catharine F. Sellew.

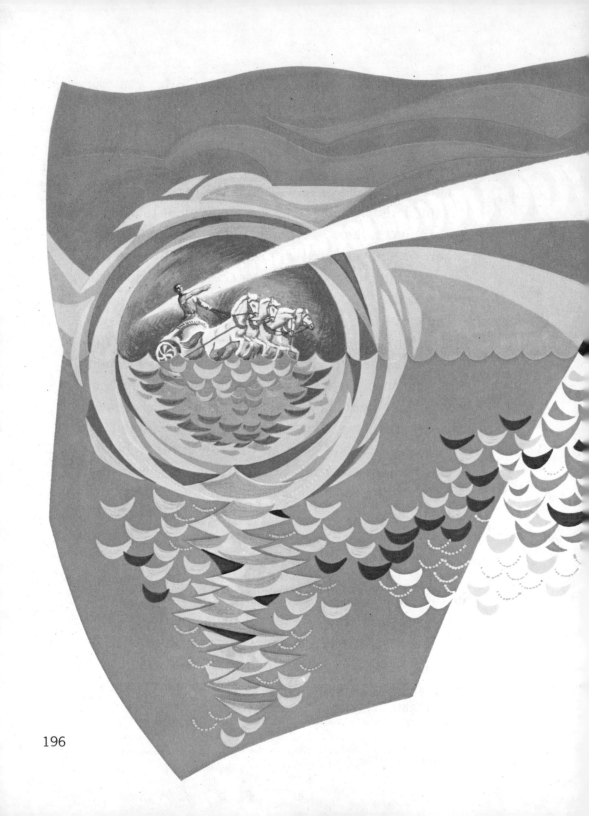

Mercury Makes a Lyre

One day a very long time ago, the god of the sun, Apollo, peeked up over the edge of the ocean. He shot one of his golden beams into the open mouth of a large, dark cave. The sunbeam fell on a newborn baby.

The baby laughed and kicked his heels joyfully in the air. He tried to catch the bright, pretty sunbeam with his hands. The sun did not know yet that this baby was his new brother, Mercury, who would one day be messenger of the gods. For Mercury's father was none other than the great Jupiter. And his mother was a beautiful nymph who lived by the sea.

Apollo soon lost interest. He rose high up in the sky—too far away to watch this wonder child.

Young Mercury sat up in his cradle and looked around. Where had that beautiful golden sunbeam gone?

But his mother was sleeping on her bed, and the cave was dark and cool again. Outside he could hear the waves washing up on the shore. He could hear the sea gulls' harsh cries. It looked bright and beautiful out there to Mercury.

Looking again at his mother and making sure that she was sound asleep, the baby climbed out of his cradle and tiptoed to the entrance of the cave. You must remember Mercury was not an ordinary baby. He was the youngest son of the great Jupiter, and he already had many godlike powers.

The sunlight was so bright after the darkness of the cave that Mercury had to blink and put his hand up to his eyes. But the air was warm and smelled of the salt of the sea. Mercury laughed with delight. It was a wonderful world!

A foamy wave slipped into the cave and ran around the moss-covered rocks and then slipped out again. The water felt cold to Mercury's toes, and he jumped to safety on a bigger brown rock.

Suddenly the brown rock began to move! It moved very slowly, but Mercury was so surprised that he was just a little bit afraid. He tried to hold on tight, but it was hard on such a smooth, round surface. Up and down! Up and down!

And then a head with two black, beady eyes came out from under the brown rock. But it wasn't a rock at all. It was a big turtle!

"Get off my back!" said the turtle in a very nasty tone of voice.

"I didn't know you were a turtle," said Mercury. And he laughed and laughed.

"Get off my back!" the turtle repeated. "I don't like little boys riding on my back. In fact, I don't like little boys at all!"

Then Mercury had an idea. It was an idea that only a very unusual baby would think of. The turtle's shell was pretty, and it made a nice sound when he tapped on it. First he killed the old turtle and took the shell from its back. Then he tiptoed into the cave and pulled nine linen threads tightly across the turtle's shell. When he touched the threads with his fingers, they made music. Mercury danced with delight out of the cave and into the sunshine. He had made a kind of small harp called a lyre.

The sand along the seashore was smooth and white and packed down hard by the pounding of the waves. Mercury ran and danced and jumped along the beach. When he looked behind him, he saw that his footprints made patterns in the sand. What fun it was!

For a long time Mercury played along the beach, going farther and farther away from his mother and the cave. After a while he came to a beautiful mountain. Its sides sloped down to the sea, and it was covered with large trees and smooth, grassy fields. Mercury was getting tired of the seashore. So he decided to climb the mountain. It was getting late. Apollo looked like a fiery red ball dropping down behind the mountain. But on the other side, the silvery white moon goddess, Diana, was sailing up into the sky. She gave plenty of light for this child, Mercury, who already could do things like a man.

Up and up the mountain he climbed, singing a gay little song all the time. Finally he came to a field. There, eating the sweet grass, was a great herd of cattle. There were oxen and cows, and they were much, much bigger than the oxen and cows that you and I see on the farms in the country. Mercury knew they were the cattle of his brother, Apollo, god of the sun! But, strangely enough, there wasn't anyone around to watch them.

"How careless of my brother," said Mercury. "He should know better than to leave his beautiful cattle unguarded." And Mercury smiled to himself.

Mercury Steals Apollo's Cattle

What a good joke it would be to drive the cattle out of the field and hide them! But Apollo would see their hoofprints and follow. Mercury hadn't forgotten his footprints in the sand on the seashore.

Mercury sat down on the ground and looked at the cattle. He thought for a few minutes. Suddenly he jumped up and began to gather some twigs. He tied them together in two bunches and then fastened one bunch on each of his feet.

"Now Apollo will never recognize my footprints," laughed Mercury. But the cattle? What was he going to do about the cattle's hoofprints? Mercury sat down again and thought some more.

"I know!" he finally said to himself. "I'll make them walk backwards." Then he broke a branch from a bush and drove the cattle backwards across wide fields and down the steep mountain.

On the way they passed an old man. The man was mending his fishing nets, and he stopped in surprise. Never had he seen such a sight in his life! Who was this baby driving a great herd of cattle backwards?

"Good evening," cried Mercury gaily.

The old man only stared at him in wonder.

"You look like a wise old man," said Mercury. "If you are, don't tell anyone that you saw me. The gods might be angry."

The old man nodded. He was unable to speak. He could not believe what he saw and heard.

Soon Mercury came to a valley into which there led only a narrow path. The steep mountains hid it from the sea on one side, and from nearby fields on the other. Here Apollo would not think to look for his cattle. Mercury laughed with glee. But he knew that his brother would be very angry. If he ever discovered that it was Mercury who had stolen them, he would punish him. Only their father, the great Jupiter, could protect Mercury from Apollo's anger.

Mercury did not think Apollo would miss just two of his great herd, and he thought that a sacrifice of such beautiful cattle would please his father very much. It was the custom in those days for people who were in trouble to make what they called a sacrifice to the gods in order to win their help. This meant burning something they liked very much on an altar. So Mercury killed two of Apollo's cattle and burned them in honor of Jupiter.

When he had finished the sacrifice, he kicked the ashes over the ground so there would be no trace of the fire or of what he had done. He was tired and sleepy after all this. So he left the cattle to graze in the hidden valley and ran back in the bright moonlight to his mother in her cave by the sea.

The next morning Apollo, great god of the sun, left his chariot standing up in the sky and came to earth to see his beautiful cattle. But, lo and behold, there was not one cow or ox in the field!

Apollo shouted, "By the great Jupiter! Someone has stolen my cattle!"

He raced across the field, calling his cattle. But the rocks threw back the echo of his voice as though mocking him. No other sound except the singing of the birds could be heard.

"By my father, the great Jupiter, the thief shall pay for this!" With these words, Apollo began to run down the mountainside. Suddenly he saw the marks of hoofs in the soft earth and, also, the crisscross print of some strange creature.

"What mark is this?" Apollo cried. "Surely no living creature has a foot like this! And the hoof-prints of my cattle lead only to their own field, but I saw for myself that they are no longer there!"

Apollo walked slowly on down the mountain. His forehead was wrinkled with thought.

At the foot of the mountain he met the old man who had been mending his fishing nets. The old man did not know that Apollo was a great god. He called out a greeting to the handsome stranger.

"Old man," Apollo replied, "have you seen any cattle passing this way?" The old man looked frightened and only shook his head. But when Apollo smiled at him and seemed so friendly, the man told Apollo about the strange thing he had seen.

"It was a young baby," the old man admitted. He hardly believed himself that what he said was true. "And he was driving a herd of cattle *backwards!*"

Apollo shouted with rage, but he thanked the old man before he raced on his way. It could be no other than his newborn brother. The great Jupiter had told him that very morning the news of Mercury's birth. Only the son of a god would be able to do such a deed when he was just a day old. How dared Mercury do such a thing!

When he reached the cave by the sea where Mercury and his mother slept, Apollo went up to his brother's cradle. Mercury lay with his head on the pillow and his lyre held tightly under one arm.

"Brother," Apollo cried, "what have you done with my cows and oxen?"

Mercury opened his eyes and said, "You woke me up."

Apollo asked his question again.

"Cows? Oxen?" Mercury said. "Brother, how should I know about such things? I was born only yesterday. I have never heard those words before. I could not have stolen those things."

Apollo was very angry. "That is a lie!" he cried. "You know where my cattle are." He picked Mercury up out of the cradle and shook him as hard as he could.

But Mercury only laughed. Then Apollo tried to tie Mercury's fists together with a rope. But with a quick twist of his hands, Mercury slipped away. He picked up his lyre and ran out of the cave.

"Mercury," Apollo called after him. "You shall be punished for this!" And he ran after his small brother and made him come with him before their father, the great Jupiter.

Jupiter listened to all that Apollo told him about the disappearance of the cattle and what the old man at the foot of the mountain had said. Then Jupiter, the king of the gods, asked Mercury to tell *his* story. Mercury saw that his father knew the truth. So he smiled and winked. His father laughed, but he did not forget what Mercury had done.

"You may have hidden your brother's cattle for a joke," Jupiter said. "But you should not have lied to him about it. Now it is right that your brother, Apollo, should punish you."

Then the great Jupiter turned to Apollo and said, "But remember, my son, it is good to be kind and forgiving to those who are yet young." Mercury heard this, but Apollo looked so angry that Mercury was afraid. Then he remembered the lyre he had made. He took it from under his arm and played on it and sang to his brother.

Apollo loved music. He had never seen or heard a lyre before, and he smiled with delight in spite of himself.

"You must give me that," he said to Mercury.

"But it's mine," Mercury cried. "I made it."

"You must pay for stealing my cattle and telling me that you did not. If you give me the lyre and show me where you hid my cattle, I will forgive you."

Mercury looked at his lyre. He ran his fingers across the strings and looked at his father.

"You must do what your brother asks," Jupiter said kindly but firmly. Mercury handed the lyre to Apollo and said that he would take him to his cattle.

"Do you promise never to do such a thing again?" Apollo asked.

Mercury looked down at his toes and nodded. He did not want Apollo to see the tears he was blinking back. He hated to give up his lyre.

Apollo smiled. "Then I will give you something to show that I have forgiven you," he said. And he handed Mercury a magic wand. It was very beautiful, with a tiny pair of wings on the end of it and two gold snakes twisted around it.

Mercury thanked Apollo for his kindness. Then taking him by the hand and clutching the new wand, Mercury led Apollo to the hidden valley. There were the beautiful cattle safely grazing in the fields.

Books to Read

Greek and Roman Myths, adapted by KAY WARE and LUCILLE SUTHERLAND. McGraw-Hill, 1952. (Webster Everyreader)

Read about Atlas, Jupiter, Apollo, etc., to learn why these names are used in the space program. Read, also, about Midas, the king with the golden touch, and Pegasus, a horse with wings.

FELTON, HAROLD W. *Sergeant O'Keefe and His Mule, Balaam.* Dodd, 1962.

Ancient peoples had legends. There are modern legends, too. These are often called "tall tales." Sergeant O'Keefe is in charge of a weather station in the mountains. He has some very funny tall tales to tell about his very strange mule, Balaam.

Like Knights of Old

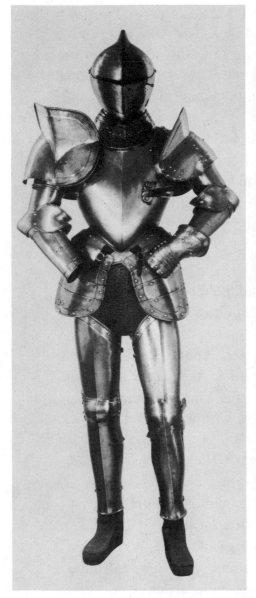

Medieval Armor

Gemini Suit

Photograph of armor from the Cleveland Museum of Art, gift of Mr. and Mrs. John L. Severance. Photographs of Gemini and Apollo suits from NASA.

Apollo Suit

In another age a warrior put on a special metal armor before he went travelling. It helped protect him if he met an enemy.

Today, spacemen wear special suits to explore a world as unknown as earth was in the age of knights.

Suits worn inside space capsules like the Gemini 4 have four layers. The materials used in the layers include nylon, rubber, and link-net. The suit worn by Edward White on his walk in space on June 4, 1965, had 22 layers instead of four.

Apollo suits to be worn when exploring the moon may look more and more like suits of armor. Aluminum will be used in Apollo suits.

Here you see, back view, the outer aluminized layer of the Apollo suit. A life-support pack is strapped to the astronaut's back.

Arthur Becomes King

adapted by WILLIAM KOTTMEYER

Many years ago Uther fought to make himself king of all England. Two true friends helped him. One was wise Merlin, the famous magician. The other was a great knight and fighter named Ulfius.

At last Uther beat his enemies and became king. Then Uther married a widow who had three daughters. Later, Uther and his wife, Igraine, had a son.

Merlin went to Uther.

"King, you know that sometimes I can tell what will happen ahead of time. Listen to what is coming. You will die soon. Your enemies will rise again. They will want to kill your son so that he will not become king. I beg you to do as I say. Let Sir Ulfius and me take him away and hide him. When he grows up, we will bring him back to be king."

"Merlin," said Uther, "you are a wise man. If I must die soon, you had better hide the boy. My enemies do not yet know I have a son."

So Merlin and Ulfius hid the boy. And a little later Uther died. Everything happened as Merlin had said. Uther's enemies rose and fought one another. Robbers and killers went free in the land. No man was strong enough to rule. The years passed. At last the chief bishop of the church sent for Merlin.

Reprinted by permission from *King Arthur and His Knights, Everyreader Series* by William Kottmeyer. Copyright 1952 by McGraw-Hill, Inc.

"Merlin," said the bishop, "men tell me that you are wiser than all others. Can you not save our land from war and killing? Can you not find a leader who is strong enough to be king over us?"

"Bishop," said Merlin, "sometimes I can tell what will happen before it does. Soon our land will have a king who is wiser and greater than Uther. I tell you, too, that he shall be Uther's true son."

"How shall we know him?" asked the bishop.

Merlin said, "I shall find a way for all to know him. You call all the lords and knights to London at Christmas time."

The bishop did as Merlin had said. When the lords and knights came to London, they saw a strange sight. Before a church was a square block of stone. On it was an iron anvil. A wonderful steel sword was stuck in the anvil. The handle of the sword was gold and set with shining jewels. On the stone were these words: *He who can pull out this sword is the king of England.*

That day there was to be a contest between two teams of knights. On Christmas Day, knights and lords and kings would try to pull the sword from the anvil.

Among those who came to London was a good knight known as Sir Ector. Sir Ector had two sons. The older was Sir Kay, already known as a brave young knight. The other was a lad named Arthur. He carried Sir Kay's spear and shield but was not yet a knight. Sir Ector and his sons set up their tents, with others, near the contest field. Sir Kay was to fight in the contest.

On the day of the battle the two teams began to fill their places. When all were ready, a horn was blown. Each team raced its horses forward. As they met with a crash like thunder, horses fell and men were thrown. Spears broke into pieces. The knights fought on with their swords.

Sir Kay threw two knights quickly before his horse went down. He fought on with his sword and brought down more knights. Then, fighting hard with another knight, Sir Kay hit him squarely on his helmet. The knight fell, but Sir Kay's sword snapped in two. He fought his way to the wall. Arthur ran to his brother.

"Brother," cried Sir Kay, "get me another sword. Hurry to the tent. Our men have some there."

Arthur ran back to the tent. But no one was there. All had gone to watch the battle. Not a sword could Arthur find.

Then he remembered seeing the sword in the anvil near the church. He ran to the church. No one was guarding the sword. Without seeing the words on the stone, Arthur quickly pulled out the sword.

Back on the contest field, Sir Kay was waiting. He saw Arthur come running.

"Here," said Arthur, handing him the sword.

Sir Kay knew the sword as soon as he saw it.

"Where did you get this sword?" he cried.

"Why," said Arthur, "I could find none in the tent. I pulled this one out of the anvil before the church. What is the matter?"

"Nothing," said Sir Kay. "Run and find our father. Tell him to come quickly to our tent. I will go on ahead."

When Sir Ector came to the tent, he saw that Sir Kay's face was white.

"What is the matter, my son?" he cried.

"Look!" said Sir Kay. He pointed to the sword.

Sir Ector's mouth fell open. He knew that sword.

"Where did you get it?" he cried.

Sir Kay said, "What's the difference? I have it."

"If you pulled it out, you are king of England!" said Sir Ector. "If you pulled it out, you can put it back again."

Sir Kay began to be afraid. But he thought if Arthur was able to pull out the sword, surely he could, too.

"Come," said Sir Ector. The two started off for the church. Arthur followed. When they came to the anvil, they found it smooth. Sir Kay pushed and pushed at the sword. He could not even scratch the anvil.

"How did you pull it out?" asked Sir Ector.

"Let me put it back," said Arthur.

"You? What right have you to touch it, boy?"

"Why, I pulled it out," said Arthur.

Sir Ector looked at him strangely. Then he looked at Kay. "Try it," he said at last to Arthur.

Arthur took the sword and jumped upon the stone. He easily pushed the sword deep into the anvil.

Sir Ector rubbed his eyes. "I can't believe it!" he cried. Then he fell on his knees before Arthur.

"Father!" cried Arthur. "Why do you kneel?"

"Boy," said Sir Ector, "I am not your father. You must be a king's son, or you could not have pulled out the sword."

"What?" cried Arthur unhappily. "Father, please do not kneel before me. Tell me what you mean!"

"Listen, then," said Sir Ector. "Years ago the wise magician, Merlin, came to me. He told me to be at King Uther's castle gate at midnight. That night I did as he said. Merlin and Sir Ulfius, Uther's best friends, came. Merlin carried a baby in his arms. That baby was you, Arthur."

Sir Ector went on, "Merlin told me to bring you up as my own son. He said that no one must know who you were. I told Merlin I would do as he said. I never knew who your father was. Now I can guess. You are Uther's son. Who else could pull out the sword?"

"I would rather be your son than be a king!" cried Arthur.

"Come," said Sir Ector. "On Christmas Day the bishop will give everyone a chance to pull the sword. You must take your turn."

On Christmas a great crowd of knights and lords and kings gathered before the church. The bishop had a horn blown to start the trial.

First came the kings who had once joined with King Uther. The husband of one of Queen Igraine's daughters stepped forward. He took hold of the sword with both hands and pulled with all his might. Again and again he tried. The sword did not move.

Now came the others—kings, lords, and knights. They pulled and pushed, but no one could make the sword move.

"What trick of Merlin's is this?" they cried. "No man can move this sword. Come, choose one of us to be king."

The bishop held up his hand. "Let no man speak against the wisest of us all. There comes Merlin. He will speak for himself."

All turned to look. Down the street came Merlin, Sir Ulfius, and Arthur. Behind them were Sir Ector and Sir Kay.

"Here is one who will try the sword," said Merlin. He laid his hand on Arthur's shoulder. "Here, lords of England, is the true son of King Uther!"

"But Uther had no son!" cried the bishop.

And so Merlin told the story of how he had hid the baby son of King Uther.

Sir Ulfius said, "Here am I to say Merlin speaks true."

"Then let Arthur try," said the bishop.

Arthur stepped up on the stone and laid his hand on the sword. Smoothly and easily Arthur pulled the sword out of the anvil. He held it high so that all could see.

The lords and knights did not know what to say. Some were ready to have Arthur as king. Others were not.

"A boy to be our king?" they cried. "No! This is a trick of Merlin and Sir Ulfius!"

But others began to shout for Arthur. "Arthur, king of England! Arthur, king of England!"

To make sure that Arthur truly was the one who should become king, the bishop repeated the trial in other parts of England. At each trial only Arthur could pull the sword from the anvil.

So Arthur became king of all England. Some of the kings and lords still did not want him, and he had to fight them. As the years went by, he became stronger and greater. Knights came from all lands to be in his court. At Camelot, Arthur established the famous Knights of the Round Table.

Books to Read

King Arthur and His Knights, adapted by WILLIAM KOTTMEYER. McGraw-Hill, 1952. (Webster Every-reader)

The story "Arthur Becomes King" is from this book of stories about the life in King Arthur's court. Read the book for more interesting stories of magic and magicians, battles and contests, and the knights and ladies of long ago.

BULLA, CLYDE ROBERT. *The Sword in the Tree.* Crowell, 1956.

Shan is the son of a knight. His father is missing. His evil uncle, Lionel, has taken over the castle. Shan has to get to King Arthur for help. Read about his dangerous and exciting journey.

Armor and Weapons of Long Ago

Arthur in "Arthur Becomes King" was not a real person. Stories about him are legends, not history. Stories were told for a thousand years before they were written. Then in 1470 Sir Thomas Malory wrote a book of King Arthur stories called *Morte d'Arthur*.

In 1470 when Malory wrote his book, armor looked like the drawing at the left.

The armor worn before that date looked like the picture at the right. It is called mail.

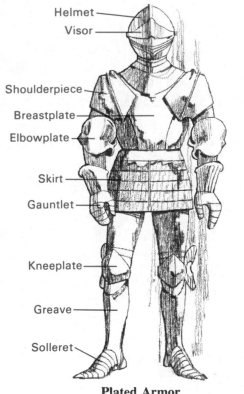

Helmet
Visor
Shoulderpiece
Breastplate
Elbowplate
Skirt
Gauntlet
Kneeplate
Greave
Solleret

Plated Armor

Suit of Mail

Armor for Man and Horse
Italy, 1575

223

Here are some weapons that knights used at about the time Malory wrote his King Arthur stories.

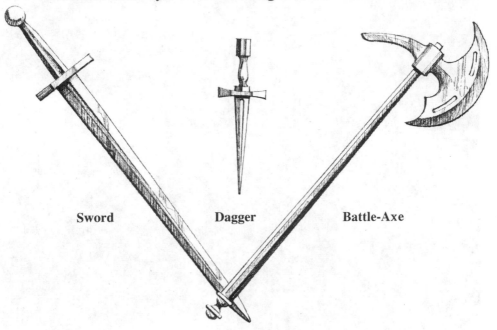

Sword   **Dagger**   **Battle-Axe**

A knight used a shield to protect himself. The shields shown below were called bucklers.

Section Four

Terry's Troubles

by JOAN M. LEXAU

F Is for Flunked

All the children but one were chanting *No more pencils, no more books* as they leaped, ran, danced out of the school building. It was Friday noon and the start of summer vacation. One second, they were still in school; the next, they were free—or would be when they crossed the street.

The only quiet one was Teresa Seth, who had an F in arithmetic on her report card.

Terry Seth kept in step with her class. She stared unseeing at the feet of the girl ahead of her.

At last her class was at the corner and crossing the street. Each boy or girl, except Terry, on reaching the opposite curb, gave a glad whoop and raced down the sidewalk.

Terry walked slowly home. She came to the end of the block, where the houses stopped. From there on, down a block and over one, all was woods. On the corner after the woods was Terry's apartment house.

One day Terry had overheard somebody walking by say that it looked like a cracker box. She

Adapted from *The Trouble with Terry* by Joan M. Lexau. Copyright © 1962 by Joan M. Lexau and used by permission of the publisher, The Dial Press, Inc.

had burned at the tone of it, but she had to admit that the apartment building did look like a huge, red-brick cracker box. It was four stories high, four windows wide in front and in back, and ten windows wide at each side. All the apartments had two rooms, and they were all exactly alike except for the furniture. Terry lived with her mother and her brother in the third-floor front that had the side windows facing the woods.

Tommy Seth was just coming out of the apartment-house door when Terry reached it. His friends were outside, waiting for him.

"Hey, what'd you get?" Tommy asked her. "I got all A's."

Terry shrugged. She was not going to yell it out before Tommy's friends.

"What's the matter? You have a fight with somebody or something?" Tommy asked, noticing how miserable she looked.

Terry shook her head. Tommy turned and followed her up the stairs. "Something's the matter," he said. "What happened?"

When they were in the apartment, she threw her books on the sofa and showed her report card.

Her brother took a long look at the card. Then he looked again to make sure he wasn't seeing things.

"Must be a mistake," he said. "It's always been your worst subject. But you never even got a D before, did you?" He looked at the year's line of marks. "Nothing below a C minus. Got to be a mistake."

"No, it isn't," Terry said. "The teacher told me about it ahead of time, during recess. She said I had improved in everything else. But during arithmetic, all I do lately is stare out the window. And my arithmetic homework's gotten abdominal."

"Gotten what?" Tommy yelled.

"Abdominal! That means it's a mess."

Tommy hooted. "You mean abominable. What do you use big words for, if you can't say them right?"

Terry flushed. If he knew what she meant, why did he have to make fun of her?

"Say, what are you going to tell Mom about your report card?" Tommy asked.

Terry shook her head. "I don't know. How mad do you think she'll be?"

"Who knows? You want me to tell her? You can stay outside till it's over," he offered.

"No. Last time we did that, remember, she caught on and only got madder than ever."

"Well, all right," said Tommy as he started for the door. "We'll be over in the woods in case you want to join us."

Terry was left alone with her misery. She huddled in a lump on the sofa and thought about all the reasons she had to be sorry for herself.

In the first place, she was always being scolded for something. Practically every minute. She wondered if there had ever been a day when she hadn't been yelled at at least a hundred times.

And then she had to be born a girl. That wasn't fair at all. Girls couldn't play football, couldn't have paper routes. They were supposed to stay clean all the time, and practically not even breathe, and certainly not have any fun.

To make life really impossible, she had to have a big brother. If it weren't for Tommy, her mother couldn't say, "Why can't you be neat, like your brother? Why can't you do what you're told right away, like your brother? How can you always lose things? Tommy never does. Tommy doesn't break everything he touches."

Tommy this, Tommy that. There were probably worse big brothers. Every time she got really mad at him, he'd do something nice that made it impossible for her to go on being mad.

Terry tried to make the tears come, but they wouldn't. They never did when she wanted them to. Not when she was alone and could cry in peace. No, she always had to burst out bawling when there were ten million people around.

F Is for Frustration

Terry shoved the report card behind a cushion on the sofa bed where she and her mother slept. She didn't want her mother to see the report card the first thing when she came in. There must be something she could do. If she did something ladylike, like housework, maybe her mother wouldn't be so mad.

What should she do? Dust? No, the last time she had dusted, she'd knocked a picture off the wall. It wouldn't have done any good to explain that she was pretending the hand with the dustcloth was a plane, landing and taking off. Her mother didn't understand things like that. To a grown-up, it was wrong to try to get any fun out of housework.

Well, she wouldn't dust, but there must be something. Yes, there was! She'd scrub the linoleum. Her mother might even notice that without being told.

Terry got a rag, soap, and a pail from Tommy's closet, and opened the doors to the kitchen part of

the living room. The water wasn't hot at this time of
day, so she poured in a lot of soap.

Floor scrubbing wasn't so bad, Terry thought as
she swished the rag around. She imagined she was on
a beach, and the tide was coming in. When the water
lapped too close to her knees, she moved up the beach.

Terry sang out heartily, "Anchors aweigh, my boys, ANCHORS AWEIGH."

Pound, pound, pound came from the ceiling.

"That old Miss Jefferson!" Terry muttered. But she went on singing more quietly.

It wasn't long before she was working toward the last corner. And look how that corner shone!

But—Good heavens! She hadn't done that yet. And then she remembered. Her mother had waxed the floor Tuesday night! All Terry would have had to do was go over it with plain water, and it would have been clean and shiny all over. What she'd done was wash all the wax off!

As soon as the floor dried, she'd have to wax it again. Otherwise, her mother would notice the difference for sure. She wouldn't appreciate it, either.

While Terry waited for the floor to dry, she read the instructions on the back of the wax can. "Wash floor," it said. Well that was done.

Terry groaned at the next words: "Rinse thoroughly." The instructions said to be sure every bit of soap was removed. Oh, no! And all that soap she'd used.

Terry rinsed the floor once and let it dry. There was still a film of soap on it. Twice more she rinsed it before all the soap was off.

She wasn't on a beach any more. Now she was in the middle of the ocean on a leaky raft. Her knees were sore, and her back ached. And she was *never, never, never* going to grow up to be a lady and do housework all her life.

When she had finished the last rinsing, she got up and hobbled to a chair by the table. She was so tired, and so hot! Except for her knees, where her skirt had gotten soaked and was clinging to her. Her school clothes! She'd forgotten to change to her jeans. Her mother would be furious.

As soon as the floor was dry, Terry changed her clothes. She buried her skirt at the bottom of the dirty-clothes pile.

In a blazing temper she unscrewed the top of the wax can and hurled the top at the floor. At the same moment, she dropped the can of wax. Wax oozed out.

"Oh, BILGE!" Terry shrieked.

Well, she'd just have to start waxing from this part of the room. Her temper soon cooled under the rhythmic movement of her hand as she covered the floor with wax. And it did look nice. Wherever she touched it with the rag, the floor took on a new look. Like King Midas turning things to gold.

She was nearly done when Tommy walked in.

"Did you have to come in now?" she yelled at him. "Couldn't you have waited till it dried?"

Tommy gaped at her. "What on earth are you doing?" he asked.

"Well, what does it look like I'm doing?" Terry snapped.

He was about to say he thought she hated housework, but he thought better of it. Instead, he said, "Look, how was I supposed to know? I only came in to get my newspaper bag. And to tell you that you could tell Mom it's my fault about the F. On account of my paper route and our not doing homework together any more to save me time."

"Oh," Terry said. "That's an idea." She didn't point out that doing their homework together had hurt her as much as it helped. After Tommy checked her homework, he showed her his. He always made his seem like fun. She knew hers wasn't. So she ended up knowing more about Tommy's decimals than her fractions. But that really wasn't Tommy's fault.

"Say, what are *you* going to do?" he asked. "About footprints," he added as she looked at him blankly.

Terry looked around her. She had waxed herself into a corner. That figured. It just *figured*.

At least Tommy didn't laugh, although he looked as if he wanted to. "I'll try not to make any more prints than I can help," he said. He took a flying leap to the door of his room, and just two leaps on the way out. "See you later," he called.

Terry looked around for a place to get off the floor. The only thing near enough was the radiator. That would have to do.

Sitting on the radiator, she finished the last bit of waxing by shoving the rag around with her foot. She looked again at the wax can. "Allow twenty minutes for drying," it said on the back.

Before one minute was up, Terry was squirming. What an uncomfortable place a radiator was! At the end of two minutes, she knew she couldn't stand it. She'd have to rewax her footprints and Tommy's.

Terry walked to the sofa. She looked through her brother's speller while the floor was drying. By the time the floor was dry, she had decided that spelling next year would be as easy as ever. Very often she was the last one to miss a word in a spelling bee.

Terry touched up the footprints and stood in the doorway to admire her work. She didn't think that her mother could have done any better. Now if she could only think of some nice way to break the news of her report card to her mother.

F Is for Finally

When Mrs. Seth came home, Terry was asleep on the sofa. She jumped up as her mother came in.

"How can you sleep on a day like this?" asked her mother. "The sun is shining, and it's your first half day of vacation."

Terry yawned. "Oh, cookies!" she said, seeing the bag her mother had. "I forgot it was payday."

Her mother worked in a cookie factory. She could buy a huge bag of broken cookies for only twenty-five cents. Once a month she brought home cookies, and on the other payday they had ice cream.

"Not till after supper," her mother warned.

"OK," Terry said meekly.

Her mother looked at her sharply. "Teresa Seth, what have you got all over you? Look at your hands. And on your face and clothes, too. Honestly, you're more of a boy than your brother."

236

Terry looked at the dried wax on her hands. She couldn't think of anything to say. After all her work, all she got for it was a scolding. She had all she could do to keep from blubbering.

"You take a shower," her mother said, "while I cook supper. And get into your other jeans and shirt."

Terry put on her rubber slippers, grabbed her clothes and a towel and soap, and stamped down the hall to the shower rooms. She always chose the middle one because she knew the handle marked "cold" was for

hot water, and the one marked "hot" was for cold. In the other two showers she could never remember which was which.

Terry's mother smiled at Terry when she came back to the apartment. "There, doesn't that feel better?" she asked. "Supper is ready now. You can whistle Tommy in."

Terry took the whistle from its nail by the window and tooted twice. Each family had its own signal for whistling the children in.

Terry still didn't know how to tell her mother about the report card. Supper was a very quiet meal. Terry had nothing to say. Her mother kept staring at her. And Tommy uneasily watched them both.

After supper Terry stacked all the dishes as her mother scraped them. With her back toward Terry, Mrs. Seth asked, "Are you out of sorts because I scolded you?"

"No," Terry mumbled. And then when her mother looked at her, "Well, I guess I was pretty dirty."

They both smiled. Terry knew she'd never have a better time to tell her mother. But she didn't want to break the spell. She hesitated, and the moment passed.

"You don't have to dry dishes tonight," her mother said. "The last day of school should be special. Just take the garbage down the hall. Then you can go play."

It was special, all right, Terry thought, as she took the bag of garbage and went down the hall toward the garbage room. Oh, she could kick herself for not telling her mother about the report card!

She was so angry that she shut her eyes, opened the
door, and hurled the bag as hard as she could toward
the ceiling, even though she knew she'd have to pick
it up to put it in one of the cans.

The bag of garbage hit the ceiling with a thud, and Terry opened her eyes. She looked straight into the eyes of Mr. Bayard, who lived in the apartment *next door* to the garbage room.

It was too much! Mr. Bayard began to laugh, and Terry burst into tears and fled.

Mr. Bayard called after her, "Don't cry, Terry. It's all right."

"What on earth——" said her mother.

Terry went straight to the sofa and dug out her report card. With tears still streaming down her face, Terry handed the card to her mother, who was standing beside her.

Mrs. Seth read the card and then looked at her daughter. All the time Terry was fighting down her sobs. There was a short silence. Terry and Tommy were hardly breathing.

Then their mother said, "Well, what do you know—an F. I got an F one time. Now finally one of my children gets an F."

Tommy laughed. "That's what the F's for—finally."

But their mother was staring at the floor. "Good heavens!" she said. "I can't believe it."

"Terry waxed it," Tommy said helpfully.

Terry wished he'd kept his mouth shut. Now her mother would say, "But what on earth for? I just waxed it."

Instead, her mother looked again at the card and back at the floor. And Terry knew that her mother understood exactly why she'd waxed the floor.

"You did a beautiful job, Terry," her mother said gently. "Thank you."

"That's all right," Terry said. She didn't know what else to say. She would have hugged her mother if they had been the hugging kind. Instead, she made a resolution to help her mother more often. Only next time she would think about what she was doing, first.

Her mother said, "I don't know why I brought those cookies home. Nobody seems to want them."

Terry and her brother ran for the cookie bag.

"First dibs on chockly graham!" Terry yelled.

SOMETHING TO SING ABOUT!

244

Words and Music by Oscar Brand.

Verse

1. I have walked cross the sand on the

Grand Banks of Newfoundland, Lazed on the

ridge of the Mi - ri - mi - chi. Seen the

waves tear and roar at the stone coast of

La - bra - dor, Watched them roll back to the

great north - ern sea.

From the Van-cou-ver Is-land to the Al-ber-ta High-land,

Cross the prai-rie, the Lakes to On-ta-ri-o's___ towers.

From the sound of Mount Roy-al's chimes out to the Mar-i-time

Some-thing to Sing A - bout, this land of ours.____

2. I have welcomed the dawn from the fields of Saskatchewan
   Followed the sun to the Vancouver shore.
   Watched it climb shiny new up the snow peaks of Caribou,
   Up to the clouds where the wild Rockies soar

I have heard the wind sing the places that I have been,
Bay Bull and Red Deer and Strait of Belle Isle.
Names like Grand' Mère and Silverthorn, Moose Jaw and Marrowbone,
Trails of the pioneer, named with a smile.

4. I have wandered my way to the wild wood of Hudson Bay,
   Treated my toes to Quebec's morning dew.
Where the sweet summer breeze kissed the leaves of the maple trees,
   Sharing this song that I'm singing to you.

Yes, there's something to sing about, tune up a string about,
Call out in chorus or quietly hum
Of a land that's still young, with a ballad that's still unsung,
Telling the promise of great things to come.

The City Enforces

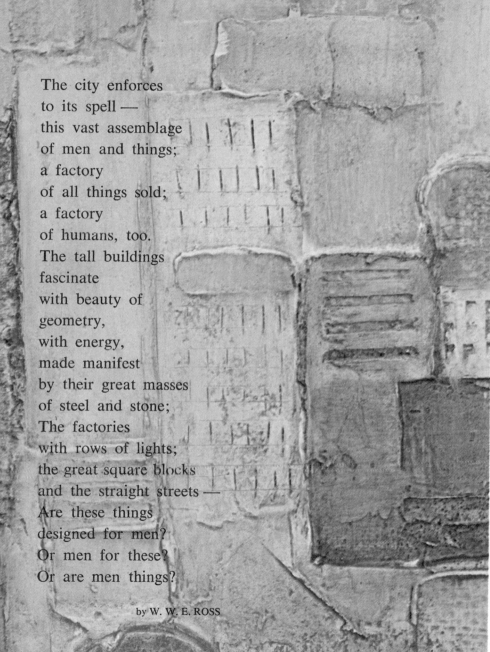

The city enforces
to its spell —
this vast assemblage
of men and things;
a factory
of all things sold;
a factory
of humans, too.
The tall buildings
fascinate
with beauty of
geometry,
with energy,
made manifest
by their great masses
of steel and stone;
The factories
with rows of lights;
the great square blocks
and the straight streets —
Are these things
designed for men?
Or men for these?
Or are men things?

by W. W. E. ROSS

From *Shapes and Sounds: Poems of W.W.E. Ross* selected by Raymond Souster and John Roberto
Colombo, copyright © 1968 by Mary Lowrey Ross, published by Longmans Canada Limited.

The Case of the
Sensational Scent

by ROBERT McCLOSKEY

This story about robbers and a skunk is the first chapter of the book Homer Price. *This is a funny story, and you will probably want to read the whole book.*

Robio Raiders

About two miles outside of Centerburg, where Route 56 meets Route 56A, there lives a boy named Homer. Homer's father owns a tourist camp. Homer's mother cooks fried chicken and hamburgers in the lunchroom and takes care of the tourist cabins while his father takes care of the filling station. Homer does odd jobs about the place. Sometimes he washes windshields of cars to help his father, and sometimes he sweeps out cabins or takes care of the lunchroom to help his mother.

When Homer isn't going to school, or doing odd jobs, or playing with other boys, he works on his hobby, which is building radios. He has a workshop in one corner of his room, where he works in the evenings.

Before going to bed at night, he usually goes down to the kitchen to have a glass of milk and cookies because working on radios makes him hungry. The family cat, Tabby, usually comes around for something to eat, too.

One night Homer came down and opened the icebox door and poured a saucer of milk for Tabby and a glass of milk for himself. He put the bottle back and looked to see if there was anything interesting on the other shelves. He heard footsteps and felt something soft brush his leg, so he reached down to pet Tabby. When he looked down, the animal drinking the milk certainly wasn't a cat! It was a skunk! Homer was startled just a little, but he didn't make any sudden motions because he remembered what he had read about skunks. They can make a very strong smell that people and other animals don't like. But the smell is only for protection, and if you don't frighten them, or hurt them, they are very friendly.

While the skunk finished drinking the saucer of milk, Homer decided to keep it for a pet because he had read somewhere that skunks become excellent pets if you treat them kindly. He decided to name the skunk Aroma. Then he poured more milk for Aroma and had some more himself. Aroma finished the second saucer of milk, licked his mouth, and calmly started to walk away. Homer followed and found that Aroma's home was under the house right beneath his window.

During the next few days Homer did a lot of thinking about what would be the best way to tame Aroma. He didn't know what his mother would think of a pet skunk around the house. But he said to himself, Aroma has been living under the house all this time and nobody knew about it, so I guess it will be all right for it to keep on being a secret.

He took a saucer of milk out to Aroma every evening when nobody was looking, and in a few weeks Aroma was just as tame as a puppy.

Homer thought it would be nice if he could bring Aroma up to his room because it would be good to have company while he worked building radios. So he got a basket and tied a rope to the handle to make an elevator. He let the basket down from his window and trained Aroma to climb in when he gave a low whistle. Then he would pull the rope, and up came the basket and up came Aroma to pay a social call. Aroma spent most of his visit sleeping while Homer worked on a new radio. Aroma's favorite place to sleep was in Homer's suitcase.

One evening Homer said, "There, that's the last wire soldered, and my new radio is finished. I'll put the new tubes in it; then we can try it out!" Aroma opened one eye and didn't look interested, even when the radio worked perfectly and an announcer's voice said, "N. W. Blott of Centerburg won the grand prize of two thousand dollars for writing the best slogan about Dreggs' After-Shaving Lotion."

"Why, I know him, and he's from my town!" said Homer.

Aroma still looked uninterested while the announcer said that next week they would broadcast the Dreggs program from Centerburg and that Mr. Dreggs himself would give Mr. N. W. Blott the two thousand dollars cash and one dozen bottles of Dreggs' Lotion for thinking up the best slogan. "Just think, Aroma, a real radio broadcast from Centerburg! I'll have to see that!"

259

The day of the broadcast arrived, and Homer rode to Centerburg on his bicycle to watch. He was there early, and he got a good place right next to the man who worked the controls so he could see everything that happened.

Mr. Dreggs made a speech about the wonderful thing that Mr. N. W. Blott had contributed to the future of

American shaving with his winning slogan: *That after-shave lotion with the distinctive invigorating smell that keeps you on your toes.* Then he gave N. W. the two thousand dollars and one dozen bottles of lotion in a suitcase just like the one that Homer had at home. After N. W. made a short speech, the program was over.

Just then four men said, "Put 'em up!"

Then one of the men said to N. W., "If you please," and grabbed the suitcase with all of the money and lotion inside it. Everyone was surprised. Mr. Dreggs was surprised, N. W. Blott was surprised, the announcer was surprised, the radio-control man was surprised. And everybody was frightened, too. The robbers were gone before anybody knew what happened. They jumped into a car and were out of sight down Route 56A before the sheriff shouted, "Wait till I send out an alarm, men! Then we'll chase them. No robio raiders, I mean radio robbers, can do that in this town and get away again!" The sheriff sent out an alarm to the State Police, and then some of the men took their shotguns and went off down 56A in the sheriff's car.

Homer waited around until the sheriff and the men came back, and the sheriff said, "They got clean away. There's not hide or hair of 'em the whole length of 56 or 56A."

While they were eating dinner that evening, Homer told the family about what had happened in town. After helping with the dishes, he went up to his room, and after he had pulled Aroma up in the basket, he listened to the news report of the robbery on his new radio. "The police are baffled," the news commentator said. "Mr. N. W. Blott is offering half of the prize money and six bottles of the lotion to anyone who helps him get his prize back."

"Aroma, if we could just catch those robbers, we would have enough money to build lots of radios and even a television receiver!" said Homer.

Keep Your Eye on 'Em

Homer decided that he had better go to bed instead of trying to think of a way to catch robbers, because he was going to get up early the next day and go fishing.

He woke up before it was light, slipped on his pants, and ate a bowl of cereal. Then he found his fishing pole and gave a whistle for Aroma (the whistle wasn't necessary because Aroma was waiting in the basket). Homer put the basket on his bike, and they rode off down 56A.

They turned into the woods where the bridge crossed the brook. Homer parked the bike and started to walk along the brook, with Aroma following right along.

They fished all morning but didn't catch anything because the fish just weren't biting. They tried all of the best places in the brook, and when they were ready to go home, they decided to go straight through the woods instead of following the brook because the woods path was much shorter.

The path through the woods was an old wood road that was not used any more. It had not been used for years, and almost everybody had forgotten that it was ever built. Before they had gone very far, Homer thought he heard voices. Then he smelled bacon cooking. He thought it was strange because nobody ever came up on this mountain to camp. So he decided to sneak up and investigate.

When Homer and Aroma looked around a large rock, they saw four men! "The robbers!" whispered Homer, and, indeed, they were the robbers.

There was the suitcase, with the two thousand dollars and the bottles of after-shaving lotion, lying open on the ground. The robbers had evidently just gotten up because they were cooking breakfast over an open fire and their faces were covered with soapy lather, for they were shaving.

Homer was so interested in what the robbers were doing that he forgot to keep an eye on Aroma. The next thing he knew, Aroma had left the hiding place and was walking straight toward the suitcase! He climbed inside and curled up on the packages of money and went right to sleep. The robbers were busy shaving and having a difficult time of it, too, because they had only one little mirror and they were all stooped over, trying to look in it.

"I can hardly wait to finish shaving and try that fragrant after-shaving lotion," said the first robber.

Then the second robber (who had a cramp in his back from stooping over and from sleeping in the woods) straightened up and turned around. He noticed Aroma. "Look at that thing on our money!" he said. The other robbers turned around and looked surprised.

"That, my friend, is *not* a thing. It is a musteline mammal (genus *Mephitis*), commonly known as a *skunk!*" said the third robber, who had evidently gone to college and studied zoology.

"Well, I don't care if it's a thing or a mammal or a skunk! He can't sleep on our money. I'll cook that mammal's goose!" Then he picked up a big gun and pointed it at Aroma.

"I wouldn't do that," said the robber with the college education. "It might attract the sheriff. Besides, it isn't the accepted thing to do to musteline mammals."

So the robbers put a piece of bacon on a stick and tried to coax Aroma out of the suitcase, but Aroma just sniffed at the bacon, yawned, and went back to sleep.

Now the fourth robber picked up a rock and said, "This will scare it away!" The rock went sailing through the air and landed with an alarming crash! It missed Aroma, but it broke several bottles of Dreggs' After-Shaving Lotion. The air was filled with "that distinctive invigorating smell that keeps you on your toes." But mostly, the air was filled with Aroma!

Everybody ran because the smell was so strong it made you want to close your eyes.

Homer waited by the old oak tree for Aroma to catch up, but not for Aroma to catch up all the way.

They came to the bike and rode off. Except to stop once to put Aroma and the basket on the rear mud-guard, they made the trip home in record time.

Homer was very thoughtful while he did the odd jobs that afternoon. He thought he had better tell his mother what had happened up on the mountain. (His father had gone into the city to buy some things that were needed around the place, and he would not be back until late that night.) At dinnertime he was just about to tell her when she said, "I think I smell a skunk around here. I'll tell your father when he gets home. We will have to get rid of that animal right away because people will not want to spend the night at our tourist camp if we have that smell around." Then Homer decided not to say anything about it because he didn't want his father to get rid of Aroma and because the robbers would no doubt get caught by the State Police, anyway.

That evening Homer was taking care of the gas station and helping his mother. In between cooking hamburgers and putting gas in cars, he read a radio-builders' magazine and looked at the pictures in the mail-order catalogue. About eight o'clock, four men got out of a car and said, "We want to rent a tourist cabin for the night."

Homer said, "All right, follow me," and he led the way to one of the largest cabins.

"I think you will be comfortable here," he said, "and that will be four dollars in advance, please."

"Here's a five-dollar bill, Buddy. You can keep the change," said one of the men.

"Thanks," said Homer as he hurried out the door.

He was just about to put the five-dollar bill in the cash register when he smelled that strange mixture, partly "the distinctive invigorating smell that keeps you on your toes" and partly Aroma. He sniffed the bill, and, sure enough, that was what he had smelled!

"The robbers! Those four men are the robbers!" said Homer to himself.

He decided that he had better call up the sheriff and tell him everything. He knew that the sheriff would be down in the barbershop in Centerburg, playing checkers and talking politics with his friends, this being Saturday night. He waited until his mother was busy getting an extra blanket for someone, because he did not think it was necessary to frighten her. Then he called up the barbershop and asked to talk to the sheriff.

"Hello," said Homer to the sheriff. "Those four robbers are spending the night out here at our tourist camp. Why don't you come out and arrest them?"

"Well, I'll be switched!" said the sheriff. "Have they got the money and the lotion with them?"

"Yes, they brought it," said Homer.

"Well, have they got their guns along, too?" asked the sheriff.

"I don't know. But if you hold the line a minute, I'll slip out and look," said Homer.

He slipped out and peeped through the window of the robbers' cabin. They were getting undressed, and their guns were lying on the table and on the chairs and under the bed and on the dresser. There were lots of guns. Homer slipped back and told the sheriff, "They must have a dozen or two."

The sheriff said, "They have, huh? Well, I tell you. I'm just about to get my hair cut, so you keep your eye on 'em, and I'll be out there in about an hour. That'll give them time to get to sleep. Then the boys and me can walk in and snap the bracelets on 'em."

"OK. See you later, Sheriff," said Homer.

Later when Homer's mother came in, Homer said, "Mother, I have some very important business. Do you think you could take care of things for a while?"

"Well, I think so, Homer," said his mother, "but don't stay away too long."

One Smell Job

Homer slipped up to a window in the robbers' cabin and started keeping an eye on them.

They were just getting into bed, and were not in a very good humor because they had been arguing about how to divide the money and the bottles of lotion that were left.

They were afraid, too, that one of the four might get up in the night and run away with the suitcase with the money and the lotion in it. They finally decided to sleep all four in one bed because if one of them got out of bed it would surely wake the others up. It was a tight fit, but they all managed to get into bed and get themselves covered up. They put the suitcase, with the money and the lotion inside, right in the middle of the bed.

After they had turned out the light, it was very quiet for a long while. Then the first robber said, "You know, this ain't so comfortable, sleeping four in a bed."

"I know," the second robber said, "but it's better than sleeping in the woods where there are mosquitoes."

"And funny little animals that don't smell so nice," added the third robber.

"You must admit, though, that our present condition could be described as being a trifle overcrowded," said the one with the college education.

"Them's my feelings exactly," said the first robber. "We might as well start driving to Mexico because we can't sleep like this. We might as well ride toward the border."

"No, driving at night makes me nervous," said the second robber.

"Me, too," said the third. Then there followed a long argument. The first and third robbers tried to convince the second and fourth robbers they should go to Mexico right away. While they were arguing, Homer thought hard. He guessed that something had better be done pretty quick or the robbers might decide to go before the sheriff got his hair cut. Homer thought of a plan, and then without making a sound, he slipped away from the window and hurried to Aroma's hole under the house. He whistled softly, and Aroma came out and climbed into the basket. Aroma had calmed down considerably, but she still smelled pretty strong. Homer quietly carried the basket to the spot under the robbers' window and listened. They were still arguing about the trip to Mexico. They didn't see Homer as he put the basket through the window onto the chair by the bed. Of course, Aroma immediately crawled out on the bed and took her place on the suitcase.

"Stop tickling," said the tall robber, because his feet stuck out and Aroma's tail was resting on his toes.

"I'm not tickling you," said the second robber, "but say, I think I still smell that animal!"

"Now that you mention it, I seem to smell it, too," said the third robber.

The fourth robber reached for the light button, saying, "That settles it! Let's get dressed and go to Mexico, because *I think I smell that animal, too!*"

Then as the light went on, Homer shouted, "You *do* smell that animal, and please don't make any sudden movements because he excites easily." The robbers took one look and pulled the covers over their heads.

"The sheriff will be here in a few minutes," said Homer bravely. But five minutes later the sheriff had not shown up. The robbers were getting restless, and Aroma was tapping her foot and getting excited.

Homer began to be disturbed about what his mother would say if Aroma smelled up one of her largest and best tourist cabins, so he quickly thought of a plan. He climbed through the window. He gathered up all of the guns and put them in the basket. Then he gathered up the robbers' clothes and tossed them out of the window. After picking out one of the larger guns, Homer waved it in the direction of the robbers and said, "You may come out from under the covers now and hold up your hands."

The robbers gingerly lifted the covers and peeked out. Then they carefully climbed out of bed, so as not to disturb Aroma, and put up their hands.

"We didn't *mean* to do it," mumbled the first robber.

"And we'll give the money back," said the second robber.

"Our early environment is no doubt responsible for our actions," said the educated robber.

"I'm sorry," Homer said, "but I'll have to take you to the sheriff." He motioned with the gun and demanded that the fourth robber pick up the suitcase with the prize money and lotion inside. Then he said, "Forward march!"

"Must we go in our pyjamas?" cried one.

"And without our shoes?" wailed another.

"Aroma is getting excited," Homer reminded them, and the robbers started marching without any more arguing, but they did grumble and groan about walking on gravel with bare feet (robbers aren't accustomed to going without shoes, and they couldn't have run away even if Homer and Aroma hadn't been there to guard them).

First came the first robber with his hands up, then the second robber with his hands up, then the third robber with his hands up, and then the fourth robber with his right hand up and his left hand down, carrying the suitcase (of course, Aroma followed the suitcase). And last of all came Homer, carrying the basket with a

dozen or two guns in it. He marched them straight down Route 56A and up the main street of Centerburg. They turned into the barbershop, where the sheriff was getting his hair cut and the boys were sitting around playing checkers.

When the sheriff saw them come in the door, he stopped talking about the World Series and said, "Well, I'll be switched if it ain't the robio raiders. I mean radio robbers!" The sheriff got out of the barber chair, with his hair cut up one side and not cut up the other, and put handcuffs on the men and led them off to the jail.

Well, there isn't much more to tell. The newspapers told the story and had headlines saying:

BOY AND PET SKUNK TRAP
SHAVING LOTION ROBBERS BY SMELL

And the news commentators on the radio told about it, too. Homer's father and mother said that Homer could keep Aroma for a pet because, instead of hurting business, Aroma was doubling business. People for miles around came to the crossroads, where 56 meets 56A, just to buy gasoline and eat a hamburger or a home-cooked dinner, and to see Aroma.

The next time Homer went into Centerburg to get a haircut, he talked the whole thing over again with the sheriff.

"Yep," said the sheriff, "that was sure one smell job of swelling. I mean one swell job of smelling!"

Postscript

Did you notice anything odd about the illustration on page 269?

Robert McCloskey wrote the story about four robbers but accidentally put five in the picture of the robbers in bed. He had to hurry to finish the pictures for the story before he went away to take part in World War II. Because he was in such a rush to get everything ready before he left, he forgot that there were only four robbers in "The Case of the Sensational Scent" and added an extra one to the picture.

The photograph below shows Mr. McCloskey with his daughters.

Photograph and text supplied by The Viking Press, Inc.

The Game of Seven Errors

An artist made the same picture twice. First he made the top one of the two pictures below. Then he copied the top picture to make the bottom one. In the second picture he made seven mistakes on purpose. Study the two pictures. On a piece of paper write all the errors you can find. Then look on page 452 to check your answers.

"The Game of Seven Errors" from *Panorama, Chicago Daily News* (June 12, 1965). Reprinted by permission of *France-Soir*.

Really?

The artist was having fun when he illustrated the terms on this page and the next. Be ready to tell what each word, phrase, or sentence really means.

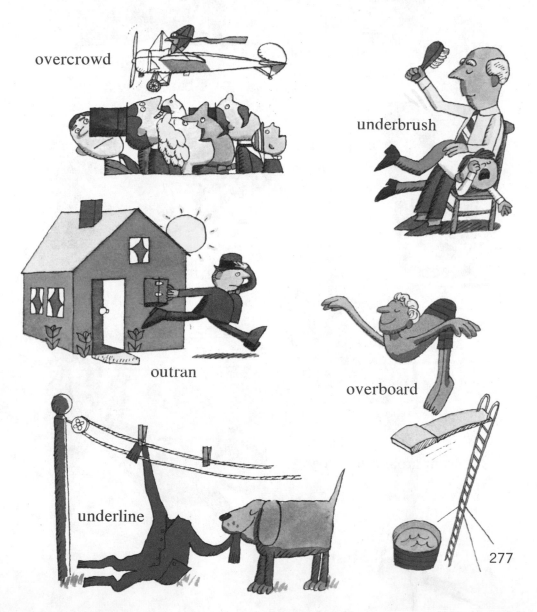

overcrowd

underbrush

outran

overboard

underline

a sunny smile

He turned into a
barber shop.

an icy stare

a flood of tears

She went around in a fog.

He breezed
through the test.

A Dream Come True

by KATHRYN KILBY BORLAND and HELEN ROSS SPEICHER

This story is about Allan Pinkerton, America's first "private eye." If you do not know what that is, you will when you finish this story.

Allan was born in Scotland in 1819. His father was a Glasgow policeman. Allan wanted to be a policeman when he grew up. But when Allan was still a boy, his father became ill and could not work. So at the age of twelve, Allan became an apprentice to a cooper. You will find out in the story what a cooper is, too.

Allan and his wife came to the United States in 1842. Soon afterward, he opened a cooper's shop at Dundee, Illinois. Dundee is a small town near Chicago.

Maybe you can guess now what the title of this story means.

Bogus Island

"I wonder who made these footprints in the mud, and why?" Allan asked himself one morning. "They are certainly not too old."

279

Allan had rowed out on the Fox River to a small island where he often cut staves for his barrels.

He was curious to know why anyone else would be coming to this tiny bit of river-bound land. It was so seldom visited that it had no name.

Allan followed the footprints. "Here someone made a fire," he continued, talking to himself. "Two others came from the opposite direction. One was a woman. The steps are less distinct and smaller."

Carefully he looked over the entire island, finding more prints.

"Whoever stayed here overnight cooked a meal— fish, I'd say. Then more people came."

Allan's imagination stopped. His memory took over. There were counterfeiters in this part of Illinois. They were very clever, and no one had caught them. Maybe these footprints were made by counterfeiters.

Allan thought, I'll row back quickly and give the sheriff the information. Maybe he can catch this gang that is passing bogus bills to the storekeepers.

Using a plan Allan suggested, the sheriff did catch the criminals. The counterfeiters, both the woman and the men, were imprisoned.

The island was given a name—Bogus Island—because of the counterfeiting.

The sheriff, B. C. Yates, was much impressed with Allan's cleverness. He made a habit of stopping at the barrel-making shop often. "Allan, I've a bit of a problem maybe you could help me with," he'd begin.

Allan would usually have some suggestion for him.

Good Money for Bad

In 1847 Allan plotted the capture of Smooth John Craig, who came from Vermont. The law had wanted to get hold of Craig for many years because he had been passing counterfeit money. Two other men engraved and printed the money, but Craig used the bills in different parts of the country and kept the good money he got in change. So far the law had not been able to catch up with him.

One morning Allan had just returned from cutting staves for his barrels. As he passed the blacksmith's shop, he heard a stranger's voice raised loudly.

"Hurry up with that horseshoe!" The tone was so disagreeable that Allan went into the shop to see who the speaker was.

Whoever he was, he gave Allan only a glance. Then he turned back to quieting his restless horse.

Again the stranger spoke harshly. "I don't have all day to wait." His huge roan horse snorted, and the man laughed. "Even Fireball says to hurry it along. Faster, man, faster!"

Allan had been mildly interested before. Now, at the stranger's demands, he became curious.

Why was this stranger in such a hurry?

Usually strange riders were glad for a chance to rest and exchange news before going on their way. This man in the well-cut city suit was too impatient.

As if he felt that he should be more chatty, the man turned to a farmer leaning against the wide-open door.

"My name's John Craig," he said easily. "I live on a farm up near Canada. I'm on my way to meet a man named Crane. Fireball threw a shoe down the road a way, and I'm late now." He smiled as if that excused his bad temper.

John Craig—Smooth John Craig, Allan thought. This must be the counterfeiter Sheriff Yates has been trying to trap.

Suddenly Allan remembered something else. He'd heard that Crane, who lived at Libertyville, had been seen lately with men who were known to be criminals. He had also made several trips out of town.

Allan watched the stranger pay the blacksmith with a crisp new bill. He had taken it from a very large roll in his pocket. Since the man had plenty of money, Allan expected him to tell the blacksmith to keep the change because he had been hurried so. But that was not what happened.

Instead, the man waited until the few coins were counted out into his hand. He carefully put them into an inside pocket of his coat.

Allan heard one of the farmers say quietly, "Andy Crane has a great deal of money to throw around all of a sudden. I wonder where he got it?"

"Hard money?" another asked.

"No, all paper."

"That's it!" Allan said to himself. "That's the way the counterfeiters get hard money for their bad paper money. Crane is buying their printed money and giving them good coins for it."

Just then Craig asked loudly, "Can someone tell me how to get to Crane's house?"

Allan was ready. Patting the restless roan, he shuffled around to Craig's side.

"Reckon I can," he answered.

Allan was glad his clothes were torn and stained with river mud. His shabby shirt and overalls served him as a disguise now. He might have been a brother to any of the four farmers standing around.

"Then let's be off," Craig urged.

Allan took him to the crossroads from which he could see Crane's house in Libertyville.

On the way Allan took great care to complain about the failure of his crops. He complained about the sad state of his leaking roof. He worried about how his children both needed shoes at the same time.

Allan talked so much like a young man in great need of money that Craig was soon interested in him. This yokel wanted some easy money soon. Craig wanted to get rid of some counterfeit money quickly.

Pinkerton played his part so well that John Craig agreed to meet Allan at a later date to exchange some counterfeit money for good.

The meeting took place. The money was exchanged. Of course Allan had told the sheriff all about it. So Sheriff Yates was able to arrest Smooth John Craig. The young barrelmaker's curiosity had paid off.

Not long after that, Sheriff Yates offered Pinkerton a job.

"Allan, how would you like to be my deputy sheriff?" asked Mr. Yates one day.

"Sheriff Yates," Allan replied honestly, "I'd like to say yes, but I think you should know something."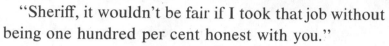

"What's that, Allan?"

"Sheriff, it wouldn't be fair if I took that job without being one hundred per cent honest with you."

"Allan," the sheriff said gravely, "did you keep some of the counterfeit money?"

"Oh, no, sir." Allan was obviously quite sincere.

"Well, then?" The sheriff was relieved.

"You see, sir," Allan admitted, "I did want to keep some. In fact, I almost did. I had an awful struggle to give it all up. I've never had very much money, and I've never seen so much before all at one time."

"You *did* give it all back?"

"Oh, yes, sir. But I thought you ought to know I didn't want to. Maybe I wouldn't be such a good deputy sheriff after all."

The older man chuckled. "Allan, my lad, you'll make the best deputy sheriff Kane County ever had."

Allan looked surprised. "I just told you——"

"That's what I mean. Allan, no man worth his salt has escaped wanting something for nothing. It's the fact that you gave the money back that's important."

"Then you'll consider me for the job?" Allan said.

"You're hired as of tomorrow morning."

Private Eye

Allan Pinkerton moved to Chicago in 1848 to work for the sheriff of Cook County.

In 1850 a group of railroad owners spoke to him. "Mr. Pinkerton, you've heard about the many railroad robberies we've had lately," they said.

"Yes, indeed. You have all lost a considerable sum of money, I'm sure."

"Somehow, information is being given to the wrong people. Can you help us?"

"Not easily. I'm busy with city business."

"We've come to ask you if you will go into private business. We will all give you our support. You will not suffer for money. Will you do it, Mr. Pinkerton?"

Allan considered. He liked the idea.

"Gentlemen, I will surely give it some thought," he said.

Allan Pinkerton organized his own agency in 1850. As a trademark he selected a picture of a wide-open eye and the words "We Never Sleep."

From the very beginning the Pinkerton Agency was successful. Allan was a good judge of character. He sensed when a man wasn't doing the right thing.

One time Allan's suspicions were aroused by a man walking nervously along Lake Street. Allan followed him to a hotel. The man gave his name as John H. Harmon of St. Louis. He was given a key to Room 29.

For hours Allan watched, but the man didn't come out again.

A friend asked, "What's the matter, Allan? Aren't you going home for dinner?"

"In a wee bit," Allan answered. "I'm watching for a bird to fly from this tree, though I don't know why."

It was late that night before the candle in Room 29 was snuffed out. Only then did Allan leave his post.

Long before sunrise Allan rose to start back to the hotel.

Quiet as Allan was, his son William heard him. "Why are you dressed like a workman, Father?" he asked.

William loved the disguises his father used.

"I'm watching a man, lad."

"Why, Father?"

"Something tells me he's up to no good, but I need proof before I speak to him."

"May I go with you?" William begged.

"Not this time, Son," Allan answered.

"You look so funny with that clay pipe between your teeth. It makes you talk funny."

"That's its purpose, lad." Allan was glad William noticed things.

"Your suit's all wrinkled, and your hat's full of dust. Mother wouldn't want you to go out like that."

"Mother would understand."

"Is there food in your lunch box, Father?"

"No, Son. It's part of the bricklayer's disguise for this job."

"Then why do you carry it?" William asked.

"It's always better to pay attention to details, lad," his father replied.

Allan's attention to his suspicions paid, also.

At sunrise Harmon, the man whom Allan had been watching, left the hotel to go to the railroad station. Allan followed him. Harmon bought a ticket.

With a half-hour remaining before train time, he walked down to the lake. There, after looking around, he dug in the sand. Allan watched from a distance.

Sunshine glinted on something. "Must be jewels," Allan decided. Allan saw the man put the jewels in his pocket.

The suspect moved rapidly. Allan had to run to the station to keep up with him. He raced into the train, close on Harmon's heels.

Seeing Allan looking so determined, Harmon tried to escape through a window.

Allan caught him just in time. "You're my prisoner," he puffed. "Now let's see what—— "

The man called to the passengers, "Somebody help me with this ruffian!"

Allan didn't look much like a policeman.

The conductor appeared. "Stop that roughhousing!" he ordered. "Stop it, or I'll call the police!"

"I *am* the police!" Allan managed to gasp.

Harmon was still struggling.

"I'm arresting this thief now. Give me my handcuffs. They are in my back pocket."

Once in jail, Harmon was searched. On him were found gold watches, rings, and many jewelled pins, as well as nine hundred dollars that he had stolen.

Allan had guessed correctly once again.

A Book to Read

SEE, INGRAM. *The Jungle Secret.*
Doubleday, 1961. (Signal Book)
Who stole the poison? Why are people upset when George kills a boa constrictor? Who is trying to kill him? These are some of the questions George has to answer in order to solve a mystery on his father's rubber plantation in Brazil.

The RCMP

It was the winter of 1966, the temperature was eighteen degrees below zero, and the high wind was about to blow up a blizzard. Somewhere in the rugged timber beyond Muskeg Lake in northern Alberta, a seventeen-year-old boy was lost. His family and friends searched for him for two days with no success. Then Constable Bob Smith and Police Service Dog Rex of the Royal Canadian Mounted Police were asked to try to trace him. When they arrived, the boy's footprints on the path were nearly invisible in the snow.

Rex and his master had been following these footprints for about two miles when suddenly Rex lifted his head from the scent. Then he left the trail and, with his master following, started off through the bushland. Across a creek, up a riverbank, through more timber they went. Then Constable Smith spotted a clump of trees where the boy had tried to light a fire. This trail was newer and fresher, only about twelve hours old.

Another three miles, and Rex again lifted his nose from the scent, sniffed the wind — and plunged down into a ravine that was partly covered with trees.

There they found the boy, exhausted and huddled in the snow, his feet, ankles, and hands severely frozen. If Rex had not scented the much shorter, fresher trail, the boy would have been dead before the rescuers found him.

Since 1935, German Shepherds like Rex have worked with their masters in the RCMP to track down suspected criminals, and to find stolen goods, lost articles, and lost

This article has been published with the approval of and from information supplied by the Royal Canadian Mounted Police, Ottawa.

A police dog signals its discovery of a lost child. RCMP photo

and missing people. But this important work is only one of the many duties carried out by the Mounties.

The Royal Canadian Mounted Police enforces the laws of the Government of Canada. It also polices all the provinces except Ontario and Quebec.

The RCMP includes an Air Division and Marine Services. The Air Division operates in all the provinces, the Yukon, and the Northwest Territories. It transports prisoners, hospital patients, and police personnel. It flies in urgently needed equipment and supplies to places that can be reached only by air. Its pilots are fully trained members of the RCMP. Vessels of Marine Services operate on Canada's east and west coasts, the St. Lawrence River, and the Great Lakes. These services help to enforce a great variety of laws, including those against smuggling and those protecting flocks of migrating birds.

The RCMP is famous for the way in which it performs all its duties. But it is respected all over the world because of its ability to prevent and solve crime. It is a well trained, up-to-date police force.

Top: An RCMP constable taking census in the Northwest Territories.
Centre: A Mountie chats with Indian boys at Campbell River, B.C.
Bottom: The RCMP investigate a highway accident. (National Film Board photos)

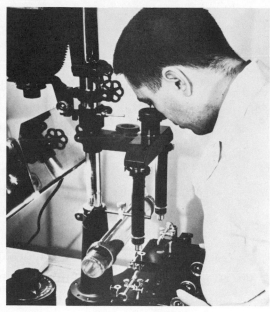

**Above: Scientists in Crime Detection Laboratories further the work of on-the-spot investigators.
Below: RCMP planes and ships pursue and transport law-breakers. They also go on errands of
mercy, such as rescuing a stranded boatman.** (First three photos by RCMP, fourth photo by NFB)

Headquarters of the RCMP is in Ottawa. This is where the Identification Branch of the RCMP is located. This branch includes a Fingerprint Section that is one of the oldest fingerprint bureaus in the world. It also includes a Crime Index Section that keeps records of criminals and their crimes — records of their personal characteristics, their manner of travelling and dressing, and the methods they use in committing crimes.

Crime Detection Laboratories are located in Ottawa, Vancouver, Edmonton, Regina, and Sackville. Here police scientists help the policemen in the field to carry on their investigations. These scientists can establish, for example, whether a stain was caused by human blood, whether a bullet was fired from a particular gun, whether the threads found on a car's fender were from the clothing of a person killed by a hit-and-run driver, and who wrote a particular message or what typewriter was used to type it.

The typical police laboratory is divided into three sections. In the chemical section, the scientists analyse drugs and poisons, investigate cases of arson and explosion. The biology section tests such things as blood, skin and other body tissues, hair, fibres, and plant specimens. In the third section, the scientists examine guns, bullets, and bullet holes; materials such as paint flakes, glass, soil, and grease; and marks made by tools or instruments.

In addition to its police work, the RCMP performs many ceremonial duties. The Mounties, in their scarlet dress-uniforms, are on duty on Parliament Hill. When Parliament opens, and on other occasions, they form an escort for the Governor General. In the next picture,

Mounties accompany Mr. and Mrs. Roland Michener as they ride in an open carriage to the ceremony in which Mr. Michener became Governor General of Canada.

Members of the RCMP who are particularly good horsemen may become members of the famous Musical Ride. The Ride is usually performed by a full troop of

295

thirty-two men and horses. It consists of a variety of intricate movements performed as the horses trot or canter to music.

The Mounties are familiar to many people in Canada and other countries because of their scarlet dress-uniforms and the Musical Ride. But they are respected throughout the world first and foremost for their outstanding police work.

Why Fingerprint Identification?

Before fingerprints became the accepted means of identification, the Bertillon System was used. About 1870, a Frenchman named Alphonse Bertillon set up a system of measuring parts of the body. The measurements were then put into a formula. It was believed that a formula could apply to only one person in the world and that the formula would not change as a person got older.

The system was used for thirty years. But in 1903 it was proved that one formula could belong to two or more different people.

Scientists had been studying fingerprints for a long time before 1900, and, after 1900, sets of fingerprints became the usual means of identification. Fingerprints do not change. The loops and spirals at the ends of the fingers are formed a few months before a baby is born. They last for a few months after a person dies. No two people have sets of fingerprints that are exactly the same in every detail. Fingerprints, therefore, give positive proof of a person's identification.

Fingerprint Yourself

Would you like to prove that no one has fingerprints exactly like yours? Would you like to compare your fingerprints with the prints of other people in your class? You can. It is easy. All you need is a white card and an ink pad. Real fingerprints are made with printer's ink; however, an ordinary ink pad will do. Roll your inked finger lightly on the paper so as not to cause a smudge, and examine the impression under a magnifying glass.

If you were having your fingerprints made by the RCMP, they would be put on a form like this:

This picture shows a girl having her fingerprints re-corded. Someone else rolls each finger in the right spot on the form.

Did you notice that there are places at the bottom of the form shown on the preceding page in which to print the four fingers of a hand at one time? This is done to make sure that each of the prints made in the squares above is in the right place.

There are ten basic fingerprint patterns. The ten patterns are shown below. The RCMP uses these patterns to classify and file fingerprints.

Compare your fingerprints with the patterns. Try to decide which patterns your prints are like.

Section Five

Twenty Minutes to Zero

by LELAND G. GRIFFIN

Three boys lay on a grassy bank above the water.
All three were looking at the old power plant across
the river. It was a useless old brick building with
windows like sightless eyes. In a few minutes a crew
would blow up the condemned building with dynamite.

To the north, upriver from the boys, clouds hung
low. Rain could be seen, slanting toward the earth.
Now and again, thunder rolled.

"Looks like nature is trying to match the show across the river," Randall Ellis said. He lifted his field glasses to his eyes and studied the old building.

Benito Lopez looked at his wrist watch. "Twenty minutes to zero," he said.

Randall's brother Bill asked, "Mind if I use those glasses for a while, Ran?"

Looking through the glasses, Bill felt that the old building was almost in his face. He looked through each of its empty windows into debris-filled rooms.

Then he studied the openings to two large tunnels under the building. Water had boiled through those tunnels when the building was in use. Now they were just hiding places for big catfish.

Suddenly Bill went rigid with shock. "The old fisherman from down the river just rowed his boat into the lower tunnel!" he cried. "What will we do?"

Benito looked at his watch. "Eleven minutes to zero," he said.

The boys jumped off the bank into the water. In seconds they were in their canoe and headed across the river. Their paddles dipped and flashed in a familiar rhythm, but with an added urgency.

Benito had turned his watch so he could see it without missing a stroke. He called out as each minute passed.

The boys were two-thirds of the way across the river when Benito said they could never make it before the dynamite went off.

Not far away and a little to the boys' left was a long finger of rocky land.

Randall shouted, "Head for the point!"

The boys sent the canoe onto the rocky point and raced to some trees close to the main shore. As they took shelter, a great blast sounded. The building shook from top to bottom. Bricks rained out over the river. The ground beneath the boys shook violently.

305

"Come on!" Randall cried, as he ran along the point toward the mainland.

When the boys reached the shore, they were met by a large, red-faced man. He stood blocking their way. There was an angry frown on his face.

"Don't you read the papers?" he yelled. "Don't you listen to the radio? Don't you watch TV? We put a ton of dynamite in that old plant. We broadcast the exact hour and minute it was set to blow. And you boys chose that time to go for a canoe ride!"

"Sorry, sir," Randall said, "but an old man rowed into the lower tunnel just before the dynamite went off. We hoped to get across in time to stop the blast."

The man's red face paled. Then his voice boomed out, "I don't believe it!"

"It's true," Benito said. "It was the old trotliner who lives downriver."

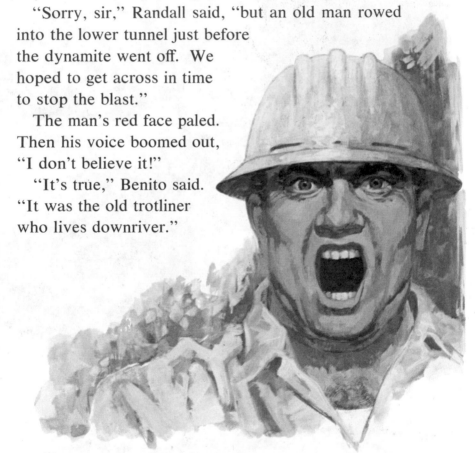

The man stared for a moment. Then he whirled and headed toward the work crew, shouting orders. The smell of burnt powder hung heavy in the air.

The boys followed the big man across the rubble. The upper tunnel was caved in. But most of the roof of the lower one had remained intact.

"There's a chance. Just a chance," the man said.

A newspaper reporter was there to write up the explosion for the Sunday paper. He called out, "What's up, Mr. Olsen?"

"Man in the lower tunnel. These boys say he rowed in before the blast," said Mr. Olsen.

The reporter turned to the boys. His eyes showed doubt. "Well, now," he said, "you boys wouldn't be pulling a prank, would you?"

The boys didn't answer. They followed the workmen down to where the opening in the tunnel had been. Bricks and broken concrete had filled the opening. There was no way into the tunnel.

Mr. Olsen spoke thoughtfully. "We can't go in from the top. The whole thing might cave in. We'll have to start from the downriver side."

Suddenly his voice changed. It cracked like a whip. "All right, men! Get started moving these bricks. Work carefully, but work fast. There's a man inside!"

As the work began, the reporter left for town to turn in his first story and to round up more men.

The three boys piled into the work of moving the bricks. Their hands were soon blistered and bruised, but they worked on.

The rescue party worked for hours. Just before dark, men from the electric company set up floodlights.

A little after dark, one of the crew yelled, "I may have found a way to get in!"

Mr. Olsen and Randall were working nearby. They ran to help the man. Soon a small passage into the tunnel was opened. The passage slanted down and to the right. And it looked dark and dangerous.

Mr. Olsen studied it for a minute. Then he shook his head. "It's too small for a man to get into," he said. "And it twists so we can't tell how far it goes. If anyone crawled into it, he might not be able to get out. We'll have to try to enlarge the passage."

It was soon plain that the opening could not be made larger without causing a cave-in.

Randall said, "Mr. Olsen, I'm pretty sure I can get through that passage. That is, if it goes all the way. The fisherman is no larger than I am. If I can get in, I figure we can both get out."

Olsen shook his head. "No," he said. "It is too dangerous. Forget it."

But Randall could not forget. He stopped to rest after a bit. While he rested, he heard thunder again. And he heard two men talking.

"If we don't get him out tonight, it's no go," one of them said. "There's high water coming down the river before morning. It will fill those old tunnels, and that will be it."

Randall jumped up and went to Olsen.

"What is it this time?" the man asked gruffly.

"I understand there's high water coming down the river before long," Randall said. "I want to go in after the old man now."

"Look," Mr. Olsen said. "It's too much. He's just an old man who's lived most of his life, anyway. You're a youngster with all your life before you. It's risking too much for too little."

Randall's eyes flashed. "Just an old man!" he said. "Nobody is *just* an old man! I want to go into that hole. You're big enough to stop me. But it will take all your strength to keep me out."

"I won't stop you," was the answer. Mr. Olsen's voice was oddly husky.

The men stopped working. The only sounds were the breathing of the men and the roll of thunder.

Slowly Randall crawled into the hole, headfirst. He was carrying Mr. Olsen's waterproof flashlight. Someone whispered behind him: "God go with you." He thought it was Mr. Olsen.

Randall's full attention was needed for the job ahead. A fallen timber lay to his right. Others had fallen across it. Bricks had tumbled down on the timbers, and bits of mortar had covered the bricks.

The boy crawled under the timbers. The passage curved to the right, and then to the left. A few feet farther on, it dropped down into the water.

Randall stopped. He knew that the water was in the outer end of the old tunnel. He did not know how long he would have to stay under the water if he tried to follow the passage. But he could not turn back.

"Hello!" he called into the darkness. "Hello!"

There was no answer. Randall could hear mortar falling behind him. There was a creaking sound as the timbers settled a little more.

He took a deep breath and stepped into the water. He did not swim. Rather he pulled and felt his way— down and down. He drew himself around timbers and pieces of concrete that almost blocked his way.

Then the passage he was following reached its lowest point and turned up. It was easier going now. He dared to hope. Suddenly his head broke water!

Randall took a deep breath and turned the light ahead. About six feet farther on, the rubble ended. At that point the roof of the old tunnel had held.

Randall swam under this roof and searched the water with his light. There was the fisherman's boat, upside down. It was kept afloat by its air tanks. The old man was clinging to the boat.

"Hello," Randall said. "You ready to leave this cosy little nest?"

The old man grinned. "I've been ready ever since I got here," he said. "Lead the way."

"Good," said Randall. "Our way out is through a small, crooked passage in the rubble. Just after we enter the passage, it dips down about five feet. Then it angles up toward the outside. I'll go first. I'll leave the flashlight shining for you at the lowest point of the passage. Give me a couple of minutes to get out of your way. Then you follow me. Got it?"

The old man nodded.

Randall swam back to the place where he had sur-
faced. The old man followed him. Then Randall took
a deep breath and went down into the narrow passage.
He left the flashlight shining at the lowest point and
clawed upward. Surfacing, he swam a little way.
Then he paused. Could the old fisherman make it?
he wondered.

More than two minutes seemed to pass.

Then the man's voice broke the stillness, and Randall saw him holding the flashlight above the water.

"Get going, youngster," said the fisherman. "I'm
ready for some fresh air."

Minutes later, eager hands were reaching out to
the old man and to Randall.

"Hank!" said Mr. Olsen to the fisherman. "Hank!
Why? Why? You knew we were going to blast this
building today. I told you so myself."

"It's that watch of mine," was the fisherman's
answer. "I guess it stopped. I thought I had a full
hour yet. And I wanted to get my trotline out."

The old man grinned and added, "There was a big
catfish on it, too."

The newspaper reporter came up to Randall. "I'll
want a story from you boys," he said. He smiled at
Randall. Then he said, "All about your prank, as I
called it."

Randall grinned. "There's not much to tell," he
said. "The three of us came out to watch the excitement. We just saw it a little closer up than we had
planned. That's all."

A Tool of Demolition

Cranes are modern wreck-
ing tools. A crane has
either a clam shell or an iron
ball fastened to the boom
by means of a steel cable.

Clam shells can bite away
walls of old buildings that
were not well built. It takes
an iron ball to knock down
high buildings or well-built
ones.

Maybe you have seen a crane being used to tear
down old buildings so that new housing developments,
schools, or expressways can be built.

The paragraphs you have just read will help you
see what is funny about the cartoon below.

"By the way, how is
your little boy?"

313

Cartoon by Ed Reed. Reproduced by arrangement with the Register and Tribune Syndicate, Des Moines, Iowa.

Miracle over the Ruhr

"I can't hold her for long, lads. You'll have to jump. Bail out!" The speaker was the pilot of an R.A.F. bomber.

The rear gunner, Sergeant Nicholas Alkemade, heard the words. His turret was not big enough for him to wear a parachute. He wore only the harness.

Adapted from "Miracle over the Ruhr" (*Finding Out*, 1964). Published by Purnell and Sons, Ltd., London, and Educational Development Corporation, Palo Alto, California.

If anything went wrong, he had to move into the body of the plane and hook on his parachute.

Something certainly was wrong now. The plane was on a bombing run over the Ruhr area of Germany. It had been hit by a fighter plane. The bomber was on fire.

Alkemade opened the turret doors with his elbows. Then he opened the door that led to the fuselage.

Inside, he saw his parachute in flames. The fire was scorching his face and hands. In an instant he decided to jump, and at 18,000 feet he leaped out into the night air.

When he came to, he could see a starlit sky through a hole above him. The hole turned out to be a space in the branches of some pine trees.

He was lying on a pile of brush that was covered with snow. It was bitterly cold. His head ached, and there was pain all over his back.

Suddenly he realized that he was alive! He was alive after falling 18,000 feet without a parachute!

He looked down at himself. His boots were gone. His clothes were burned and torn. But his watch was still ticking. He saw that the time was 3:20 a.m. It had been midnight when the plane had caught fire.

Fastened to Alkemade's collar was a whistle that airmen used to keep in touch with one another in case they had to ditch their plane at sea. Alkemade thought, After that fall I shall be happy even to be taken prisoner of war. He blew sharp blasts on the whistle again and again and again.

Shortly he saw torchlights flashing. Then some men walked out of the darkness.

"Get up!" came an order in German. When the men saw he couldn't, they carried him across a field to a cottage. From there he was taken to a hospital.

Alkemade was in the operating room a long time. His legs, face, and hands had been badly burned. His right knee had been twisted. There was a wound in his thigh. His back was strained. He had a cut on the head and a brain concussion.

For three days he was questioned by a German officer, who became very angry every time Sergeant Alkemade told his story.

After three weeks, Alkemade's wounds had healed. So he was taken to a prison near Frankfort. Clearly the Germans thought he was a spy. A week later he was taken before the commandant.

In very good English the commandant said, "We have to congratulate you, I understand. Would you tell me all about your escape? It's a very tall story."

Sergeant Alkemade told him. He also explained how the story could be proved. He pointed out that his plane must have crashed near where he fell and that what was left of his burned parachute must be in it. He said that they could also look at the parachute harness he had worn and see that it had not been used.

The commandant spoke to a lieutenant, who saluted and went away. For fifteen minutes the prisoner and the commandant talked. Then the lieutenant and three other officers rushed back into the room.

They put Alkemade's parachute harness on the commandant's desk. There for all to see were the snap-hooks still in their clasps. The lift-webs were still fastened down on the chest straps.

The commandant looked at the harness. He stared at the Englishman. Then he turned to the German officers. "Gentlemen," he said, "a miracle—no less!"

He shook Alkemade's hand. "What a story you will have to tell your grandchildren! Tomorrow, I promise, the story of how you became a prisoner of war will be told here."

That was what happened. Before two hundred other captured airmen, a German soldier told the story.

After the war, R.A.F. Intelligence men checked the records at the prison camp. These men agreed with the commandant. It was a miracle—no less.

The Escape

by KATHERINE B. SHIPPEN

Nobody knows why André Garnerin was imprisoned in the 1790's in the high tower at Budapest. Maybe he did not have enough money to pay his debts. Maybe he had said insulting things about the government. Whatever the reason was, one thing was sure. He didn't want to stay there. And he kept trying to think of a way to get out.

It was not a particularly bad prison. It was just a high tower built of granite blocks, with the kites and the hawks wheeling over it all day. Three times a day an old guard with a heavy bunch of keys at his belt climbed up the narrow, winding stairs to bring food. Otherwise, André was alone all day. He watched the sun as it went swinging on its way across the sky. He watched the stars at night.

He was not uncomfortable. The prison supplied a good bed for him. You might have expected a heap of straw spread on the floor. But Garnerin had a real bed. And oddly enough, the prison bed was equipped with sheets and blankets.

However, he didn't like being there. He was the kind of man who liked doing things for the world of men to admire, not sitting alone in a tall tower all day. Sometimes he sat at the edge of the parapet, looking out across the red roofs of Budapest at the bending Danube River and the blue hills that folded away toward the horizon.

320

There was a green vine growing at the foot of the tower. But its growth was very slow. André figured that if it continued at the rate it was growing now, he would be a man of ninety before it reached the place where he could climb down it. Then he would be too old. And what good would it do him if he could escape then? Little of his life would be left, anyway. People who sit in prison towers often pass the time in trying to work out arithmetic problems like that.

Another way that André passed his time was in thinking about all the books he had read and all the stories he had heard so that he could see whether any of them would be useful to him now. It didn't take him long to go over the books, for he hadn't bothered to read very many. But when he began to think over the stories he had heard, it took him a long time. For André had been in many places and talked with many people and sat for many hours at tables of little inns. And that is the best place to listen to stories.

So one day as he sat beside the parapet of his high prison tower, André remembered a story that he had heard in England. He had heard that a scientific gentleman named Lenormand, wanting to prove certain things about air pressures, had stepped off the top of a high stone wall, holding two open umbrellas in his hands. This Lenormand, according to the story, had arrived safely on the earth, unharmed.

It was obvious that André Garnerin had no umbrellas. And he did not think he could get his guard to bring him any, for the weather was generally fair.

And at any rate, his prison had a very good roof. So André gave up the idea of the umbrellas.

But it is a curious thing that when the seed of an idea is planted in the mind, although it is untended, it often grows like a weed. The idea of the umbrellas did not perish. It grew.

At night when André Garnerin lay in his bed, he thought about the umbrellas. And all his dreams were filled with their rounded, floating shapes. What were they made of? Cloth probably. What made them float in the air? Their shape probably. Their rounded, curving shape, like a child's soap bubble.

He was dreaming of umbrellas and soap bubbles when suddenly one night he found himself wide awake. He was so wide awake that he jumped out of bed and stood on the cold stone floor. From his bed he took the bedsheet which the prison had provided. He went to the edge of the parapet, and all that night he sat holding his bedsheet, watching the stars, and waiting for them to fade.

When the stars were dim, and the gray light of the morning had come, and the white mists were rising from the quiet earth as if to protect a man who was about to escape, André Garnerin stood up.

He took the big, square bedsheet and put four hard knots in the corners. Then he fastened the four knots into one. Then he held the sheet up. And a puff of wind filled it until it was rounded like an umbrella. Then he closed his eyes, paused for a moment on the wall of the parapet, took a step forward, and jumped.

The bedsheet billowed in the wind, then filled like a good, strong sail set sideways. André Garnerin, clinging to the knots with both hands, dropped down, swinging from side to side. The air rushed past him. But he kept his eyes tight shut. Down and down he dropped from the high tower, from his prison, into freedom.

He landed with a crash in a thorn bush and sat still, waiting to see if anyone would come to get him. But no one came. The old guard was quite deaf.

André rubbed his ankles and rubbed his elbow and found that he was not hurt. Then he tore a corner about six inches square from the sheet. Folding it carefully, he put it in his pocket for a souvenir.

Now that he was free, what did André Garnerin do? He made his way to France. There, wherever he heard that a crowd was to gather—for a horse race, for a fair, or for any other reason—he went aloft in a balloon. Standing on the edge of the basket, and with a wave to the crowd, he held on to his parachute and jumped. He loved to do it. Sometimes he jumped a thousand feet, and sometimes two thousand feet.

Everybody began to talk about how he had escaped from prison. This could have made the prison authorities nervous. But most of the prisons in Europe did not have towers. They had dungeons.

Men standing in the crowds to watch him shouted and cheered, and women fainted. At first the swinging motion made him sick, so he couldn't fully enjoy the excitement of the crowds.

But after a while André learned to cut a little hole in the top of the parachute so that the air passing through it stopped the swinging and made him fall straight and graceful as an angel from heaven.

You might say it was not worth while for André Garnerin to get out of prison just to spend the rest of his life jumping out of a balloon. Yet every man to his taste, as they say. And I think the airmen who fly the Douglas B-19's and the Curtiss P-40's and the Bell Airacobras, each man with his parachute neatly folded on his back, must be glad that André did it. That is, if they know anything about him at all.

? ? ?

You can find information in this book to help you answer the following questions. You might, also, look in a reference book. Write your answers, the information you found, and where you found it.

Do you think the last paragraph of the article is talking about planes that are commonly flown today?

Do you think they were World War II planes?

"All I know is I was supposed to show up here at three a.m."

327

Cartoon courtesy *American Youth* magazine.

Dog Paratroopers

THE PART OF PARATROOPER FOR THE GERMAN SHEPHERD WAS DECIDED UPON ONE DAY WHEN AN AVALANCHE TRAPPED SKIERS IN THE AUSTRIAN ALPS.

AT THE AUSTRIAN MOUNTAIN RESCUE SERVICE . . .

THOSE SKIERS CAN'T BE REACHED BY FOOT.

IF WE COULD ONLY REACH THEM FROM THE AIR!

WHAT GOOD WOULD THAT DO? WHO COULD SNIFF THEM OUT EXCEPT DOGS?

OUR PROBLEM WOULD BE TO GET A DOG TO PARACHUTE.

HOW ABOUT TRYING LUX? IT'S TOO LATE TO SAVE THOSE SKIERS, BUT WE COULD TRAIN HIM FOR THE NEXT AVALANCHE.

328

Text and pictures from *The Illustrated Story of Dogs* appearing in *Classics Illustrated* from *The World Around Us* series, September 1958. Published by Gilberton Company, Inc.

THE NEXT DAY THERE WAS A TEST.

LUX, YOU'RE GOING TO BE THE FIRST DOG PARATROOPER IN HISTORY.

WE HOPE.

THEY WENT TO THE TRAINING TOWER.

WHAT WORRIES ME IS-- CAN A DOG RELAX IN THE AIR?

WE'LL SOON KNOW THE ANSWER.

THEN LUX JUMPED.

HE'S FALLING BACKWARD!

THAT'S BECAUSE OF HIS FUR AND LONG BODY. HE'LL RIGHT HIMSELF.

Then came the trial.

An S.O.S. WAS SENT OUT.

CALLING ALL RESCUE AND FIRST-AID STATIONS. PARTY OF SKIERS TRAPPED UNDER AVALANCHE!

AT THE AUSTRIAN MOUNTAIN RESCUE SERVICE . . . .

WE'LL SEND LUX!

LUX WAS STRAPPED INTO HIS PARACHUTE.

THIS IS THE REAL THING, LUX.

SOON THEY WERE FLYING OVER THE ALPS.

THERE'S THE SPOT-- BETWEEN THOSE CLIFFS.

IT LOOKS RUGGED.

Lux' first mission as a paratrooper was a success.

Dog Daze

"Well, that's half the battle."

? ? ?

What does *that's half the battle* mean?

At what point in learning to roller-skate or ice-skate might you use those words?

In working an arithmetic problem?

In making a kite?

Sidelights on AVIATION

Unnoticed in the publicity surrounding the two newest jets, the B-70 and F-111, is the fact that none of the crew in either plane will wear a parachute. Each aircraft is equipped with "escape capsules," which can be blasted free of the fuselage.

A capsule is airtight, with self-contained oxygen, and watertight so it will float if it lands in water. Huge parachutes float the capsules down to earth safely.

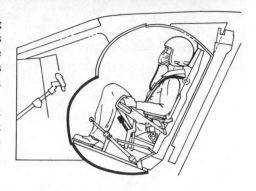

Kevin V. Brown
Aviation Editor

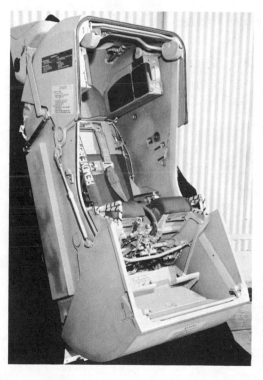

335

Adapted from *Popular Mechanics* (March 1965). Published by Popular Mechanics Company. Photographs and drawing from U. S. Air Force.

What Makes a Jet Plane Work?

Jet engines work by a law of nature discovered by Sir Isaac Newton. *For every action, there is an equal and opposite reaction.*

In a jet engine, compressed oxygen is set afire and exploded out the back. This backward action causes a reaction in the plane, making it move in the opposite direction—forward.

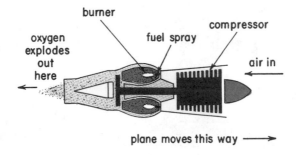

336

Photograph of jet courtesy Air Canada. Text and other pictures from *The Illustrated Story of Whaling* appearing in *Classics Illustrated* from *The World Around Us* series, December 1960. Published by Gilberton Company, Inc.

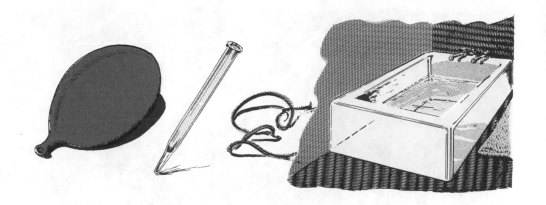

To see how a jet engine works, you will need a small balloon, the glass tube from an eyedropper, a piece of string, and a tub half filled with water.

Blow up the balloon. Close the opening of the balloon with the string, but don't tie the string. Insert the wide end of the dropper into the balloon opening. Keep your finger on the small opening in the eyedropper while you loosen the string.

Put your jet into the tub. Don't take your finger away from the small end of the dropper until it is underwater. Take your finger away, and air will shoot backward out of the eyedropper, causing your balloon jet to move forward.

A Spear for Omar

by HEDDY RADO

Omar's Fear

Omar let his hand drift in the cool water of the Red Sea. He loved this hour of the day, heading home with the dugout canoe deep in the water, heavy with a day's catch of fish. It usually made him feel peaceful to watch the sun begin to sink behind the mountains that lined the dry, hot desert.

Today, however, there was no peace in Omar. He had failed again! As if in answer to his thoughts came his father's voice. "Do not worry too much, my son. Tomorrow you will be able to hold your breath underwater longer than you did today."

Omar's father was the best spear fisherman from Suez all the way to Port Sudan. He stood tall and had developed strong muscles. He now paddled toward home with even, powerful strokes.

Omar's older brother, Gomez, was sitting behind Omar in the canoe. Gomez was cleaning his underwater goggles with the tail of his shirt. Gomez laughed. "Tomorrow Omar will be bobbing up for air every few seconds just as he did today. How can he ever be a spear fisherman if he is afraid he might drown as soon as he is underwater for more than a few seconds?"

"Tomorrow I shall stay underwater for hours! You will see!" cried Omar. Deep inside he was very much ashamed of his fear of drowning.

"There will be no more fighting between you two," said the boys' father. Turning to Gomez, he said, "And as for you, it would not harm you to use more caution. It is not well to show fear. But it is also not wise to disregard danger as you so often do. The sea is full of danger for the reckless spear fisherman."

After that, no one spoke again.

Omar sighed and looked with longing at the spears at the stern of the canoe. His father had promised him a spear of his own as soon as he had conquered his fear. The spears were slender, long shafts of smooth wood with metal points that gleamed dark red in the last rays of the sun. To Omar, the spears were beautiful and well worth the effort he silently promised to make tomorrow.

The next morning the boys' father announced that he would stay home that day. "I want you two to go to sea alone," he said. "Gomez is well able to do some fishing alone if he is careful. And as for you, Omar, I expect you to do some real diving today."

Omar respected his father too much to argue. Even though he didn't want to go without him, reluctantly Omar nodded.

"I'll race you to the beach!" cried Gomez.

Gomez won the race. But as soon as the boys had taken the boat out into the deeper water, Omar forgot about the race. He could not help but admire the way Gomez gripped the spear tightly and shot downward in the clear, blue water. In a few seconds Gomez came up with his first catch. He threw the fish into the canoe and grinned at Omar.

"Come on down yourself," Gomez teased his brother.

Omar held on to the canoe. "I will! I will!" he said. "But, Gomez, please don't take chances and stay down too long. You know father warned you yesterday."

"You worry about yourself," Gomez called. Then he took a few deep breaths, and down he went again.

This was the moment for Omar to dive. He was determined to dive well. He let go of the canoe and submerged quickly.

A few feet below the surface, the water seemed to be alive with fish. The rays of the sun entered the clear water and showed the colorful fish in a soft light. Yet the scene did not seem real because there was no sound.

Omar's breath began to give out, and he felt like darting to the surface. However, he made himself swim deeper toward a pink coral reef. It was covered with flaming red sponges and nodding heads of purple worms. Scattered over the coral were thousands of sea gems, shining like diamonds.

There were also many clams half hidden in the reef. Their wide-open jaws seemed to be waiting for Omar. If he swam too near, they would close their shells as quick as a flash over a finger or an arm. Omar kept away from the jaws of the clams, swimming with smooth, careful strokes.

When he finally came to the surface, he was very happy. His father would be proud when he heard how well Omar had dived today.

Gomez emerged a few feet away with another fish. He was panting for air. But he didn't linger long, treading water. He took a deep breath and quickly shot down again.

A breeze had come up that brought gusts of hot air from across the desert. The water, however, was as cool and smooth as satin. Omar turned on his back and swam slowly to the canoe. He held on to the crudely carved wood, and it tickled in his palms. Suddenly the water seemed to become as cold as ice. Omar went limp.

He knew a shark must be near. In great panic he looked closely at the water below him. He saw that most of the fish had disappeared. That was all he needed to know. Quickly he slipped into the boat.

Then the shark slowly emerged from the deep water and started circling the boat.

The shark had a huge, silvery body. Its eyes were small but shone with murder. It had pointed teeth that made Omar shudder.

The boy leaned over one side of the dugout canoe and looked for his brother. The water was almost deserted. Only a few herring fish darted about.

There was no sign of Gomez.

Omar's Bravery

Omar studied the water from the other side of the boat. He saw Gomez fifteen feet below, half hidden by a ridge in the reef. His hand was caught in one of the many clams, and he was trying to free himself. But he was weakened by lack of air and did not seem able to pry his hand loose.

How could he have been so careless! thought Omar frantically. He knew that he had only a few seconds to save his brother.

There was a chance that the shark might not attack if Omar could disregard him. Omar's mouth went dry as he lowered himself into the water. He did not turn his head when the shark moved closer. Without any outward sign of fear, Omar went straight down.

Never before had he dived as deep as this, and he felt as if his lungs would burst. For a second everything seemed to go black before his eyes.

Then he saw Gomez in front of him. His brother's body was swaying, helpless from the terrible lack of air.

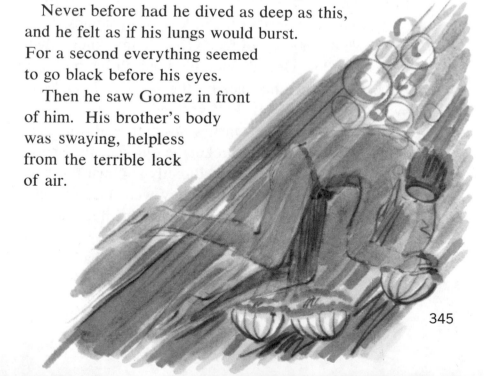

The cocky expression Gomez usually wore was gone. He looked at Omar with horror in his eyes.

Omar acted quickly. Prying the clam loose from the coral, he left it fastened to Gomez' hand. There was no time to waste now. He would attend to the clam when they were safe in the canoe, if they ever reached it.

The shark, whose giant shadow had been hovering above the boys' heads, swam toward them. As Omar grabbed Gomez and started upward, he tried to ignore the shark. Suddenly the shark seemed to look straight at Omar with its murderous, yellow eyes. It came closer, almost brushing Omar with its fanlike, powerful fins. Omar's fingers began to loosen their hold on his brother, and the boys started to sink. The water around them had grown cloudy from the churning of the shark.

It *might* be true that a shark will not attack if its victim shows no sign of fear. If so, Omar knew what he had to do. He tightened his hold on his brother.

Then he turned his back on the shark and began to swim upward in calm, slow motions.

The effort took all Omar's strength and courage. When the boys' heads broke the surface, the shark came in for attack. He shot directly at Omar through boiling waves. For a second they were face to face. The shark was a terrible sight with its huge set of razor-sharp teeth.

In desperation Omar did what his father had taught him he must do in an emergency like this.

Omar raised his right hand and slapped the shark across its pointed nose. He struck again and again.

For a long moment the shark was still. Then it churned about, brushing against Omar's face with its rough fins, and headed toward the deep water.

Omar pulled his brother into the canoe. Gomez sank to the floor, too exhausted to move. For a moment Omar also gave way to the feeling of faintness that washed over him.

But only for a moment. Then he grabbed a knife and his brother's arm. With the handle of the knife, Omar chipped away part of the clam shell. Gomez winced with pain, but Omar kept working until he could open the clam.

"It's only a flesh wound and will heal fast," said Omar after he had examined his brother's wrist. He wrapped his dry shirt around the wound to stop the bleeding.

Gomez opened his eyes and smiled weakly at Omar. His smile was full of love and admiration. "Thank you, my brother," he said. "Thank you."

Omar gave the makeshift bandage a last tug. "Shh," he said. "Do not speak now. You must rest."

Suddenly he felt very tired. His body ached, and his right hand was bruised from hitting the shark. But there was not time to rest yet. Omar took the paddle and brought the boat safely to the beach.

The next morning when Omar woke up, he found a spear next to his sleeping mat. His father stood looking down at him. There was love and pride in his father's eyes. Omar jumped to his feet, holding the spear tightly in his hand.

"You will be a fine spear fisherman, my son," his father said. Omar lowered his head as a great wave of happiness rushed through him.

349

Adventuring Underwater

Since earliest times, man has been able to swim. But for centuries he found the water a mystery. He could swim on its surface and a few feet below, but he could not drop into the depths that lay beneath.

In time, man invented equipment and machines to carry him deeper underwater.

Leonardo da Vinci, the Italian artist and engineer who lived from 1452 to 1519, designed a breathing tube and mask, and webbed flippers for the hands and feet.

In the sixteenth and seventeenth centuries, diving bells were developed. When they were lowered into water, the air inside them was trapped. Men dived out of the bells but returned when they ran out of breath.

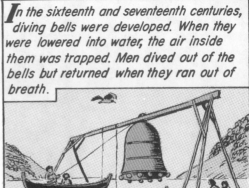

In the early seventeenth century, this diving platform was used in Venice. Air stayed in the box when the box was lowered into water.

350

Text and pictures from *Underseas Adventures* appearing in *Classics Illustrated* from *The World Around Us* series, February 1961. Published by Gilberton Company, Inc.

The efforts of other men resulted in improved devices for staying underwater. This outfit was used by a diver to go beneath the Oder River in Germany in 1797.

In 1819, in England, August Siebe made a diving dress. Its wearer wore weights on a belt, and weighted shoes. Siebe's dress was the forerunner of the modern diving suit.

In 1865, August Denayrouze and Benoît Rouquayrol of France invented the aerophore. The small tank held compressed air. Modern diving equipment follows this design.

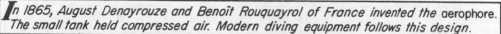

Skin and Scuba Diving

Just before World War II, skin diving as a sport became popular in France and Italy. Now it is a favorite pastime for many persons around the world.

For warm-water skin diving, equipment is simple. It consists of flippers and a mask. The mask keeps water out of the eyes. The flippers help one swim faster and for longer periods without tiring.

Many divers use snorkels. These are breathing tubes about a half-foot long. They are either built into the mask, or inserted directly into the mouth.

mask
snorkel

tube
snorkel

When using a snorkel, the diver swims along with the tube out of the water. When he sees something he wishes to explore, he dives. Valves in the snorkel close automatically so water will not fill the tube.

Spear fishing is an exciting sport. The speargun uses rubber strands, springs or compressed gas to shoot out the spear. Some spear fishermen prefer long spears which they propel by hand.

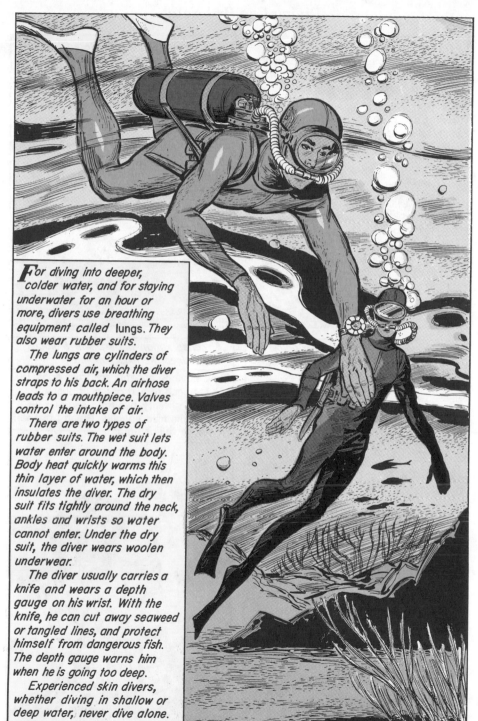

For diving into deeper, colder water, and for staying underwater for an hour or more, divers use breathing equipment called lungs. They also wear rubber suits.

The lungs are cylinders of compressed air, which the diver straps to his back. An airhose leads to a mouthpiece. Valves control the intake of air.

There are two types of rubber suits. The wet suit lets water enter around the body. Body heat quickly warms this thin layer of water, which then insulates the diver. The dry suit fits tightly around the neck, ankles and wrists so water cannot enter. Under the dry suit, the diver wears woolen underwear.

The diver usually carries a knife and wears a depth gauge on his wrist. With the knife, he can cut away seaweed or tangled lines, and protect himself from dangerous fish. The depth gauge warns him when he is going too deep.

Experienced skin divers, whether diving in shallow or deep water, never dive alone.

353

Diving Can Be Useful

 *Besides being an exciting sport, skin diving can be useful. Recently, one of the state conservation departments in the United States was concerned.*

No matter what we do, we can't keep Green Lake stocked with trout. Fishermen can't catch enough in a whole season to make a single good fish fry.

A skin diving club volunteered to help the department. Ten divers were taken out into the lake in motorboats.

 *One hundred and twenty feet below the surface, the divers captured a species of salamander called mud puppies.*

A conservation department biologist examined the mud puppies.

They have an appetite for trout eggs. In the stomach of just one mud puppy, I counted seventy-two trout eggs. If we control the mud puppies, Green Lake will again be full of trout.

354

Skin diving is of tremendous value to marine biologists, who study underwater plant and animal life. Often, they take color photographs. They use these photographs to identify and classify the fish of a particular area.

By charting the habits of fish, marine biologists have learned much about their life cycles. These studies are of value to commercial fishermen.

Scientists spear fishing in the South Seas have found that some species of fish have poisonous flesh. They have learned which fish not to eat.

Throw that one back. It is not good.

Some scientists gather underwater plants and prepare extracts from them. Many sea plants yield medicines. One is kelp, from which we get iodine.

355

Police often use skin divers in their fight against crime. Once, in a southern California coast resort, police arrested some burglary suspects.

We caught them at the end of the pier, chief, but they didn't have the stolen jewelry.

If we want to convict them, we'll have to have evidence.

The police chief remembered there were several youths at the resort who had formed a skin diving club.

Do you fellows think you could explore the waters around the pier? I'm especially interested in what might be on the bottom.

That afternoon, the youths dived. On the bottom, they clawed through the mud. Suddenly, one found a watch.

After a half-hour search, the divers recovered all the stolen jewelry.

That does it! Now we've got the evidence we need.

Elephants!

by FRANK BUCK

Elephants are the largest animals that roam the Far East jungles. A full-grown male elephant will weigh anywhere from four to six tons. That is eight to twelve thousand pounds—as heavy as the largest motor truck you have ever seen.

A full-grown elephant stands from nine to twelve feet high at the shoulder. In other words, he would have to stoop far down to get into most rooms. And his head, if he held it up, would touch the ceiling of many schoolrooms.

With his great size and strength, the elephant is the most powerful animal that lives in the jungle. There is no other animal that can stand against his charge. Even the lordly tiger fears him and will move silently away to avoid a fight. The elephant, with his long ivory tusks, his strong trunk, and his heavy, dangerous feet that can stamp out the life of any other living creature, is the master of the land where he lives.

Yet, in spite of the elephant's huge size, it is possible for a man, with less than a fiftieth of his weight, to capture these greatest of jungle beasts. And this is because man, small as he is in comparison, has a brain that reasons.

357

Adapted from *On Jungle Trails*. Published by J. B. Lippincott Company.

A few years ago I received an order for two fine, husky male elephants. This order had me a bit worried. I knew that in order to get just those two male elephants, I would have to capture a whole herd.

I decided to try to capture them on the island of Ceylon, off the southern coast of India. Some of the finest work elephants in the East come from Ceylon.

Now I could have captured my elephants in India or Siam or Burma—all countries in Asia—or in Africa. But I knew that in Ceylon, at Kandy, I could get the help I needed for my elephant drive.

Strange as it may seem, in order to capture wild elephants, tame elephants are needed. These tame elephants must be hired from an elephant man. They are rented out in much the same way as are trucks or freight cars in North America. You pay so much rent, and the animal will work for you under the direction of his master.

I knew I should need a number of tame work elephants. So at Kandy I hunted up an old friend of mine, an elephant man named Ratwatti.

Ratwatti comes from an old Ceylon family. His father, and his grandfather before him, were in the elephant business. Ratwatti has a fine group of work elephants that he rents out. I made a deal with him for thirty of his best elephants and for two hundred men. The elephants would carry all the equipment and supplies needed for a long stay in the jungle.

But another thing was necessary before I could try to capture my two male elephants. You can't just walk into the jungle and capture or shoot elephants. Elephants are too rare and valuable as working animals to take any chance of their becoming extinct. I had to get permission to hold an elephant drive. So I went to the Kandy District Officer for the papers that I needed.

After I got them, I was off into the Ceylon jungles on the back of Ratwatti's biggest elephant.

We went fifty miles into the interior. Fifty miles is not far in an automobile on a smooth road. But fifty miles through a Ceylon jungle is a long trip. It seems very long if you make it on the gray back of a swaying, slow, shuffling elephant. Those big feet can throw up a lot of dust. And when thirty elephants are moving along, there is thirty times as much dust! I breathed it mile after mile, and I was very glad when we finally made camp and picked out a level place to build a kraal.

This business of a kraal—a pen into which to drive the herd of elephants—is very important. We would have to build one that covered eight acres of land.

Our camp was in the centre of a great jungle that stretched dozens of miles in all directions around us. Somewhere in that jungle, we knew, were elephants. But where? We intended to build a huge pen of logs into which to drive them. But unless we could find our elephants, the kraal, no matter how big or how strong, would do no good. So Ratwatti sent out scouts. They set out in all directions in the jungle to find an elephant herd.

There was no telling where they might find a herd. Perhaps a mile away—perhaps ten—perhaps twenty. They had their orders to search over hundreds of square miles for elephants. Once a herd was found, the scouts were to send in a runner to report. Then the scouts had to stay with the herd, no matter where it went. They were to eat, sleep, and live on the trail of that herd until the kraal was built and it was time for the drive.

While Ratwatti's scouts were busy in the jungle, trying to find an elephant herd, Ratwatti and I were not idle. To build an elephant kraal that covers eight acres of land is a huge job.

The first thing I did was to mark off eight acres in a rough circle. Eight acres would hold a village of a hundred or more houses. With the ground marked off, I set some of Ratwatti's men to digging postholes around the edge of the whole circle. Other men were ordered to chop down trees both inside and outside the circle.

From these trees I wanted big logs. Each log had to be over fifteen feet long and at least a foot thick. I knew the power of an elephant charge. Any log less strong than this would be likely to give way before the power and weight of a herd of wild elephants. Then the herd would be able to break loose and stampede off into the jungle.

This is where Ratwatti's tame work elephants began to help me. To bring in one of the logs from the place where it was chopped down in the forest would have taken twenty men. But it took only one work elephant to do the same job.

When a log was cut and trimmed of its branches, we fastened a chain around it. To the chain we tied a five-foot pole. Then a big work elephant would come up. Guided by the driver on his back, that elephant would simply take the pole in his trunk and walk away with the whole log! An elephant trained in this work can even set the end of the log in the hole dug for it and push the log upright with his forehead and trunk.

These logs, fifteen feet high, had to be set eighteen inches apart around the whole eight acres of the kraal. But building the pen didn't finish the job. As an approach to the single opening—through which I hoped the wild elephants would come—great fences had to be built of logs in exactly the same way as the wall around the kraal itself.

These fences are called flange fences, and they are for a very important job. They spread out on either side of the gate in the shape of a fan, getting wider apart as they go deeper into the jungle. They reach four hundred feet from the gate and make a runway leading, like a funnel, straight into the kraal itself. These flange fences keep the wild elephants running straight ahead after they are started.

It took two full months to get my great kraal built. One of the last things we did was to make a sliding gate at the entrance. And the fences had to be covered with leaves and brush so that the elephants wouldn't suspect they were being driven into a trap.

Before the drive could be held, there were two other things that had to be done. The first was to test the strength of the wall of the kraal. For this test, I had Ratwatti send his biggest work elephant into the pen. This was an enormous beast, weighing nearly five tons and almost as strong and powerful as a railroad locomotive. I ordered the driver on the elephant's back to charge the great animal against the wall of logs. If the wall would not stand the charge of this tame elephant, it would not hold up against the attack of wild ones. So I held my breath as the man drove his huge, strong beast against the log wall again and again!

The wall held! In some spots logs creaked and cracked. In others they bent outward in the earth from the power of nearly five tons of trained elephant. But around the whole kraal the wall stood up!

There was one other thing that had to be done before the elephant drive could be held. This was a ceremony that all mahouts—elephant drivers—go through before they will risk their lives on a drive.

All the mahouts of Ceylon are Buddhists. And although they worship Buddha, they have not forgotten the gods of their ancestors. So before the drive, my mahouts called on all the old forest and jungle gods and spirits to protect them. The ropes we were to use were blessed. Each mahout led up his elephant. Before us all, he dropped on his knees and asked his elephant to carry him safely.

At last we were ready for the wild-elephant drive!

But what had the scouts been doing during the two months it took to build the kraal? They had been out in the jungle, trailing a herd of elephants that they had found. For two months the scouts had followed that herd. There were twenty-two elephants in it. The scouts had eaten and lived and slept within sight of those twenty-two great gray beasts.

A week before the date set for the drive, they had begun working the herd slowly toward the kraal. This had to be done very carefully, for the elephants were likely to stampede and be lost for days. But by breaking a single dry stick to windward of the herd, the men could set the elephants moving slowly in the desired direction.

By the time we were ready for the drive, Ratwatti's scouts had the whole herd at a spot about four miles away from the opening of our flange fences. But my helpers and I had to circle through the jungle for miles to get behind the herd. We did not dare come too near for fear the great beasts would stampede.

The men who work on these elephant drives are called beaters. They move very slowly in a great half circle behind the herd and always very quietly. The sound of a breaking branch, now and then, will keep the wild elephants moving ahead. If the elephants start off to one side, a branch is broken on that side of the half circle. This sets the herd straight again. So it goes for hours until the elephant herd is in front of the opening of the flange fences.

Strange as it may seem, it is not the bull, or herd leader, that really leads the herd. Always in times of danger it is some wise old cow elephant that hears the sound. She lifts her trunk, sniffs the air, and then moves off slowly with the rest of the herd behind her.

During the working of the herd toward the kraal, I had my first sight of the elephants. Through the trees and brush, far ahead, I was able to count the twenty-two great beasts. And you can imagine how glad I was to see among them two young males! They were exactly the elephants I wanted to fill my order back in America.

As the wild herd and the beaters got closer and closer to the flange fences, I had the men move even more slowly. The real danger comes when the fences are reached. If a herd senses that it is being driven into a trap, it is likely to turn about without warning and charge anything or anybody that stands in its path.

Soon I saw the ends of the flange fences just ahead. The elephant herd was moving slowly, straight into the wide mouth. Now was the time!

I glanced quickly about at the beaters. They were all in place, ready for the drive. Raising my gun in the air, I fired three quick shots. The signal!

A second later it was as if a wild battle had broken out in that quiet jungle. Two hundred men raised their voices to the skies and shouted with all their power. They beat on hollow tree trunks with clubs. They pounded drums and tin pans. Their cries could be

heard a mile away. And all the time I kept loading and firing my gun into the leaves of the trees as fast as I could.

And the elephants? The elephants were startled. Naturally, they ran away from the noise. As the noise was behind them, they ran straight ahead. Their path ahead was between the fences, toward the gate!

Faster and faster they went. Dust rose in clouds from the feet of the stampeding herd. The thunder of the elephants' great feet added to the noise two hundred men were already making. And we ran behind the elephants, keeping up our noise, stampeding them toward the narrow gate into the pen.

They went through that gate like a train through a country crossing. They went through it and straight into the eight fenced acres!

It was then I yelled to the beaters. "Light those fires!" I shouted. "Light them quickly!"

On each side of the gate we had piled up heaps of brush and soaked them with oil. A match tossed into the brush started flames roaring. No animal would dare those flames to escape by the opening he had entered.

With the fire keeping back the herd, we put up the sliding bars across the gate. I had captured twenty-two savage, fighting elephants in the jungles of Ceylon.

For a few minutes they circled madly around the kraal. Then a young bull discovered that he was in a pen. Lowering his head, he charged the logs with the

force of a battering ram. Another elephant joined him. Together they threw their bodies wildly against the logs, again and again. But those logs stood under the attack.

Presently the herd seemed to sense that it was trapped and that there was no escape. One elephant after another calmed down and began to feed on the rich grass and leaves inside the pen. After a short time all twenty-two elephants were quietly feeding inside their new prison.

I had captured the herd. But if you think this ended my job, you're wrong. Here is where Ratwatti's tame elephants came in again. From twenty-two savage elephants I had to pick out just two. I had to get them outside the pen away from the others and into strong cages I had built. A job? Rather! But Ratwatti's tame elephants did it.

Four of them moved through the gate into the kraal. Each had a driver on his neck and another elephant man with a coil of rope mounted on his back. Tame elephants used in this sort of work with wild elephants are called decoys. The decoy elephants, which are always powerful bulls, walk right up to the wild ones. Even the best elephant man could not go near the wild elephants inside the kraal on foot. He would probably be trampled to death. But mounted on the decoy elephants, men can get close to the wild elephants.

With drivers guiding them, two tame elephants came up, one on each side of the young bull I had picked out. Using their weight against his sides, they

held him still until two other tame elephants came
up to his head and tail. Then he was hemmed in, at
both sides and at front and rear, by a wall of tame
elephants.

The men with ropes slid to the ground and put the ropes around the legs and body of the wild elephant. The ropes were then brought up over the necks of the tame elephants on either side of the wild one. In that way he was lashed to a decoy on each side.

With this done, the rest was easy. The wild jungle elephant was marched out of the kraal with a decoy elephant on each side of him to keep him in line. And straight into a training cage he went. The other male I wanted was handled in the same way.

The most fun I got from that whole elephant drive was at the very end of it. With the two I wanted in their cages, I had a pleasant task before me. This was to let the other twenty of the herd go. We tore down the gate of the kraal and let them run back into the jungle.

I shall never forget how, when we let down the last bar of the gate, those elephants scented freedom. Their trunks were all raised toward the open gate. They sniffed the free air. Then trumpeting until the jungle rang with the sound, their tails held grandly up, the elephants ran back into their native home!

Animals Around the World

Six continents are named on this map. Write the
names on a sheet of paper, leaving space below each

name. For each continent write the names of the animals pictured on the continent. You may check your answers by looking on page 453.

Riddles Around the World

by JOSEPH LEEMING

What country has a good appetite?

Hungary.

What country is popular on
Thanksgiving Day?

Turkey.

What part of London is in France?

The letter *n*.

What country does the cook use?

Greece.

What country is useful
at mealtime?

China.

376

Reprinted from *Riddles, Riddles, Riddles*. Published by Franklin Watts, Inc.

What is it that is found in the very centre of America and Australia?

The letter *r*.

What continent do you see when you look in the mirror in the morning?

You see Europe.

Which was the largest island before Australia was discovered?

Australia.

If you throw a white stone into the Red Sea, what will it become?

Wet.

What happens to a cat when it crosses the Sahara Desert on Christmas?

It gets sandy claws.

Books to Read

ADAMSON, JOY. *Elsa,* rev. ed. Pantheon, 1963.

True story of a lioness cub raised by a game warden and his wife. They had to teach her to kill so that she could be set free in the African jungle. Story is short, but the book is full of wonderful photographs.

BALCH, GLENN. *Indian Paint,* adapted by Ardis E. Burton. McGraw-Hill, 1962. (Webster Everyreader)

The son of an Indian chief fights animals and men to protect his wild pony.

BUCK, FRANK. *On Jungle Trails,* adapted by Ardis E. Burton. McGraw-Hill, 1962. (Webster Everyreader)

A leopard loose in a storm at sea! A strange animal that eats with his scales! These stories and others are told in this book written by a man whose job it was to capture wild animals alive.

HITTE, KATHRYN. *Hurricanes, Tornadoes and Blizzards.* Random House, 1960.

True story of raging storms and the terrible damage they do. Many drawings and diagrams help the reader understand storms on land and at sea.

JOHNSON, ANNABEL AND JOHNSON, EDGAR. *The Grizzly.* Harper, 1964.

An exciting story about a boy who is afraid of his father. David faces many dangers when his father takes him camping in the wilds of Montana.

Burma Boy

Burma Boy

by Willis Lindquist

Pictures by
Nicolas Mordvinoff

Pronunciations and Meanings of Some Words
Used in This Story

You may need to use the pronunciation key on page 454.

cardamons (kär′də mənz), large plants.

Chinwa (chin′wä′), Haji's home village.

Irrawaddy (ir′ə wod′ē), a river in Burma.

kaing (kīN), tall grass.

Karen peddler (kə rän′), a peddler from the Karen states.

mango (mang′gō), a tropical fruit.

maung (mouN), Mister.

nullah (nul′ə), a gully.

oozie (ü′zē′), an elephant rider.

paddy (pad′ē), a rice field.

paijaik (pī′jīk′), a boy helper.

pye-dog (pī′dôg), a stray dog.

sambur (sam′bər), a deer of Asia.

sayah (sä′yä′), a witch doctor.

tamarind (tam′ə rind), a tree that grows in Asia.

thakin (thä′kin′), Master.

Yomaks (yō′mäks), a mountain range in Burma.

Runaway Elephant

Stars twinkled over the teak forest of the upper Irrawaddy. The hour was late, but no one could sleep in the elephant camp, least of all the boy Haji. Word had come down from the jungle country to the north that mighty Majda Koom, the father of all elephants, had been seen in the hills with a herd of wild elephants.

For two long years Haji had awaited news of the elephant he loved so dearly, and now he was almost afraid to believe what he heard. Joy bubbled up in him.

"Majda Koom has been seen! He is alive!" his heart sang over and over again. "He lives! He did not fall into an elephant trap. The hunters were not able to harm him. Someday he will come back to me and we will be together again in the jungle."

Haji edged closer to where the *oozies,* as the brown-skinned Burman elephant riders were called, sat about their campfires. They spoke of Majda Koom in hushed voices. Many of them had known the great elephant well before he ran away and became a wild beast in the jungle. Even those who were new in camp had heard of him, for the fame of Majda Koom had spread to the far corners of Burma, from the jade-green jungles of Shan to the distant borders of Tibet and India.

"Never was there an elephant like him," said an *oozie.* "His tusks are as thick around as the pillars in the pagoda temple at Chinwa."

"For thirty years," declared a wrinkled *oozie,* "Majda Koom did the work of three elephants in this very teak

From *Burma Boy* by Willis Lindquist, with pictures by Nicolas Mordvinoff. Published by Whittlesey House/McGraw-Hill Book Company. Copyright © 1952, 1953 by Willis Lindquist and Nicolas Mordvinoff.

forest. He stood over other elephants as a mountain stands over the hills. Yet, truly, he was gentle as a fawn till the madness came over him."

"It was even so," whispered Haji to his young friend Byoo.

Though only thirteen years of age, Haji could have told them much about the mighty elephant his father had ridden and cared for so long. But he said nothing. It was not polite for a boy to speak before his elders.

"Why did Majda Koom run away?" asked a new *oozie*.

The wrinkled one poked into the campfire with a stick. Sparks swirled up into the purple night and disappeared in the arching branches of the fig trees. "Some say it was grief that drove him into the jungle. Who can say what is in the mind of an elephant who has lost his master?"

No one tried to answer that, though several *oozies* glanced at Haji as if they thought he might know.

The man who had brought the news from the north spoke up, "They say Majda Koom has killed all who tried to capture him. Now he leads a herd of wild elephants. Only a week ago they trampled a village and drove off the people. Many might have been killed had they not been quick. I think there will be much trouble with the big bull."

Byoo tugged at Haji's arm. "The boys," he whispered. "They are calling you."

Haji looked at the campfire where his young friends were gathered. They were looking at him and making signs that he should come. Like himself, they were all ground helpers. They handled the big elephant chains, hooked them around the teak logs that were to be dragged to the river, and took their orders from the *oozies* who rode the elephants.

Haji went to join them. With them he could speak freely. They felt as he did about elephants. They loved elephants, and each lived only for the day when he would be given an elephant to ride and command. But there were never enough elephants to go around. Some of the boys would have to be content as camp cooks, others as tree choppers. Some would be chosen to ride the teak logs down the river to the sawmill. Only a few lucky ones who showed special skill with the elephants would ever have a chance to become *oozies*.

"Haji," said one of the boys, "would you be afraid to go out and look for Majda Koom?"

Byoo laughed. "Why should he be afraid? He was climbing on Majda Koom's tusks almost before he could walk. Some say Majda brushed the flies away from Haji while he slept."

They all laughed.

"*Wah!*" Haji said, grinning. "That is not true about the flies." He liked the way they were looking at him, as if they expected some wonderful thing of him now that the mightiest of all elephants had been seen. "But I do remember this: If a wild animal ever came too close to me, Majda Koom was sure to chase it away."

"He even chased me away once when I was fighting with Haji," laughed Byoo. "Majda Koom was very jealous. He never liked it when I played with Haji. If I did not go away soon enough to suit him, he would pick Haji up and carry him off into the jungle."

"It was even so," Haji agreed. "When I was older, I went always into the jungle to be with Majda Koom on his resting days. I would ride on his head and watch the tiger and the water buffalo run away when we came close. With Majda to protect me, I felt like the prince of all the jungle. There was nothing to fear."

"All that was long ago," said one of the boys. "Majda Koom is wild now. They say he hates all men. I would not trust him."

A smile came to Haji's lips. They did not know how much Majda Koom loved him. "I would never be afraid to trust him," he said. "Majda would know me."

"Look!" Byoo whispered. "Oo Yan comes. There is bad news for someone this night."

The low murmur of voices died quickly away as Oo Yan, the chief of the *oozies,* walked from fire to fire. He was clearly searching for someone. All eyes turned to follow him anxiously. He did not walk among them often at night, and they were more than anxious about his business.

He stopped before Haji. "You!" he said, pointing. "Come with me. *Thakin* Jensen would speak with you."

Haji's heart took a sudden dive. He swallowed. "With —with me?" He was certain a mistake had been made. The white master, *Thakin* Jensen, was a person of great importance. He was boss man for the Rangoon Lumber Company, which owned all the elephants. He did not even know Haji by name. What could he want of him?

Oo Yan's Plan

"Come," said Oo Yan again, more firmly this time, and turned back the way he had come.

Haji rose and followed on stiff legs. All were watching him now, and his heart began racing with fear. There were few who could please the stern *thakin*.

"Have I done some wrong?" Haji asked anxiously. "Please, *Maung* Oo Yan, tell him not to send me away from the elephant camp."

Oo Yan did not bother to answer him. They entered the jungle darkness. Fireflies twinkled about them. A jackal howled in the lonely hills, and from all sides came the ringing of wooden elephant bells.

No two elephant bells ever sounded alike, for each *oozie* made the bell for his own elephant. He carved it out of a chunk of teakwood and fixed two clappers to it, one on each side, hanging outside the bell.

Oo Yan and Haji reached the lighted tent, and as they entered, *Thakin* Jensen looked up from his papers and stared at Haji. He seemed surprised and not at all pleased.

"Have you lost your mind?" he asked Oo Yan angrily. "This is only a child."

"He is the one, *thakin*. He is Haji, the son of the *oozie* who trained and worked Majda Koom for thirty years." Oo Yan placed a hand on Haji's shoulder. "Haji was born in the elephant camp. Most of his days were spent in the shadow of the big elephant. He played at its feet. With my own eyes I have seen him use the

389

elephant's trunk for a swing. They went into the jungle, the two of them, and swam in the river together."

Haji heard the words and felt proud. He stood as straight and tall as he could.

"And now you expect miracles of this boy?" asked *Thakin* Jensen.

Oo Yan was not disturbed. "Majda Koom loved only two—his *oozie* and this boy. When his *oozie* was injured by the falling tree, we sent the family and the boy back to live in the rice village of Chinwa. That was when the elephant went wild, was it not?"

"What are you trying to say?"

"Why did the elephant come into our camp night after night?" asked Oo Yan. "There is only one explanation. He came to search for the boy and the *oozie* and could not find them. His grief was such that none could go near him."

"That was your opinion," said *Thakin* Jensen. "We brought the boy back here. What good has it done?"

"We brought him back too late. Majda Koom had already disappeared in the jungle."

Thakin Jensen lighted his pipe and shook his head. "It's no good, Oo Yan. It's been all of two years since the beast went wild. My best *oozies* were unable to capture him. He killed the last two who tried. He's gone mad, I tell you. He's a killer."

Haji trembled with sudden rage. He wanted to shout that it was not so. Majda Koom was not mad. It was all he could do to hold in the words by pressing his lips tightly together.

"Love is a power above all others," Oo Yan said gently. "Majda Koom and the wild elephants with him have already destroyed one village. They may destroy others. Many lives may be lost unless Majda Koom is captured, *thakin*. This boy is our only chance."

So excited was Haji that he forgot his fear of *Thakin* Jensen. "Please, *thakin,* let me search for him. I am not afraid."

"No!" snapped *Thakin* Jensen. "I have heard quite enough. Now get out of here, both of you. I will not send a child to face a killer elephant."

They went quickly.

Haji tightened his hands into hard fists as they walked away in the darkness. "I could do it," he said between his teeth. "I could bring Majda Koom back. I know I could! Maybe, if I run away from the elephant camp——"

"If you do, then *Thakin* Jensen will never allow you to work here again," said Oo Yan. "There is a better way. We shall prove to him you can handle elephants. Tomorrow I want you to work the young elephant See Po."

Haji looked up in surprise. He was only a *paijaik,* as boy helpers were called, and was not expected to know about handling elephants.

"Is it true?" he asked breathlessly. "Am I really to be the *oozie* of See Po tomorrow?"

"I have said it," replied the chief of the *oozies.* "It is true you are young, but I have not forgotten how your father trained you to work the big elephant. You did very well. Tomorrow you shall work See Po. If all goes well, *Thakin* Jensen will see your skill and send you to capture Majda Koom."

"I shall try to be a good *oozie,*" Haji promised, so thrilled he could hardly keep from jumping up and down for joy. See Po was small and young, with no tusks, but she was an elephant for all that.

Much as he wanted to tell his young friends, he kept his lips tightly sealed. The plan was a secret that had to be kept between Oo Yan and himself. If *Thakin* Jensen heard of it, he might spoil everything.

Jungle Dawn

He slept very little that night. Sometimes he listened to see if he could hear See Po's wooden bell. Any good *oozie* could name an elephant a mile away in the jungle merely by listening to the sound of its bell.

No elephant bell Haji had ever heard had the deep, rich tones of the one Majda Koom had worn at his neck. Majda had loved his bell, though sometimes when he did not wish to work, he would pack mud into the bell so that Haji and his father would be a long time in finding him. Haji chuckled, remembering how Majda had fooled them.

When at last he fell asleep, he dreamed of bringing back Majda Koom. With Majda Koom as his elephant he would become a great *oozie,* as his father had been before him.

Before the break of day he was up. With a white cloth wrapped about his hips and another about his head in a loose turban, he went to the elephant watering place by the river.

There, hobbled with chains on their front legs, the working elephants had been given their freedom to wander in the jungle and to feed during the night.

The tracks of elephants were everywhere in the soft mud. Some were several days old. Haji looked only for fresh tracks. There were many of these, but the daintiest of all were those of See Po. Her front pads were as round as cooking pots, her hind ones narrower, shaped rather like coconuts.

He followed her tracks with the skill of an experienced *oozie*, for many were the times he had trailed Majda Koom with his father in the half-light of morning.

See Po's tracks led through the marsh grasses where the snipe and the wild geese had their nests. There were many frogs, and they leaped out of his path as he came. He caught one of them because he had many wonderful things to tell. He had always liked talking to frogs. They blinked so wisely as he talked that he was certain they understood everything.

Up over a hill of jack trees went the trail. Now and then See Po had paused to eat branches and leaves from the trees, or tufts of short grass. Every bamboo clump in her path had been torn apart and stripped of its tender green shoots.

A brown-and-yellow weaverbird scolded Haji from the fronds of a tamarind tree. He grinned up at it and

said, "Have no fear, little friend. It is only Haji, seeking his elephant."

He could hardly blame the weaverbird for being upset. It probably had not slept very well. Right under its tree was a flat place in the grass where See Po had made her bed. And See Po snored!

With his heart singing the song of morning, Haji went on. He met a sambur deer and a grandfather porcupine on the trail and shouted cheery greetings. He wanted all the creatures in the jungle to be happy on this very special morning, for today he was an *oozie*.

But then, quite unexpectedly, he came upon the tracks of a large tiger. Jungle cats were not interested in elephants as a rule. Yet the tracks of this one crossed and recrossed See Po's trail.

Haji was puzzled at first. He dropped to his hands and knees and examined the tiger's tracks more closely. He found dark, wet drops of blood. Tiger's blood!

Somehow, the big cat had been wounded, and a wounded cat would attack anything in the jungle, even an elephant.

For another mile the tiger had followed See Po's trail. Finally it had lost interest and gone about other business. Haji felt better.

On a ridge he paused to listen for the sound of the wooden bell that hung from See Po's neck. All he heard was the faint moo-aw, moo-aw of a wild water buffalo from some distant wallow.

See Po's trail then led uphill again, toward the bamboo clumps above. But Haji did not follow. From his experience with elephants, he knew See Po would soon have her fill of bamboo. Then she would head down again to feed on the sweet *kaing* grass that grew in the nullah, the gully at the foot of the slope.

He started down the slope toward the nullah. There he would find her now, he felt certain. The slope grew steep and rocky. He had to pick his way carefully through thorny brush. Everything about him was strange and new. He wondered why he and his father had never come this way.

Ahead, large boulders suddenly loomed against the sky of gray morning like weird monsters. It was then, with a catch in his breath, that he recognized the evil place.

At campfires he had heard that bats sometimes flew up from the boulders in dark clouds. The wicked nats —the bad spirits of the jungle—were said to meet there in the dark of the moon and take the shape of bats.

With a little shiver up his spine, Haji turned and went wide of the place. It was a very unlucky chance that had brought him this way. Wise *oozies* always carried charms to protect themselves against the evil nats. But Haji had no charm.

In his haste to get away, he stumbled on a stone. He wondered fearfully if the nats had cursed him for coming so close. If they had, it would mean bad luck for him. With all his heart he wished he could see a cobra slither across his path. Then all would be well. The sight of a cobra, as everyone in the Burma jungle knows, brings good luck.

Several times Haji paused to listen for See Po's bell. What was the matter, he wondered. Why couldn't he hear it? Had the evil nats stopped the bell from singing?

He began to run like a frightened deer. "If I do not find See Po," he told himself, "*Thakin* Jensen will be very angry. He will have me thrown out of the camp."

Then he would never live with the elephants again. He would have no chance to go in search of Majda Koom. It was too terrible a fate to think about.

On and on he ran till he reached the tall sea of *kaing* grass in the nullah. Even then he could not hear the sound of See Po's bell. But once more he came across the tracks of a jungle cat and saw where the creature had entered the tall grass. Along its trail were drops of blood, shiny and fresh.

"*Wah!*" he exclaimed. "The very same wounded tiger that followed See Po!"

He hurried on, keeping a wide space between himself and the tall grass. Perhaps he had gone half a mile from the tracks of the tiger when he heard the sweetest music that ever an *oozie* knew—the faint ticky-tok, ticky-tok-tok-tok of See Po's wooden bell in the distance.

The voice of the bell grew louder as he approached. "I come! I come!" sang Haji at the top of his voice. See Po had to be warned of his coming so she would not be startled and run away.

His voice echoed so loudly in the lonely hills that it frightened him a little. He glanced back over his shoulder anxiously, hoping the wounded tiger had not heard him, too.

Charge of the Wounded Tiger

Presently he could hear the flopping of elephant ears, and the tearing and crunching and blowing that are the sounds of a feeding elephant. He kept singing loudly to calm See Po's fears.

"The eyelids of morning have opened," he sang. "Darkness has folded her wings, and there is nothing to fear. Your new *oozie* seeks for you. It is I, Haji. I come. I come."

The morning song of the *oozie* went on and on so that See Po would know exactly where he was at all times. There were no special words he had to use. Any would do. He sang of the flycatcher birds that were sweeping the gray skies above with their long tails. He sang of the eye of day—the sun—which would soon come leaping up from the eastern hills like a great ball of fire.

> "All is well, little sister!
> There is nothing to fear.
> My song is for you;
> I hope you can hear."

He came as close as he could to where See Po was feeding without entering the *kaing* grass. There no *oozie* would enter. In the thick grass, so tall that it could hide the largest elephant, lurked unseen dangers. There, royal tigers and panthers lay in hiding. There, wild buffalo and the ill-tempered rhinoceros charged and killed without warning.

"Lah! Lah! Lah! Come on! Come on! Come on!"
he cried.

The tearing and blowing sounds of See Po's feeding
still continued. Every two or three minutes he called
again. He chased a lizard from a flat rock and sat down
to wait.

There was no use being impatient. Only See Po could
know how much food she needed, and she would keep
on eating until she was satisfied. Even the best of *oozies*
could not hurry an elephant. When See Po had finished
her breakfast and was ready for work, she would come.

He had waited for perhaps ten minutes when suddenly, out of the corner of his eye, he saw a movement
in the tall grass. He stiffened. Something was in there,
to the left of the feeding elephant.

Changing his tone, he called sharply, *"Digo lah! Digo
lah!* Come here! Come here!"

See Po, of course, paid no attention. For several
minutes, Haji watched the place where the grass had
moved, but he saw nothing more to arouse suspicion.

Finally See Po stopped eating. All grew quiet in the
kaing grass. Even the flopping of elephant ears had
ceased, and that meant See Po was listening for his call.
This was her way of asking, "Where are you?"

Haji leaped to his feet. "Over here, little sister! Come
on!"

He could hear her coming. The grass tops swayed
and swirled about her as she pressed through. But even
before she came into sight, another movement to the
left caught Haji's attention.

He sucked in his breath. The thing was moving toward his elephant in quick starts and stops, in the stealthy manner of a jungle cat stalking its victim. Had there been the slightest breeze, See Po might have been able to catch the tiger's scent and rush off to safety, trumpeting her alarm.

But the still morning air hung like a curtain. She had no warning. She came slowly out of the grass, as if she had all the time in the world. She stopped only a few yards in front of Haji, fanning her big ears, raising her trunk high and waving it from side to side to catch his scent.

Though she was looking right at him, Haji did not dare move so long as her trunk remained in the air. He knew that elephants relied chiefly on their keen sense of smell. Until See Po caught his scent and recognized it, she would not allow him to approach. But finally her trunk came down, and she stood there as if to say, "Well, come on. I recognize you now."

"*Wah!*" said Haji, trying to keep fear out of his voice. "Would you keep stuffing yourself all day? Do you think I have nothing to do but wait for you?"

He had to keep talking, as *oozies* usually did, so that See Po would sense nothing unusual. "Already the sun shines on the peaks of the Yomaks, and, because of you, I have not yet had one bite of breakfast."

Then his voice rang out in firm command, "*Hmit! Lie down!*"

See Po dropped obediently to her haunches and rolled over on her side. Haji advanced slowly, his eyes round as coins as he watched the grass beyond her for some sign of the tiger.

He saw nothing. But his heart was hammering loudly and his skin prickled as he came up and gave See Po an affectionate pat on her trunk.

"*Tah!* Get up!" he ordered.

See Po got to her feet. Quickly he stooped and unfastened the chain from her front legs.

Once more he ordered her down and climbed onto her neck. "Home, little sister! Home!"

It seemed to him that it took her forever to get to her feet. She was just rising when he heard the thrashing of grass behind them. He whirled—and suddenly his heart stood still.

Just a stone's throw away, the big jungle cat streaked out of the tall grass. It snarled as it came in mighty bounds. He saw the open jaws, the flashing fangs. Straight at them it came, and all Haji could do was watch in helpless horror.

See Po trumpeted her alarm. She wheeled to meet the charge, but her great weight made her much too slow.

With a savage leap the tiger was upon her, ripping with its claws, slashing her back with yellow fangs.

The elephant screamed in pain and terror. She reared. Up on her hind legs she went, up and up.

Haji was tossed high, sailing and turning in the air. For an instant he hung between sky and earth. Then he came down with a crash in the *kaing* grass.

That was all he remembered, for suddenly it was very dark and very still.

Haji Meets the Great Elephant

Haji blinked and looked up at the *kaing* grass waving above him, wondering where he was. Then Haji remembered. The wounded tiger—it had leaped on his elephant's back!

He sat up with a jerk and looked wildly about. Where was the tiger? What had happened to See Po?

He listened, heard nothing but the whispering of morning breezes through the tall grass.

Quickly he got to his feet. He was stiff and his back hurt a little, but there was no time to worry about himself. He could smell death even before he burst from the *kaing* grass. See Po was nowhere in sight.

He approached a dark stain on the slope of the nullah. For a long moment he stared at it. His whole body trembled with weakness, and he wanted to cry and laugh at the same time.

The tiger was dead.

With the keen senses of one born in the jungle, he read the story of the struggle. See Po had reared up and fallen over on her back to crush the tiger beneath her. Then she had trampled it into the earth with her mighty pads and broken every bone in its body. The stained skin was all that remained, and that was as flat as the tiger-skin rug in the *thakin*'s tent.

"Wah!" Haji exclaimed. He was very proud of See Po.

But then he remembered her deep wounds. She was in pain. He had to find her quickly and take her back to *Thakin* Jensen for treatment.

Her trail led into the tall *kaing* grass. He followed, though he knew the dangers that lurked there. The trail was long. Hour after hour, he ran at a steady jog trot that ate up the miles. The sun rose over his head, and the day grew hot. Perspiration rolled down his slender brown body. His breath came in torn gasps. But never once did he slacken his pace.

He could tell, from the distance between See Po's tracks, that she was travelling faster than a man could run. That was proof that she was still frightened and in pain. She had never paused for an instant to feed on the *kaing* grass.

Finally her trail led into the hills, into the green twilight of jungle shade. Haji was thankful. He drew the cool air into his burning lungs. Even the thorns of the jungle brush that ripped at his arms and legs were easier to bear than the terrible heat of the midday sun.

In a strange part of the jungle he had never seen before, he came to a brook of clear mountain water. He dropped to the cool, mossy bank and drank deeply. He could not resist the temptation to roll into the stream and let the cool water flow over his burning body. How good it felt.

He meant to stay there only for an instant. But he lingered. Something far down the stream, where it widened into a sun-bright pool, suddenly drew his attention. Slowly, as if in a daze, he sat up. It couldn't be true. He rubbed his eyes and looked again.

There was no mistake about it, and it was not a dream! Drinking at the edge of the sunny pool stood the mightiest of all the Burma elephants—his beloved Majda Koom!

What a beauty the big elephant was! His great, curving tusks were more than twice the length of Haji's body, and as thick around as Haji's chest.

In the two long years Majda Koom had lived in the jungle as a wild elephant, he had not changed at all, except that his tusks were darker. Haji's father had spent many hours scrubbing and polishing and keeping them bright. He had been very proud of those tusks, and rightly so, for not in all Burma was there another set of tusks half so magnificent.

Haji remembered, as he stared at the mighty beast, that people said Majda Koom had gone mad, that he was

a killer. But these things Haji could not believe. What was there to fear from an old and trusted friend?

Yet, even an old friend should never be taken by surprise in the jungle. Haji rose quietly. Far from being afraid, he was happier than he had been for a long time. He had found Majda Koom. Now, all he had to do was to bring him back into camp.

Step by step, he advanced along the mossy margin of the brook until he was only a stone's throw from the giant elephant.

Then he stopped and called softly, "Majda. Majda Koom."

Up jerked the mighty head. Ears cocked forward like enormous fans.

"I am Haji, the son of your *oozie*. I have come for you. *Lah! Lah! Lah!* Don't you remember me, big brother?"

For an instant Majda Koom stared at him. Haji held his breath. The babbling of the brook seemed like a roaring sound in the jungle stillness.

Suddenly the great beast came to life. He smacked the surface of the pool sharply with his trunk—a warning signal of danger—and, turning, disappeared in the jungle as quickly and quietly as a jungle cat.

"Majda Koom!" shouted Haji in sudden alarm. "Come back! Come back! There is no danger. It is Haji who comes for you."

Again and again he called—but in vain. Majda was gone. And from high up on a distant jungle slope came crashing sounds and the trumpeting of a wild elephant herd, put to sudden flight by the warning signal of its leader.

Stunned, Haji stood there, staring at the place where Majda had disappeared. His elephant, his beloved Majda Koom, had not recognized him.

He swallowed hard. Tears stung his eyes. He wanted to cry, but the terrible empty feeling within him made him too weak even for that. All his dreams of capturing Majda Koom, all his hopes of becoming the *oozie* of the great elephant, died in his heart. There was nothing left for him.

As if walking in a dream that could not be real, he went back to the trail of See Po. For several hours he followed it without once hearing the sound of See Po's bell.

Finally, when the sun stood low in the western sky, he gave up. Without chain hobbles to hinder her, See Po had travelled so fast and so far that now she could only be caught by *oozies* mounted on elephants.

It was long after dark when he returned, weary and hungry, to the elephant camp. His young friends and the *oozies* quickly gathered around him at a campfire. Oo Yan heard their shouts and came running.

"Where have you been?" he demanded angrily. "What did you do with See Po? Where is she?"

Haltingly, Haji told what had happened.

"He lies!" cried an *oozie*. "Only a toad could be that stupid."

Another said, "Who ever heard of an *oozie* calling to his elephant when a wounded tiger is near?"

Even Oo Yan looked at him in dismay. "You have lived your years in the jungle," he said. "You know the ways of a wounded tiger. Did you not know it would come when you called to See Po?"

"I—I thought the tiger was far away," Haji mumbled, knowing what a poor excuse it was. He realized now, when it was too late, that he should have waited quietly on the slope of the nullah, waited till the sun grew hot and See Po came out of the tall grass to seek the cool shade of the jungle.

"The good *oozie* thinks first of his elephant," Oo Yan said sternly. "Because you did not, your elephant has been injured. We may never find her again. One who thinks so little of elephants belongs in the rice fields of Chinwa."

"*Ay,* back to the paddy with him," grumbled an *oozie*. "Is it not the price any of us would have to pay for letting harm come to an elephant? Away with him!"

"Even the son of an owl," said another, "should know that once an elephant has been betrayed, he becomes difficult to handle."

Haji looked about at the unfriendly faces. The *oozies* loved their animals. He, by exposing his elephant to danger, had done the one thing none of them could forgive. Now they wanted him banished, sent back to the rice fields of his father's village.

His eyes filled with tears. Never to live with the elephants again—it would be worse than death.

He fell to his knees before the chief *oozie*. "Mercy, *Maung* Oo Yan," he sobbed. "Mercy! Kick me! Beat me with staves of split bamboo. Tie me to the tree of the biting ants for an hour. Punish me as you will, but do not send me away."

In the flickering light of the fire, Oo Yan's grim face did not soften. "In the morning you go," he said. "Be gone before the sun touches the cardamons."

Haji hung his head and turned to go. He could hear the *oozies* as they spat in the dust to show their contempt. He stumbled into the darkness, not caring whether he lived or died. It was the end of all things for him.

Banished

Before any of the others were up the next morning, Haji was well on his way to the valley of rice fields. Even so, it was a full day of walking through jungled foothills and along the dusty yellow road of the bullock carts before he finally came to the village of Chinwa.

He went directly to the house of his father. Like all the other houses of the village, it was made of thatch and bamboo, and stood on high stilts so that the animals of the jungle could not enter.

There, as the last dusty tatters of the setting sun filtered through the bamboo slats, Haji told of his banishment from the elephant camp.

His crippled father, who had been helpless since the tree fell on him two years ago, stirred on his straw-mat bed. "The thing is done," he sighed. "My heart is heavy for you, my son."

Haji looked at his mother. Her joyous smile of welcome had faded. Quickly she came to sit by him and held his hand, sharing his sorrow. His small sister, with her glossy black hair and a jasmine flower above her ear, stared at him. She had been so proud of him. What could she think now?

Haji hung his head. His lips trembled. "If I have offended—if—if I have brought shame upon this house, my father, then—then send me away to some far village."

"Foolish talk," scolded his father gently. "Oo Yan is not without blame in this. He made you an *oozie* before your time."

The gong in the pagoda temple at the edge of the village sounded the hour of sunset. Haji's mother and his sister went down the ladder to prepare the evening meal on the fire before the house. His father spoke of many things to take Haji's mind away from the elephants.

All had been well in the village, he said. But an owl had hooted over the house of the tinker three nights in a row—a sign of sickness and death. Something very bad would surely have happened had the tinker not gone to the *sayah*—the witch doctor—who made a charm to break the evil spell. The charm must have been very strong, for there had been no sickness or death in the tinker's family, and no one had heard the hoot of an owl since that day.

"With such a powerful charm," said Haji, "I could have saved See Po from the tiger."

"Nothing is sure," said his father. "I wore the *sayah*'s charm the very day the tree fell on me." His withered hand reached out and touched the wooden bell of Majda Koom, which had been torn from the elephant's neck by the falling tree. "It was Majda Koom who saved my life by lifting the tree from my body."

Haji told of meeting Majda Koom in the jungle. "But he is as wild as any elephant," he said. "He did not know me."

"An elephant's eyes are not sharp at a distance," reminded his father. "And you have changed. You have grown much these past two years."

"But I called to him!"

"Your voice also has changed, my son. It is deeper now. You are no longer the child Majda Koom loved so well."

Haji could see how hopeless it was. He had changed so much that Majda Koom would never again be able to recognize him.

His new life in the village began before dawn the following morning. With his sister leading the way, he went to the pagoda temple and joined the children of Chinwa under the sacred bo tree. They chanted prayers until the light of dawn swept the stars from the sky. Then a priest in yellow robes gave out books—long, narrow books made of palm fronds—and the reading lesson began.

Everyone read aloud. Some read slowly, others with great speed. It did not matter, for the books were not all the same anyway.

The priest went to this one and that one, cocking his head, listening for mistakes. Haji, like most of the others, read at the top of his voice so the priest would think he could read very well and pass him by quickly.

The shrill voices made such a din that the monkeys in the bo tree above began jabbering complaints and shaking the branches. Parrots screeched. A pye-dog howled, for the noise hurt its ears, and all the other pye-dogs in the village joined in the swelling chorus.

It was dawn, and no mistake, and the sounds of new-born day thundered over the village of Chinwa.

The reading lesson did not last very long. Before the morning mists had lifted from the lowlands by the river, Haji was in the rice fields with the villagers, busy with the new harvest.

He could not understand why people joked and laughed and sang while they worked so hard in the fields. But then, none of them had ever known how fine it was to live in an elephant camp.

Sometimes he slept by day and sat the night through on one of the bamboo watchtowers that stood over the paddy fields. The precious rice crop had to be guarded carefully now from the animals of the jungle—the sambur deer and wild pigs and buffalo—whose feasting and trampling could do great damage in a single night.

It was rarely lonely on those night watches, Haji discovered. The boys in the towers kept up a constant chatter among themselves to frighten off animals and to keep each other awake. They never tired of asking Haji about the elephants.

"Tell us more about Majda Koom," Ket Kay shouted one night. "Did you ever tease him?"

"*Ay.* Almost every day when work was done, Majda came searching for me," said Haji. "I never found a hiding place where he couldn't smell me out. He liked hunting for me. But best of all he liked to take me to the river and play the water game."

"Could he swim?" asked Ket Kay.

"All elephants can swim! You perhaps never saw one swimming because they like better to walk on the deep river bottom and hold up their trunks for air."

"*Ay!*" laughed the boys in the nearby towers. "That we have seen."

Ket Kay asked, "How did you play the water game?"

Now it was Haji who laughed. "When we came to the deep place in the river, I would try to drag his trunk underwater so he could not breathe. It was a game to see who could fight the longest underwater without breathing. Sometimes I would win, and Majda had to throw me off and poke up his trunk for air."

Such happy memories of the big elephant lived always in Haji's mind. Whenever he picked a mango from a tree, he was reminded of the times that Majda Koom had lifted him high so that he could pick the ripest fruit from the tree.

Whenever his father rang the bell of Majda Koom, Haji could almost see the big elephant standing before him.

The clatter and squeaking of a bullock cart made his heart race, for bullock drivers sometimes had news from the elephant camp. One day they brought word that See Po had been caught and was almost well again.

But late one afternoon another sound broke over the peaceful valley of rice fields like a clap of thunder.

A Warning from the North

Gongs boomed. Shouts of alarm came from the village. For a stunned moment those in the rice fields stopped to listen. And then they were running, Haji along with them.

"It must be a fire," someone cried.

Ket Kay caught up with Haji at the edge of the village. "Maybe a big storm is coming," he gasped. "See, the people are coming from the houses."

Never had Haji beheld such confusion. People were everywhere in the streets, milling, shouting questions, glancing anxiously toward the sky. No one seemed to know why the alarm had been sounded.

Whole families of monkeys were leaping wildly from one thatch roof to another, headed for safety among the trees. Pye-dogs barked and scurried for cover.

"To the gong-beating place," yelled Ket Kay in Haji's ear. "Follow me."

Under the houses he ran, with Haji at his heels. They reached the thronged market square just as a Shan pony reared and slashed the air with its hoofs. It broke from its master and went plunging through the crowd, spreading panic and knocking over the fruit stalls of the seller-women.

The thundering of the gong ceased suddenly, and the beater of the gong held up his hands for silence. People moved toward the wooden platform where he stood.

Above the clamor and bustle came his voice. "Majda Koom!" he cried. "He comes to destroy us. He has gone mad." He beckoned with his hands. "Draw near, you

people of Chinwa, while the elders decide how best to protect your lives and your homes."

Haji's blood went cold. Frantically he pressed through the throng, squeezing and pushing, until he made his way to the open place where the council of elders sat.

Before the elders stood a tall Karen peddler. His robes were covered with the dust of a hard journey. "Hear my report, O noble elders of Chinwa. I bring a warning from the north. A mighty herd of wild elephants has come down from the hills to feed on the rice harvest. Many paddy fields have been flattened. Whole villages have been destroyed."

"Are the elephants coming this way?" asked an elder.

"*Ay*. They come down this valley," replied the Karen. "I have been sent to warn you. Majda Koom leads the wild herd. He is the cause of this. He fears nothing. Noisemakers and torches of fire do not stop him."

Wails of dismay went up from the villagers.

"Majda Koom has surely gone mad," said an elder. "Majda Koom must be killed before harm comes to our village."

Killed! Haji choked back a cry. But when he thought for a moment, he felt better. There were no hunters in the village. The people had no weapons that could harm Majda Koom.

"Send for the soldiers," said the Karen. "Let them hunt down this beast and shoot him."

"No!" The cry broke from Haji's lips like a sob. He rushed forward to face the elders. "Majda Koom is not mad! He is not mad!"

"Silence!" ordered the chief of the elders. "What nonsense is this? Have you a better plan for saving the village?" he asked Haji.

Haji swallowed and looked about in sudden confusion. Plan? He had not had time to think of a plan. The eyes of all were upon him, waiting, but his thoughts were only of his beloved elephant. Majda Koom was in danger. Something had to be done. He said the first thing that came into his head.

"Majda Koom is not mad," he said again. "He belongs to me. I, Haji, will capture him and turn back the herd. The village shall not be harmed. Let the safety of your rice fields and the village be on my head."

There were angry rumbles in the crowd.

"He speaks with the tongue of a jackal," growled the Karen. "Do not listen to him. What boy could stay the charge of a hundred wild elephants?"

"Enough of this foolish talk," cried an elder. "Send the boy away."

"*Ay,* send the boy away," said the chief elder. "The Karen speaks wisely. We shall send for the soldiers at once. Who will ride for them?"

Shoved roughly aside, Haji heard no more. He worked his way through the press of people and blindly struck out down the street with the speed of a black panther.

Where he was going he did not know—nor did he care. What difference could it make? Majda Koom would soon be shot, and nothing could be done to save him, nothing at all.

Secret of the Little Temple Bell

He ran until he reached the river. There his friend Ket Kay caught up with him.

"Never have I known one as brave as you, Haji," he gasped in admiration. "They did not believe your words, but I believe them. Where do you go now?"

Haji brushed the hot tears from his face. Across the river he saw the lonely cliff where the *sayah*—the witch doctor—lived, and he remembered the strange powers of magic charms. That was it. A magic charm! It would be just the thing.

"I go to the *sayah*," he said recklessly.

Ket Kay gasped. He glanced at the cliff, at the sunset sky. "At this hour?" he asked.

Pretending not to be afraid, Haji tugged at the boat drawn up on the shore. Ket Kay helped him draw it into

the water, for the boat was very heavy, hollowed out of a log.

The cliff was a place of mysterious moans and groans and rattling things where few villagers cared to venture even by the light of day. Haji brushed aside his fears. There was no time to lose if Majda Koom was to be saved.

Daylight faded quickly as they paddled across the river. Where the evening shadows were gathering under the cliff, they found the climbing path. It grew darker as they started up, and the sky above seemed to fade to the color of blood. Surely this was an evil place. The cliff, and even the sky above, seemed to have fallen under the magic spell of the powerful *sayah*.

Halfway up they were startled by a sound—an eerie, wailing sound that might have been the wind in the lonely rock crags. But there was no wind.

The boys looked at each other. Ket Kay's eyes were so wide that they looked white. He took a step backward.

"The *sayah* might be angry if two of us come," he whispered. "I shall wait for you here."

Haji nodded and went on alone. He could not turn back now. Cold chills went up and down his back, and he wondered what kind of creature this was that had such powers over the evil nat spirits.

Presently he reached the top and stood before a cave covered with tiger skins. Scattered about the entrance were broken bones and tufts of fur and feathers, as if hyenas had feasted there.

The wailing sound, which came from within the cave,
suddenly stopped.

"On what business did you come?" asked a high-
pitched voice.

Haji at last found his tongue. "M-make me a charm
to keep wild elephants away."

"What price will you pay?"

Haji had not thought of payment. "I—I have nothing," he said.

"Nothing!" screeched the high voice behind the tiger skins.

"It is to save the village and the life of Majda Koom," pleaded Haji.

Angry rattling and hissing sounds came from the cave.

Haji trembled, afraid he might have offended the powerful *sayah*. "Tell me the price," he begged. "Let me serve you. I will———"

"Away!" screeched the voice. "Away with you, and be quick. Darkness comes on swift wings, and the nats do not wait with their curses."

Haji fled, running down the path. To be cursed by the wicked nats would surely mean death to himself and Majda Koom.

He rejoined Ket Kay at the base of the cliff. They crossed back over the river again and returned to the village even more quickly than they had left it.

In the thickening twilight, cooking fires glowed before the houses on both sides of the street like angry red eyes. A strange restlessness hung over the village. People spoke in low, anxious voices. The soldiers had been sent for, they said. It would take them a day to come.

Here and there at the edge of the village, men were now gathering torches with which to frighten away the elephants.

"Why do you gather torches?" Ket Kay asked one of them. "Did you not hear the Karen say Majda Koom fears nothing?"

"*Ay,* we heard the Karen," replied the man. "It may be that Majda Koom fears nothing. But when he is shot by the soldiers, we will frighten the other elephants away with our torches. Without their brave leader, they can be frightened easily."

Haji turned away. He did not want to hear any more talk of Majda Koom being shot. It was too horrible to think about.

As he wandered restlessly through the village with Ket Kay, they met old ones and lame ones who were already carrying their blankets and cooking pots beyond the stone wall near the pagoda temple, where the elephants could not trample them.

"If only there were something I could do," said Haji.

"Why don't you do what you told the elders you would do?" asked Ket Kay. "Go into the jungle and call Majda Koom."

Haji shook his head. "Even if I found him, he would not know me. In two years I have grown tall. My voice has changed. My smell is wrong, too. I smell of the paddy fields now. If there were only some way I could make him remember me."

Ket Kay pulled his ear and blinked as thoughtfully as a frog. "Come," he said. "Maybe there is a way. We shall ask the wise one at the pagoda temple."

It seemed like a good idea. It was dark now, and, approaching the temple, they moved wide around the flat stone under which the sacred cobra had its hole.

In the flickering light of the temple, before the gilded image of the Holy One, they found the old priest who knew more, and said less, than anyone else in the rice valley. He had a round, gentle face, and long finger-nails on his left hand. He listened to them with patience, nodding wisely now and then. Yet he did not offer to tell them how Majda Koom could be made to recognize Haji.

"Sit here," he told them. "Meditate. All is possible for those who have found favor."

Haji took a seat on the cool stone floor. He lifted his eyes to the golden image beyond the curling banners of smoke that rose from the incense pots. He waited

eagerly, listening for an answer from the mysterious spirits of the temple.

The great gong crashed. Its booming shook the air of the temple, then faded to a thousand humming echoes. Silence came again, and the small whisperings of night.

For long minutes the priest chanted his prayers. He clicked his prayer beads and sometimes rang the small brass bell of his ceremony. But one hour passed, and another—and no answer came.

When Haji finally left the temple, it seemed to him that even the gods had forsaken him. But as he turned his steps toward home, he was not at all certain of that. Something troubled him, something about the little brass bell of the ceremony. He kept remembering the sound of it. Why? Was there some secret it wished to tell?

All at once, he stopped short. He knew! He had the answer. The little brass bell reminded him of yet another bell, the great wooden bell of Majda Koom that lay at his father's bedside. Of course, that was it!

His heart pounding with new hope, Haji raced for home. He caught up the wooden bell and ran to one of the watchtowers in the rice fields, where Ket Kay awaited him.

"Look, Ket Kay!" he shouted as he climbed the bamboo ladder to the platform high over the fields. "Here is the answer. The bell of Majda Koom! I should have thought of it before. The bell has not changed its voice. Majda Koom will remember it when I ring it for him."

Ket Kay looked at the bell Haji had brought. "Good. Now you must find Majda Koom."

"*Ay,*" replied Haji. "At dawn I go into the jungle."
He stretched out on his back. "It will not be easy to find
him. Let me rest till the big star shines over the bend
of the river."

Wild Elephant Raid

For a time he dozed, trying to sleep so that he would be well rested for his long journey through the jungle.

Presently something brought him out of his sleep. He was suddenly wide awake, and he could not understand why. He sat up.

"What is it?" Ket Kay asked.

"I don't know. Did you hear anything?"

"There was nothing to hear."

That was odd, Haji thought. He knew only that his keen senses had brought him a warning. He listened, turning his head this way and that.

Somewhere in the paddy a porcupine called softly to its mate. Frogs and crickets were singing their usual song to the starry heavens. But Haji knew these sounds would not have awakened him.

Perhaps it was not a sound at all. He tested the cool night breeze coming down from the jungled hills, and his sensitive nostrils caught a familiar smell, like the spicy fragrance of crushed grasses.

"Elephants!" he whispered. "And very close, too, or I couldn't smell them."

"Do you think Majda Koom——"

"Look!" Haji pointed to a dark shape moving into the paddy.

Other dark shapes followed. Like ghostly shadows they came, large elephants and small, slipping quietly out from the fringe of the jungle to feast on the precious rice.

Ket Kay grabbed Haji's arm so hard that it hurt. "All our rice will be eaten. The soldiers will not be here until tomorrow. What can we do?"

"I don't know," Haji said.

He had hoped to find the elephants in the jungle, before they reached the rice fields. Even the tame animals from the elephant camp would be hard to manage if they got in a rice field.

The whole margin of the jungle now was alive with shadowy motion. On they came, without making a sound. Haji had never seen such a large herd. He bent forward, trying to locate Majda Koom.

"Quick!" Ket Kay said. "Ring the bell of Majda Koom!"

An elephant hungry for rice would pay no attention to a bell, Haji knew. But he rang the bell just the same, more to please Ket Kay than anything else.

The voice of the bell brought the boys in the other watchtowers to life. They saw the elephants and began shouting and banging gongs and throwing stones to frighten away the herd. The hail of stones and the noise merely annoyed the elephants.

Haji did not like this. If the boys made the elephants angry, there would be bad trouble. Stones and noise were not going to stop a mighty herd.

But one of the stones must have found its mark, for suddenly, above the din, came a scream and a crash. A watchtower disappeared at the end of the field. Then there were more screams from the boys, and more crashes.

"It's Majda Koom," cried Haji. "They made him angry with their stones. Now he's charging the towers!"

In frozen horror, the boys watched.

"We'll all be killed," cried Ket Kay. "Now he's coming this way! Do something, Haji. Stop him!"

What could he do? Down went the towers, one by one. Boys leaped for their lives as the bamboo frames of the towers exploded beneath them. Haji couldn't think. He couldn't move. Was there nothing that could stop that furious charge?

Down the line of towers rushed the enraged elephant. He smacked into the tower next to theirs, and over it went with a sickening crash.

"Here he comes!" screamed Ket Kay.

"Jump aside when he rams," Haji told him. "Jump that way. No harm will come if you hide in the rice and leave him alone."

In his haste to get ready for the leap, Ket Kay accidentally kicked the elephant bell from the platform. Not that it mattered. It could not help them now.

Haji had no thought of saving himself. The mighty beast would soon pass under the platform as he rammed their tower. He had to be stopped if the rice fields and the village were to be saved. But how?

He had only seconds to think, for rushing at them out of the night came the giant elephant, trumpeting with rage.

Only one thing could stop him now—fear! If he could be frightened somehow, his fear would spread through the entire elephant herd like wildfire. The elephants would scatter in panic and never come back.

"I have to try to scare him," Haji thought. His heart hammered as he braced himself. There was still hope, if he could do it right. If he failed, he would die.

He waited till the elephant was almost beneath him. Then, with the savage snarl of a tiger breaking from his lips, he jumped.

Nimble as a cat he twisted in midair and came down where he wanted to land—squarely on the back of the huge elephant.

Majda Koom was taken completely by surprise. His screams of terror filled the night. He turned in sudden panic and bolted for the jungle, as if ten tigers were clawing his back.

Haji clung desperately with fingers and toes. With all the power of his lungs, he kept snarling like a royal tiger making a kill.

He could hear the frightened trumpeting of the other elephants. Panic spread in the herd. The elephants had seen their great leader frightened off by some mysterious attack, and now they scattered and fled from the unknown danger.

Haji saw them disappearing into the jungle far to the left of him. A tight smile came to his lips. He had won. His plan had worked. The village and rice fields were saved, for elephants never came back to a place where they had been badly frightened.

But Haji had little time to be pleased with himself. The wild, swaying ride took all his attention and strength.

Now he had to find a way to escape from Majda Koom —if he could. It wouldn't be easy.

He did not think he could hang on the broad back for long. His fingers were not strong enough to dig into the rough hide. There was nothing to which he could hold. One slip would bring sudden death, for, if he fell, the desperate beast would wheel instantly and trample him into the earth in a few seconds.

When they were deep in the jungle, Majda Koom slackened his pace suddenly. Haji caught his breath. The battle for his life was just beginning.

Without warning, the great trunk lashed back at him. It whipped so close to his face that he could feel the wind of it. Again and again Majda struck out with his trunk, mighty blows that could have crushed the skull of a tiger. But Haji knew how far back an elephant could reach with its trunk and stayed clear.

Then Majda abruptly changed his method of attack. Tossing his mighty head, he reared, went up and up and over on his back to crush the unknown thing beneath him, just as See Po had killed the tiger.

Haji was not to be caught so easily. He jumped aside at the last moment.

With a rumble of disgust, the big tusker rolled over on its side. As it made to rise, Haji sprang up on a huge hind knee and vaulted onto the broad back again.

"*Tah! Tah!* Stand up! Stand up!" he shouted. "I am not a tiger. I am Haji."

Now that they were alone in the jungle, Haji began to hope that somehow, by his actions and words, he could make Majda Koom recognize him. "If I had not lost your bell in the rice field," he said, "you would soon remember me."

The sound of his voice seemed only to anger the beast. It went off through the brush and made for the river. Soon it was splashing out through the shallows.

"*Ay,* big brother," said Haji. "What you need is a bath in the river. Perhaps it will cool your temper."

The big bull made a rumbling answer in his throat and plowed deeper and deeper into the river, until at last the muddy water closed over the elephant completely. Soon the water was up to Haji's neck. Then he had to swim. All he could see of Majda, who was walking on the bottom, was the tip of the trunk, held above water for breathing.

It reminded Haji of the water game they had played so often together. He looked at the tip of the trunk only a few feet ahead of him. To play the game, he had only to swim over, grab the trunk, and pull it below the surface. Did Majda Koom want him to play the game now? Was the animal testing him to find out if he really was the boy Haji?

There was no way of being sure. Haji was afraid to go near. How could he be certain the trunk would not coil about him and drag him down to an awful death?

Slowly the tip of the trunk moved toward the far shore. Once it stopped and waved from side to side, as if inviting Haji to grab it.

Suddenly the trunk disappeared altogether. Haji knew what that meant. It was the trick of a killer elephant!

Majda Koom's Battle with Haji

In the muddy water an elephant could turn unseen below the surface and drag down a swimmer in a matter of moments. Haji took no chances. He dived, found the elephant's tail, and hung on. So long as he could hang on to the tail and hold his breath, he was safe enough.

Twice he had to kick up to the surface for air and dive for the tail again. But when Majda Koom emerged on the far bank of the river, Haji was once again perched on his back.

Again the mighty elephant had failed to get rid of him. But the battle was far from over. With a bellow of rage as big as six tiger roars, Majda Koom rammed into the thickest of the jungle to brush the pesky man-thing from his back.

It was what Haji had most dreaded. He would be helpless against such an attack. A terrible fear gripped him as they smashed headlong through snarled entanglements that lashed and tore at his body.

Though he flattened down, it did not help him. There was no protection against the scraping jungle. Branches clubbed him. Twigs jabbed into his flesh like hot needles. Thorns ripped the length of his back till he cried out in pain. No one could take such bruising punishment for long.

Again and again he screamed for Majda to stop.

Tears blinded him. Dizziness and pain took the strength from his body. His fingers grew numb. The end was near, he knew, for he couldn't hold on much longer. Death would come quickly and take away the pain. He was thankful for that.

Just when he thought he would have to give up, a strange thing happened. The terrible punishment ceased as quickly as it had begun. They were in the open now, rushing through milky morning mists. It was almost too good to be true.

Cautiously, Haji raised his head to look in front of them. Too late he saw the branch—a low branch coming at him like a swinging club.

It struck with a solid jolt. Stars burst in his head. The world spun and dipped and turned on edge so that he couldn't tell up from down. It began to grow dark. For a terrible instant he hung on, fighting the swirling grayness that was closing over him.

But it closed down just the same. He went limp. He could feel his fingers lose their hold. He was slipping —slipping—sliding off into space—falling down, down, down into a bottomless pit of darkness.

It seemed like a long and restless sleep. And when he opened his eyes at last, the sun was lacing down through leafy bowers in the roof of the Burma jungle. How peaceful it was! Flies buzzed around him. Birds were chattering.

Nothing seemed quite real at first. It felt good to rest. But after a time he remembered his fall from the elephant's back. His arms and legs felt as stiff as sticks, and his head hurt where the branch had struck him.

Slowly he tested his arms, then his legs. He could move them. He felt of his head. There was a lump on the top. That was all. There was nothing to worry about. He could get up and go home as soon as he had rested.

For a time he tried to sleep. Then, suddenly, all the little lazy sounds of the jungle morning were shattered by the loud flopping of elephant ears.

Haji sat up with a start. His eyes went wide.

Only a few feet away stood the mighty Majda Koom, swaying gently back and forth, as elephants usually do. Majda stopped swaying. They looked at each other.

For an endless moment Haji forgot to breathe. He had not been trampled—not yet—but he knew that was not the miracle it seemed. When he had fallen and hit the ground, he had lain there in a lifeless heap—and elephants rarely attacked anything that did not move or show some sign of life.

But now! Now that he had moved, what would the elephant do? Had it waited to kill him? Or had it touched and smelled of his body and recognized him?

As if in answer, Majda reached slowly out with his long trunk. He touched Haji's chest gently, as he had done so many times before, and made the small whistling sounds of a happy elephant.

A cry broke from Haji's lips. With both hands he caught the trunk and laid his cheek against it. Majda Koom knew him and loved him still!

Two years, two long years of waiting and hoping— and now it was over. They were back together again.

Haji knew his father had been right. An elephant's eyes were not very sharp at a distance. All Majda had needed was to get a close look at him, and to touch and smell of him.

Late the following afternoon, with Haji riding proudly on the mighty head of his tusker, they entered the elephant camp. In a moment the entire camp was in an uproar. People came running from all directions, and among them were Ket Kay and several others from the village.

"I said you would bring him here!" cried Ket Kay. "They did not believe me, but I knew it. We told how you saved the village. They did not want to believe that, either."

Byoo, Haji's young friend from the elephant camp, stared. "We believe it now," he said. "It is Majda Koom. No one but Haji could have brought him back."

The villagers from Chinwa pressed forward, and one of them said, "The elders have sent us to take you back to the village for a day. They wish to honor you."

Oo Yan, the chief of the *oozies,* was nodding his head. "It is well," he said. "For one day he may go. But you will remind your elders that this boy is one of the elephant people. He belongs here with us."

At a word from Haji, the great tusker lowered him to the ground with his trunk. Haji turned to face *Thakin* Jensen and the amazed *oozies. Thakin* Jensen still acted as if he could hardly believe what he saw.

Oo Yan stepped forward and placed a hand warmly on Haji's shoulder. "If our faith in you has been small, my son, you have at last opened our eyes. You have done what our best *oozies* could not do."

Ket Kay's dark eyes sparkled. "I knew he would do it. I knew it! Was there ever anyone so brave?"

Slowly a smile grew on *Thakin* Jensen's lips. "Many are brave," he said. "What this boy Haji has done took far more than courage. It took love—the kind of love that a great *oozie* has for his elephant."

Thakin Jensen turned to Oo Yan. "Majda Koom will need careful watching for a time. See that no one handles him but this boy, and make sure the boy is properly trained as an *oozie*."

The *oozies* smiled and nodded. The wrinkled one said, "Truly this boy is the son of his father. He will make a good *oozie*."

Oo Yan seemed more pleased than anyone. He raised his hands for silence. "Hail! Hail to the new *oozie* of Majda Koom!"

Loudly and long they hailed him.

Haji could not keep the painful lump from swelling in his throat, or the tears from his eyes. He stepped back and, resting one of his hands on a great curved tusk of his elephant, stood proudly.

Then a smile broke upon his lips, for he heard the best hail of all. It came from the great beast beside him—the happy whistling sounds of the lord of all elephants.

Answers

For page 45:

1-D	baseball	*healthy cut*
2-G	basketball	*baskets*
3-J	tennis	*serves, net*
4-C	swimming	*Australian crawl*
5-E	golf	*par, putt, cup*
6-I	bowling	*alley*
7-A	track	*high hurdles*
8-B	archery	*arrows, bow*
9-F	boating	*waters, Tampa Bay, Flying Dutchman*
10-H	hockey	*Leafs, goalie, puck*

For page 114:

1. It was 6:00 p.m.
2. He wore a brown suit, white shirt, and dark glasses.
3. Yes. (His right hand was bleeding.)
4. He cut his hand when he broke the store window.
5. He probably used the wrench, which is now on the sidewalk.
6. He had a white sack in his left hand.
7. The car was green.
8. The licence number of the car was A-1234.

9. No. (There was a man at the steering wheel.)
10. Yes. (A man, woman, and little girl were walking along the sidewalk. A man was looking out a second-floor window. A man was standing at the corner.)
11. Yes. (The man at the corner seemed to be acting as a lookout.)

For page 193:

bird watchers: onlookers at a launching
Big Joe: an Atlas D booster rocket
clear the pad: clear the launching area
beast: booster rocket
blast-off: rising into the air
bug: special problem
scrub: cancellation
lox: liquid oxygen
shed her skirt: give off a spray of ice
go juice: rocket fuel
hot rock: flashy astronaut
greenhouse: Plexiglas covering of the craft
go condition: readiness
lift-off: rising into the air
in the green: proceeding as planned

For page 276:

1. The dog's tail is not the same length.
2. The mower wheel is different.
3. The man's neck in relation to his ear is different.
4. He has two pockets in his overalls in one picture, one pocket in the other picture.
5. There is a different number of branches on the big tree.
6. There is a different number of small cone-shaped trees.
7. Windows at the right on the first floor of the building are different.

For pages 374–375:

North America	South America
walrus	tapir
moose	jaguar
bison	llama
lynx	macaw
alligator	rhea
armadillo	penguin

Europe	Asia
reindeer	bear
horse	fox
wild boar	yak
	rhesus
	rhinoceros
	tiger

Africa	Australia
dromedary	kangaroo
ostrich	koala
lion	
gorilla	
elephant	
zebra	

Glossary

Full Pronunciation Key

The pronunciation of each word is shown just after the word, in this way: **ab bre vi ate** (ə brē′vē āt). The letters and signs used are pronounced as in the words below. The mark ′ is placed after a syllable with primary or strong accent, as in the example above. The mark ′ after a syllable shows a secondary or lighter accent, as in **ab bre vi a tion** (ə brē′vē ā′shən).

Some words, taken from foreign languages, are spoken with sounds that otherwise do not occur in English. Symbols for these sounds are given at the bottom of the page as "Foreign Sounds."

a	hat, cap	j	jam, enjoy			u	cup, butter
ā	age, face	k	kind, seek			ù	full, put
ã	care, air	l	land, coal			ü	rule, move
ä	father, far	m	me, am			ū	use, music
		n	no, in				
		ng	long, bring				
b	bad, rob						
ch	child, much						
d	did, red					v	very, save
		o	hot, rock			w	will, woman
		ō	open, go			y	young, yet
e	let, best	ô	order, all			z	zero, breeze
ē	equal, see	oi	oil, voice			zh	measure, seizure
ėr	term, learn	ou	house, out				
f	fat, if	p	paper, cup				
g	go, bag	r	run, try			ə represents:	
h	he, how	s	say, yes				a in about
		sh	she, rush				e in taken
		t	tell, it				i in April
i	it, pin	th	thin, both				o in lemon
ī	ice, five	ŦH	then, smooth				u in circus

foreign sounds

Y as in French *du*. Pronounce ē with the lips rounded as for English ü in **rule**.

œ as in French *peu*. Pronounce ā with the lips rounded as for ō.

N as in French *bon*. The N is not pronounced, but shows that the vowel before it is nasal.

H as in German *ach*. Pronounce k without closing the breath passage.

This pronunciation key is based on the key in the *Intermediate Dictionary* in the Dictionary of Canadian English series (W. J. Gage Limited), from which this glossary was compiled.

ab do men (ab′də mən or ab dō′mən), the part of the body containing the stomach, the intestines, and other digestive organs. *n.*

ab dom i nal (ab dom′ə nəl), of the abdomen; in the abdomen: *abdominal muscles. adj.*

-able, suffix meaning:
1. that can be _____ed, as in *enjoyable.*
2. adapted for or suitable to, as in *comfortable.*
3. inclined to, as in *peaceable.*
4. deserving to be _____ed, as in *lovable.*

abom i na ble (ə bom′ə nə bəl), 1. disgusting; hateful. 2. very unpleasant; very bad. *adj.*

ac cus tomed (ə kus′təmd), usual; customary. *adj.*

accustomed to, used to; in the habit of: *He was accustomed to hard work.*

acre (ā′kər), a measure of land, 160 square rods or 43,560 square feet. *n.*

ad vis er or **ad vi sor** (ad vīz′ər), 1. person who gives advice. 2. teacher appointed to advise students. *n.*

ahoy (ə hoi′), a call used by sailors to attract the attention of persons at a distance. *interj.*

air-con di tion (ãr′kən dish′ən), 1. supply with equipment for air conditioning. 2. treat (air) by means of air conditioning. *v.*

air conditioner, equipment that washes the air (in a room, building, etc.) and controls its humidity and temperature.

-al, suffix meaning:
1. of; like, as in *natural, accidental.*
2. act of, as in *arrival, refusal.*

Alps (alps), a mountain system in S Europe, famous for its beautiful scenery. The **Austrian Alps** are that part of this mountain system lying in Austria. *n. pl.*

al tar (ôl′tər), 1. table or stand in the most sacred part of a church, synagogue, or temple. 2. a raised place, built of earth or stone, on which to make sacrifices or burn offerings to a god. *n.*

alu mi nize (ə lü′mə nīz′), coat with aluminum. *v.,* **alu mi nized, alu mi niz ing.**

alu mi num (ə lü′mə nəm), a silver-white, very light metal that does not lose its brightness easily. Aluminum is much used for making kettles and pans. *n.*

am pli fy (am′plə fī), 1. make greater; make stronger. 2. increase the strength of a sound or an electrical impulse. *v.,* **am pli fied, am pli fy ing.**

-an, suffix meaning:
1. of or having to do with, as in *Mohammedan.*
2. native or inhabitant of, as in *Missourian.*

an ces tor (an′ses tər), person from whom one is descended. Your father, your mother, your grandfathers, your grandmothers, and so on back, are your ancestors. *n.*

an cient (ān′shənt), 1. of or belonging to times long past: *We saw the ruined temples of ancient Rome.* 2. old-fashioned: *"Mother, this dress is positively ancient!" complained the girl. adj.*

ant eat er (ant′ēt′ər), a toothless animal with a long, slender, sticky tongue. The anteater eats ants and termites. *n.*

Anteater (total length 3½ feet)

anx ious (angk′shəs or ang′shəs), 1. uneasy because of thoughts and fears about what may happen; troubled; worried: *Mother felt anxious about the children, who had been gone an hour too long.* 2. wishing very much; eager: *Jim was anxious to please his father. adj.*

ap pren tice (ə pren′tis), 1. person learning a trade or art. A plumber begins as an apprentice. After he learns his trade, he becomes a journeyman. 2. take as an apprentice: *On leaving school, Bob was apprenticed to a butcher.* 1 *n.,* 2 *v.,* **ap pren ticed, ap pren tic ing.**

Ar bois (är bwä′), town in E France. *n.*

arm[1] (ärm), 1. the part of a person's body between the shoulder and the hand. 2. something that is shaped or used like a person's arm: *the arm of a chair.* 3. power, authority: *the long arm of the law.*

arm[2] (ärm), 1. a weapon, *usually plural.* See **arms.** 2. provide with weapons: *Policemen in England are not allowed to arm themselves with guns, except by special order.* 1 *n.,* 2 *v.*

aro ma (ə rō′mə), fragrance; spicy or strong odor: *the aroma of cooked cabbage. n.*

arouse (ə rouz′), 1. awaken: *The buzzing of the alarm clock failed to arouse Nick.* 2. stir to action; excite: *The attack on Pearl Harbor aroused the whole country. v.,* **aroused, arous ing.**

ar son (är′sən), the crime of intentionally setting fire to a building or other property. *n.*

as sem blage (ə sem′blij), a collection; group. *n.*

as ton ish (əs ton′ish), surprise greatly; amaze. *v.*

as tron o mer (əs tron′ə mər), an expert in astronomy. *n.*

as tron o my (əs tron′ə mē), the science that deals with the sun, moon, planets, stars, and other heavenly bodies. *n.*

at mos phere (at′məs fēr), 1. air that surrounds the earth; the air. 2. mass of gases that surrounds any heavenly body: *The atmosphere of Mars is very different from the earth's atmosphere.* *n.*

at mos pher ic (at′məs fer′ik), of or having to do with the atmosphere. *adj.*

atmospheric pressure, pressure caused by the weight of the air pressing down upon the surface of the earth.

au thor i ty (ə thôr′ə tē), 1. power; control: *A father has authority over his children.* 2. right: *A policeman has the authority to make arrests.* 3. person who has power or right. *n., pl.* **au thor i ties.**

av a lanche (av′ə lanch), 1. a large mass of snow and ice, or of dirt and rocks, sliding or falling down the side of a mountain. 2. anything like an avalanche: *an avalanche of water smashing down upon the ship's deck, an avalanche of questions.* *n.*

award (ə wôrd), 1. give after careful consideration, grant. 2. something given after careful consideration; prize. 1 *v.*, 2 *n.*

ay (ā), *Burmese.* exclamation of approval or agreement; yes. *adv.*

Az tec (az′tek), 1. member of a highly civilized people who ruled Mexico before its conquest by the Spaniards in 1521. 2. their language. 3. of the Aztecs or their language. 1, 2 *n.*, 3 *adj.*

baf fle (baf′əl), 1. be too hard for (a person) to understand or solve: *This problem baffles me.* 2. a wall or screen to turn aside or stop the flow of air, water, etc. 1 *v.*, **baffled, baf fling;** 2 *n.*

bal lad (bal′əd), 1. a simple song. 2. a poem that tells a story in simple verse form, especially one that tells a popular legend. *n.*

bam boo (bam-bü′), 1. a treelike plant belonging to the grass family. The plant's stiff, hollow stems, which have hard thick joints, are used for making canes, furniture, and even houses. 2. of bamboo; made of the stems of this plant. 1 *n., pl.* **bam boos;** 2 *adj.*

Bamboo

ban ish (ban′ish), 1. condemn to leave a country: *Napoleon was banished to the island of Elba.* 2. force to go away; send away; drive away: *The judge banished photographers from the courtroom.* *v.*

ban ish ment (ban′ish mənt), 1. act of banishing. 2. state of being banished. *n.*

bar ren (bar′ən), 1. not producing anything: *The desert was barren.* 2. a stretch of barren land. 1 *adj.*, 2 *n.*

bat ter[1] (bat′ər), beat with repeated blows; pound: *The fireman battered the door down with an ax.* *v.*

bat ter[2] (bat′ər), mixture of flour, milk, eggs, or the like, that becomes solid when cooked. Cakes, pancakes, etc., are made from batter. *n.*

bat ter[3] (bat′ər), player whose turn it is to bat in baseball, cricket, etc. *n.*

battering ram, 1. a military machine used in ancient times for battering down walls, gates, etc. 2. any heavy object used to break down a door, wall, etc.

Soldiers using a battering ram

Belle Isle, Strait of, (bel īl strāt uv), the N. outlet of the Gulf of St. Lawrence between the coasts of Labrador and Newfoundland.

ben zine (ben′zēn or ben zēn′), a colorless liquid obtained from petroleum and used in cleaning and dyeing and as a motor fuel. It vaporizes and is set on fire easily. *n.*

Ber til lon (ber′tē yōN′), **Al phonse** (äl-fôNs′), *French.* *n.*

be tray (bi trā′),   **1.** give away to the enemy: *The traitor betrayed his country.* **2.** be unfaithful to; let down: *She betrayed her friends by breaking her promise.* **3.** mislead; deceive: *He was betrayed by his own enthusiasm.* **4.** show; reveal: *His answer betrayed the fact that he had not listened.* *v.*

bi ol o gist (bī ol′ə jist), an expert in biology. *n.*

bi ol o gy (bī ol′ə jē), the science of life or living things; study of plant and animal life. *n.*

blun der (blun′dər), **1.** a stupid mistake. **2.** make a stupid mistake. 1 *n.*, 2 *v.*

bo gus (bō′gəs), counterfeit. *adj.*

bon vo yage (bôn vwä yazh′ *French*), good-bye; good luck; pleasant trip.

Bor deaux (bôr dō′), seaport in SW France. *n.*

Bor ghe se (bôr gā′zā), **Sci pi o ne** (shē-pyō′nā), *Italian. n.*

bo tree (bō), a fig tree of India. *n.*

Bu da pest (bü′də pest), capital of Hungary, on the Danube River. *n.*

Bud dha (būd′ə or bü′də), 563?-483? B.C., great religious teacher of Asia, founder of Buddhism. *n.* Also, **Gautama.**

Bud dhism (būd′iz əm or bü′diz əm), religion that originated in the sixth century B.C., in N India and spread widely over central, SE, and E Asia. It teaches self-control and right living. *n.*

Bud dhist (būd′ist or bü′dist), **1.** having to do with Buddha or Buddhism. **2.** believer in Buddhism. 1 *adj.*, 2 *n.*

Bur ma (bėr′mə), country in SE Asia. *Capital:* Rangoon. *n.*

bur row (bėr′ō), **1.** hole dug in the ground by an animal for protection or shelter. Rabbits live in burrows. **2.** dig a hole in the ground: *The mole quickly burrowed out of sight.* 1 *n.*, 2 *v.*

bush (būsh), **1.** a woody plant smaller than a tree, often with many separate stems starting near the ground. **2.** open forest or wild land. *n.*

bush land (būsh′land′), bush. *n.*

bush man (būsh′mən), **1.** settler in the Australian bush. **2.** person who knows much about life in the bush. *n., pl.* **bush men.**

bust er (bus′tər), *especially Australian.* sudden, violent wind. *n.*

Byoo (bū), *Burmese. n.*

ca cao (kə kā′ō or kə kä′ō), **1.** a small tree from whose seeds cocoa and chocolate are made. **2.** the seeds of the tree. *n., pl.* **ca ca os.**

cal lus (kal′əs), a hard, thickened place on the skin. *n.*

cam el (kam′əl), a large, four-footed animal with one or two humps on its back, used as a beast of burden. The **Arabian camel**, or dromedary, has one hump; the **Bactrian camel** of Asia has two humps. *n.*

Dromedary (6 ft. high at the shoulder)

Bactrian camel (7½ ft. high at hump)

cam paign (kam-pān′), **1.** in a war, a number of related military operations with a special purpose, such as gaining control of important cities and highways: *The British Army lost many men in the campaigns during World War II.* **2.** series of connected activities to do or get something; planned course of action for some special purpose: *an advertising campaign.* **3.** take part in a campaign. 1, 2 *n.*, 3 *v.*

ca na li (kä nä′lē), *Italian. n. pl.*

ca not du maître (ka nō′ dᵸ me′tre *Cdn. French*), the "master's canoe" or Montreal canoe, a large freight canoe, capable of carrying 4 to 5 tons, used by the fur traders for the voyage from Montreal to the Grand Portage. *n.*

ca not du nord (ka nō′ dᵸ nôr′ *Cdn. French*), a birchbark canoe capable of carrying some 1½ to 2 tons, used primarily on the waterways north and west of Lake Superior. *n.*

---

hat, āge, cãre, fär; let, bē, tėrm; it, īce; hot, gō, ôrder; oil, out; cup, pút, rüle, ūse; ch, child; ng, long; th, thin; ᵺ, then; zh, measure; ə represents *a* in about, *e* in taken, *i* in April, *o* in lemon, *u* in circus.

Cape Kennedy, place in Florida from which the United States launches rockets, formerly called Cape Canaveral.

cap sule (kap′səl or kap′syúl), **1.** a small case or covering. Medicine is often given in capsules. **2.** that part of a rocket that contains instruments, a man, etc., which is separated in flight from the motors and goes into orbit or is recovered at a later time. **3.** an enclosed section of an aircraft or rocket, as a cockpit, which can be handled or ejected as a unit. *n.*

ca reer (kə rēr′), **1.** a general course of action or progress through life: *It is interesting to read of the careers of great men and women.* **2.** occupation; profession: *Stan chose the Navy for his career.* **3.** rush along wildly: *The runaway horse careered through the streets.* 1, 2 *n.*, 3 *v.*

Car i boo or **Car i bou** (kar′ə bü′), a mountain range in British Columbia at the northernmost part of the Fraser River Valley and west of the Rocky Mountains.

cat nip (kat′nip), a plant somewhat like mint, with strongly scented leaves of which cats are fond. *n.*

cen ten ni al (sen ten′ē əl), **1.** a period of 100 years or the 100th anniversary. **2.** 100 years old. *n.*

cen tu ry (sen′chə rē), **1.** each 100 years, counting from some special time, such as the birth of Christ. The first century is 1 to 100; the sixteenth century is 1501 to 1600; the twentieth century is 1901 to 2000. **2.** period of 100 years. From 1824 to 1924 is a century. **3.** body of soldiers in the ancient Roman army. Originally, it probably consisted of 100 soldiers. *n., pl.* **cen tu ries.**

Cey lon (si lon′), island in the Indian Ocean, just off S India. *Capital:* Colombo. *n.* See **India** for map.

cham ois (sham′ē), **1.** a small, goatlike antelope that lives in the high mountains of Europe and SW Asia. **2.** a soft leather made from the skin of sheep, goats, deer, etc. *n., pl.* **cham ois.**

Chamois (2 ft. high at the shoulder)

chant (chant), **1.** a short, simple song in which several syllables or words are sung in one tone. It is used in a church service. **2.** sing in this way. A choir chants psalms or prayers. **3.** say over and over again. 1 *n.*, 2, 3 *v.*

charge (chärj), **1.** load; fill. A gun is charged with powder and shot. A battery is charged with electricity. **2.** care; management: *Doctors and nurses have charge of sick people.* **3.** ask a price: *They charge a lot for hamburgers at that restaurant.* **4.** attack; rush with force: *Our soldiers charged the enemy* (*v.*). *The charge drove the enemy back* (*n.*). 1, 3, 4 *v.*, **charged, charg ing;** 2, 4 *n.*

Chi na (chī′nə), a large country in E Asia. *Capital:* Peking. *n.*

clap (klap), **1.** a sudden noise, such as a single burst of thunder, the sound of the hands struck together, or the sound of a loud slap. **2.** make such a noise, especially with the hands: *When the show was over, we all clapped.* **3.** put or place quickly and effectively: *The police clapped the thief into jail.* 1 *n.*, 2, 3 *v.*, **clapped, clap ping.**

clap per (klap′ər), **1.** person or thing that claps. **2.** inside a bell, the movable part that strikes and rings the outer part. *n.*

clear (klēr), **1.** not cloudy; bright; light: *a clear day.* **2.** transparent: *clear glass.* **3.** easily seen, heard, or understood; plain; distinct: *a clear idea, a clear voice.* **4.** make clear; get clear: *He cleared the land of trees.* **5.** without touching; without being caught; out of the way: *The ship was clear of the iceberg.* **6.** completely; entirely: *The bullet went clear through the door.* 1-3, 5 *adj.*, 4 *v.*, 6 *adv.*

clear ance (klēr′əns), **1.** act of making clear, such as the removal of buildings to permit new construction: *slum clearance.* **2.** distance between things. *n.*

clear ing (klēr′ing), an open space of cleared land in a forest. *n.*

co bra (kō′brə), a poisonous snake of S Asia and Africa. It can dilate the head and neck so that they assume a hoodlike form. *n.*

Cobra (4½ ft. long)

col or ful (kul′ər fəl), **1.** full of color. **2.** picturesque; vivid: *a colorful parade. adj.*

come (kum), **1.** move toward the speaker or the place where he is or will be; approach. **2.** arrive. *v.*, **came, come, com ing.**
come in, enter.

com man dant (kom′ən dant′), the commanding officer of a fort, navy yard, military prison, etc. *n.*

com merce (kom′ərs), trade; business. *n.*

com mer cial (kə mėr′shəl), **1.** having to do with commerce. **2.** the part of a radio or television program that advertises something. 1 *adj.*, 2 *n.*

com plex (kəm pleks′ or kom′pleks), **1.** made up of a number of parts. **2.** complicated. *adj.*

con cus sion (kən kush′ən), **1.** a sudden, violent shaking; shock: *The concussion caused by the explosion broke many windows.* **2.** an injury to the brain, spine, etc., caused by a blow, fall, or other shock. *n.*

con demn (kən dem′), **1.** express strong disapproval of: *We condemn cruelty and cruel people.* **2.** declare not sound or suitable for use: *This bridge has been condemned because it is no longer safe. v.*

con di tion (kən dish′ən), **1.** state in which a person or thing is: *A sick person is in poor condition.* **2.** good condition: *People who take part in sports must keep in condition.* **3.** put in good condition: *Exercise conditions your muscles.* **4.** thing on which something else depends: *I'll help you on one condition: that you make an effort to help yourself.* 1, 2, 4 *n.*, 3 *v.*

con fec tion er (kən fek′shən ər), person who makes or sells candies, ice cream, and cakes. *n.*

confectioners' sugar, a finely ground sugar specially suited for use by confectioners.

con flict (kon′flict for 1, 2; kən flikt′ for 3), **1.** fight; struggle: *an armed conflict between two nations.* **2.** disagreement: *a conflict of opinion.* **3.** be directly opposed; disagree; clash: *opinions that conflict.* 1, 2 *n.*, 3 *v.*

con quer (kong′kər), **1.** win in war: *conquer a country.* **2.** get the better of: *conquer a bad habit. v.*

con ser va tion (kon′sər vā′shən), a preserving from harm or decay; protecting from loss or from being used up: *The conservation of forests is very important. n.*

con serve (kən sėrv′ for 1; kon′sėrv for 2), **1.** keep from harm or decay; protect from loss or from being used up; preserve: *Try to conserve your strength for the end of the race.* **2.** fruit preserved in sugar; jam. 1 *v.*, con served, con serv ing; 2 *n.*

con sid er (kən sid′ər), **1.** think about in order to decide: *Take till tomorrow to consider this offer.* **2.** be thoughtful of: *Why not consider the feelings of other people once in a while? v.*

con sid er a ble (kən sid′ər ə bəl), **1.** worth thinking about; important. **2.** not a little; much: *considerable difficulty. adj.*

con sid er a bly (kən sid′ər ə blē), much; a good deal. *adv.*

con sult (kən sult′), seek information or advice from: *You can consult persons, books, or maps to find out what you wish to know. v.*

con tempt (kən tempt′), **1.** the feeling that a person, act, or thing is mean, low, or worthless; scorn: *We feel contempt for a liar.* **2.** disobedience to or open disrespect for the rules or decisions of a law court. A person can be put in jail for **contempt of court.** *n.*

con ti nent (kon′tə nənt), one of the seven great masses of land on the earth. The continents are North America, South America, Europe, Africa, Asia, Australia, and Antarctica. *n.*

con vict (kən vikt′ for 1; kon′vikt for 2), **1.** prove guilty. **2.** person serving a prison sentence for some crime. 1 *v.*, 2 *n.*

con vince (kən vins′), make (a person) feel sure; cause to believe: *The mistakes Sue made convinced me she had not studied her lesson. v.*, con vinced, con vinc ing.

cor al (kôr′əl), **1.** a hard red, pink, or white substance. Coral is made out of the skeletons of tiny sea animals. **2.** deep pink or red. 1 *n.*, 2 *adj.*

Cor tés or **Cor tez** (kôr tez′), **Her nan do** (her nän′dō), 1486-1547, Spanish soldier who conquered Mexico. *n.*

coun ter feit (koun′tər fit), **1.** copy (money, pictures, handwriting, etc.) in order to deceive: *He was sent to prison for counterfeiting money.* **2.** not genuine. 1 *v.*, 2 *adj.*

crag (krag), a steep, rugged rock rising above others. *n.*

cra ter (krā′tər), **1.** the depression around the opening at the top of a volcano. **2.** a bowl-shaped hole. *n.*

---

hat, āge, cãre, fär; let, bē, tėrm; it, īce; hot, gō, ôrder; oil, out; cup, pút, rüle, ūse; ch, child; ng, long; th, thin; ŦH, then; zh, measure; ə represents *a* in about, *e* in taken, *i* in April, *o* in lemon, *u* in circus.

curse (kėrs), **1.** ask God to bring evil or harm on. **2.** the words that a person says when he asks God to curse someone or something. **3.** bring or call forth evil or harm on. **4.** a bringing or calling forth of evil or harm. 1, 3 *v.*, **cursed** or **curst, curs ing;** 2, 4 *n.*

cus cus (kus′kəs), a small, tree-climbing mammal of Australia. *n.*

cus tom (kus′təm), **1.** a usual action; habit: *It was his custom to rise early.* **2.** the regular business given by a customer: *That store would like to have your custom.* **3.** made specially for individuals; made to order: *custom clothes.* 1, 2 *n.*, 3 *adj.*

custom-built, built to order; built specially for individuals. *adj.*

cy cle (sī′kəl), **1.** any period of time or complete process of growth or action which repeats itself in the same order. The seasons of the year—spring, summer, autumn, and winter—make a cycle. **2.** ride a bicycle or tricycle. 1 *n.*, 2 *v.*, **cy cled, cy cling.**

dain ty (dān′tē), **1.** having delicate beauty: *a dainty flower.* **2.** marked by delicate form: *The ballerina took dainty steps.* **3.** something very good to eat; a delicious bit of food: *a dainty made of whipped cream and custard and jelly.* 1, 2 *adj.*, **dain ti er, dain ti est;** 3 *n.*, *pl.* **dain ties.**

da Vin ci (də vin′chē; *Italian* dä vēn′chē), **Le o nar do** (lē′ən är′dō; *Italian* lā′ən är′dō). *n.*

de bate (di bāt′), **1.** discuss reasons for and against (something); consider: *I am debating buying a car.* **2.** discussion of reasons for and against: *There has been much debate about whom to choose for captain.* 1 *v.*, **de bat ed, de bat ing;** 2 *n.*

de bris or **dé bris** (də brē′ or dā′brē), **1.** scattered fragments; ruins; rubbish: *The street was covered with debris from the explosion.* **2.** a mass of fragments of rock, etc.: *the debris left by a rockslide.* *n.*

de coy (di koi′ for 1; dē′koi or di koi′ for 2, 3), **1.** lead (wild birds, animals, etc.) into a trap or within gunshot. **2.** an artificial bird used to lure birds into a trap or within gunshot. **3.** a trained bird or animal used for the same purpose. 1 *v.*, 2, 3 *n.*

de gli Or ma ni (dā′lyē ôr mä′nē), **An sal do** (än säl′dō), *Italian.* *n.*

dei Fi fan te (dā′ē fē fän′tä), **Gio con do** (jō kōn′dō), *Italian.* *n.*

De nay rouze (də nā rüz′), **Au gust** (ō gyst′), *French.* *n.*

des ert[1] (dez′ərt), **1.** a dry, barren region, usually sandy and without trees: *the Sahara Desert.* **2.** not inhabited or cultivated; wild: *Robinson Crusoe was stranded on a desert island.* 1 *n.*, 2 *adj.*

de sert[2] (di zėrt′), **1.** go away and leave; abandon: *He found that he could not desert his fellow miners who had been trapped by the explosion.* **2.** leave military service without permission. *v.*

de sign (di zīn′), **1.** a drawing, plan, or sketch from which to work: *a design for a house.* **2.** arrangement of detail, form, and color in painting, weaving, building, etc.: *a wallpaper design in tan and brown.* **3.** make a first sketch of; plan out: *to design a dress.* **4.** intend; plan: *The nursery was designed for the baby's use.* 1, 2 *n.*, 3, 4 *v.*

de spair (di spãr′), **1.** loss of hope; a feeling that nothing good can happen: *She was filled with despair on hearing the bad news.* **2.** lose hope: *Doctors despaired of saving the sick man's life.* 1 *n.*, 2 *v.*

des per ate (des′pər it), **1.** reckless because of despair; willing to run any risk: *a desperate robber.* **2.** with little or no hope of improvement; very dangerous or serious: *a desperate illness.* *adj.*

des per a tion (des′pər ā′shən), recklessness caused by despair. *n.*

de vice (di vīs′), **1.** a mechanical invention used for a special purpose. A can opener is a device. So is an electric razor. **2.** a plan; a scheme; sometimes, a trick: *By a clever device the burglar got past the night watchman.* *n.*

di gest (də jest′ for 1; dī′jest for 2), **1.** change (food) in the stomach and intestines so that the body can absorb it: *We digest our food.* **2.** a brief statement of what is in a longer book or article; summary: *You will find digests of the latest books in every issue of that magazine.* 1 *v.*, 2 *n.*

di ges tion (də jes′chən), **1.** the digesting of food. **2.** ability to digest. *n.*

di go lah (dē′gō′ lä), *Burmese.*

dim (dim), **1.** not bright; not clear; not distinct: *dim light.* **2.** make or become dim: *We dimmed our bright lights.* 1 *adj.*, **dim mer, dim mest;** 2 *v.*, **dimmed, dim ming.**

din (din), **1.** a loud, confused noise that lasts. **2.** make a din: *Hundreds of horns began to din as the traffic jam worsened.* **3.** say (one thing) over and over: *He was always dinning into our ears the importance of hard work.* 1 *n.*, 2, 3 *v.*, **dinned, din ning.**

dis-, prefix meaning:
1. the opposite of, as in *disagree, disbelieve.*
2. not, as in *disagreeable, dishonest.*

dis may (dis mā′), **1.** loss of courage because of fear of what is about to happen: *She was filled with dismay when her son confessed that he had robbed a store.* **2.** trouble greatly; make afraid: *The thought that she might fail the history test dismayed her.* 1 *n.*, 2 *v.*

dis tinct (dis tingkt′), **1.** not the same; separate: *Every snowflake is distinct in pattern from every other snowflake.* **2.** clear; plain: *distinct handwriting. adj.*

dis tinc tive (dis tingk′tiv), distinguishing from others; special: *Policemen wear a distinctive uniform. adj.*

di vi sion (di vizh′ən), a part, group; section. *n.*

Dôle (dōl), town in E France. *n.*

douse (dous), **1.** plunge into water or any other liquid: *to douse the wash in soapsuds.* **2.** *Informal.* put out; extinguish: *douse a fire. v.*, **doused, dous ing.**

drom e dary (drom′ə der′ē), a swift camel for riding, usually the one-humped camel of Arabia. *n., pl.* **drom e dar ies.**

Due sen berg (dü′zən bėrg). *n.*

dun geon (dun′jən), a dark underground room to keep prisoners in. *n.*

Dur yea (dúr′yā). *n.*

echid na (i kid′nə), a small mammal of Australia with a covering of spines and a long, slender snout. *n., pl.* **echid nas, echid nae** (-nē).

eco nom i cal (e′kə nom′ə kəl or ek′ə-nom′ə kəl), avoiding waste; saving; thrifty. *adj.*

econ o my (i kon′ə mē), thrift; freedom from waste in the use of anything: *A good housewife practises economy. n., pl.* **econ o mies.**

ee rie (ir′ē), causing fear; strange; weird. *adj.*, **ee ri er, ee ri est.**

eld er (el′dər), **1.** older: *my elder brother.* **2.** an older person: *Children should respect their elders.* **3.** one of the older and more influential men of a tribe or community; chief, ruler, member of council, etc. 1 *adj.*, 2, 3 *n.*

em bark (em bärk′), **1.** go on board ship: *Many people embark for Europe in New York.* **2.** set out; start: *After leaving college, the young man embarked upon a business career. v.*

em bar ka tion (em′bär kā′shən), an embarking. *n.*

em brace (em brās′), **1.** clasp or hold in the arms to show love or friendship; hug: *The soldier embraced his mother before getting on the train.* **2.** an embracing; a hug. 1 *v.*, **em braced, em brac ing;** 2 *n.*

en force (en fôrs′), compel; force. *v.*, -forced, -forc ing.

en grave (en grāv′), **1.** cut in; carve artistically; decorate by engraving: *The jeweller engraved the boy's initials on the back of the watch.* **2.** cut in lines on a metal plate, block of wood, etc., for printing. *v.*, **en graved, en grav ing.**

en vi ron ment (en vī′rən mənt), surrounding things, conditions, or influences: *A child's character is greatly influenced by his home environment. n.*

equip (i kwip′), furnish with what is needed; fit out; provide: *The soldiers were equipped with rifles. v.*, **equipped, equip ping.**

es ca la tor (es′kə lā′tər), a moving stairway. *n.*

eu ca lyp tus (ū′kə lip′-təs), a very tall tree that grows in Australia and elsewhere. It is valued for its timber and for an oil made from its leaves. *n., pl.* **eu ca-lyp tus es, eu ca lyp ti** (-tī).

Escalator

Eu rope (ūr′əp), a continent east of the Atlantic Ocean and west of Asia. *n.*

ex ist (eg zist′), **1.** be; be real: *Cities may exist on faraway planets.* **2.** continue to be; live; have life: *A man cannot exist without air. v.*

ex tinct (eks tingkt′), **1.** no longer existing: *Dinosaurs are extinct.* **2.** gone out; not burning: *an extinct volcano. adj.*

---

hat, āge, cãre, fär;   let, bē, tėrm;   it, īce;   hot, gō, ôrder;   oil, out;   cup, pùt, rüle, ūse;
ch, child;   ng, long;   th, thin;   ₜн, then;   zh, measure;   ə represents *a* in about, *e* in taken, *i* in April, *o* in lemon, *u* in circus.

extract

ex tract (eks trakt′ for 1; eks′trakt for 2),
1. pull out or draw out, usually with some
effort: *extract a tooth.* **2.** something drawn
out or taken out: *He read several extracts
from the poem. Vanilla extract is made from
vanilla beans.* 1 *v.*, 2 *n.*

fair[1] (fãr), **1.** not favoring one more than
the other or others; just; honest: *a fair
judge.* **2.** according to the rules: *fair play.*
3. average; not good and not bad: *His
schoolwork is fair.* **4.** considerable. **5.** favorable; promising: *a fair wind.* **6.** light; not
dark: *She has fair hair and skin.* **7.** not
cloudy or stormy; clear; sunny: *The weather
will be fair today. adj.*
fair[2] (fãr), a gathering of people for the
buying and selling of goods, often held at
regular times during the year. *n.*
Far East, China, Japan, and other parts
of E Asia.
Feast of Stephen, St. Stephen's Day.
fi bre or **fi ber** (fī′bər), a substance made
up of threads or threadlike parts. *n.*
fi bre glass (fī′bər glas), very fine flexi-
ble threads of glass that can be made into
materials, fabrics, boats, etc. *n.*
flesh wound, wound that merely injures
the flesh; slight wound.
floun der[1] (floun′dər), struggle awkwardly
without making much progress: *Men and
horses were floundering in the deep snow-
drifts. v.*
floun der[2] (floun′dər), flatfish that has a
large mouth. *n., pl.* **floun ders** or **floun der.**
flour ish (flėr′ish), **1.** do well; be prosper-
ous: *His business continued to flourish as the
years went by.* **2.** an extra ornament or
curve in handwriting. 1 *v.*, 2 *n.*
fly catch er (flī′kach′ər), any of a
family of songless,
perching birds having
small, weak feet, short
necks, and large heads
with broad, flattened
bills hooked at the
tip. *n.*
Flying Dutchman,
1. a legendary Dutch
sea captain con-
demned to sail the
ocean until the Day

Flycatcher
(about 7½ in. long)

of Judgment. **2.** his ghostlike ship, supposed
to appear at sea.

fuselage

fon dant (fon′dənt), **1.** a creamy substance made of sugar and used as a base for
candy. **2.** a candy made mostly of fondant. *n.*
fore run ner (fôr′run′ər), **1.** sign or warning of something to come. **2.** something that
comes before; ancestor: *The curbside gasoline
pump was the forerunner of the modern filling
station. n.*
for mi da ble (fôr′mə də bəl), hard to
overcome; hard to deal with; to be dreaded.
adj.
fra grance (frā′grəns), a sweet smell;
pleasing odor. *n.*
fra grant (frā′grənt), having or giving off
a pleasing odor; sweet-smelling. *adj.*
fran tic (fran′tik), very much excited;
wild with rage, fear, pain, grief, etc. *adj.*
fringe (frinj), **1.** border or
trimming made of threads,
cords, etc., either loose
or tied together in small
bunches: *a fringe on a shawl.*
2. anything like this; border: *fringe of the forest. n.*
frond (frond), the leaf of
a fern or of a palm tree. *n.*
frus trate (frus′trāt),
1. foil; bring to nothing;
defeat; baffle: *Heavy rains
frustrated our plans for a picnic.* **2.** cause to
feel discouraged. *v.*, **frus trat ed, frus trat ing.**
frus tra tion (frus trā′shən), a frustrat-
ing or being frustrated. *n.*

Frond of maiden-
hair fern

-ful, suffix meaning:
1. full of, as in *colorful.*
2. having; characterized by, as in *careful,
thoughtful.*
3. having a tendency to, as in *harmful.*
4. enough to fill a, as in *cupful, handful.*
5. other meanings, as in *manful, useful.*
fun nel (fun′əl), **1.** a small
tapering tube with a wide,
cone-shaped mouth. A fun-
nel is used to prevent
spilling in pouring liquids
into containers with small
openings. **2.** pass or feed
through a funnel. 1 *n.*, 2 *v.*,
fun neled, fun nel ing.
fu se lage (fū′zə läzh or
fū′zə lij), body of an airplane. The wings and tail
are fastened to it. The fuselage holds the
passengers, cargo, etc. *n.*

Funnel

462

gage (gāj), gauge. *n.*, *v.*, **gaged, gag ing.**

ga lah (gə lä′), a grayish cockatoo of Australia with a pinkish-red breast. *n.*

game[1] (gām), 1. way of playing; amusement: *a game of tag.* 2. the things needed for a game: *This store sells games.* 3. contest with certain rules. One person or side tries to win it. 4. wild animals, birds, or fish hunted or caught for sport or for food. 5. brave; plucky: *The losing team put up a game fight.* 1-4 *n.*, 5 *adj.*, **gam er, gam est.**

game[2] (gām), *Informal.* lame; crippled; injured: *He has a game leg. adj.*

gape (gāp), 1. open wide: *A deep hole in the earth gaped before us.* 2. open the mouth wide. *v.*, **gaped, gap ing.**

Gar ne rin (gär nə reN′), **An dré** (äN′drā), *French. n.*

gauge (gāj), 1. instrument for measuring. A steam gauge measures the pressure of steam. 2. estimate; judge: *We tried to gauge the speed of the train.* 1 *n.*, 2 *v.*, **gauged, gaug ing.** Also, **gage.**

Gau ta ma (gô′tə mə or gou′tə mə), Buddha. *n.* Also, **Gotama.**

Gem i ni (jem′ə nī or jem′ə nē). *n.*

Gen oa (jen′ō ə), seaport in NW Italy. *n.*

ge nus (jē′nəs), 1. kind; sort; class. 2. group of related animals or plants ranking below a family and above a species. The scientific name of an animal or plant consists of the genus written with a capital letter and the species written with a small letter. *n.*, *pl.* **gen era** (jen′ər ə) or **ge nus es.**

ge om e try (jē om′ə trē), the branch of mathematics that deals with lines, angles, surfaces, and solids. *n.*

gey ser (gī′zər), a spring that sends a column of hot water and steam into the air at intervals. *n.*

gild (gild), cover with a thin layer of gold. *v.*, **gild ed** or **gilt, gild ing.**

gin ger ly (jin′jər lē), with extreme care or caution. *adv.*, *adj.*

glow worm (glō′ werm′), wormlike insect that glows in the dark. Fireflies develop from some glowworms. *n.*

Go ta ma (gō′tə mə), Gautama. *n.*

grat i tude (grat′ə tüd or grat′ə tüd), thankfulness; kindly feeling because of a favor received; desire to return a favor. *n.*

graze[1] (grāz), feed on growing grass. Cattle and sheep graze. *v.*, **grazed, graz ing.**

graze[2] (grāz), touch lightly in passing; rub lightly against: *The car grazed the garage door.* *v.*, **grazed, graz ing.**

grief (grēf), 1. deep sadness caused by trouble or loss; heavy sorrow. 2. cause of sadness or sorrow. *n.*

gru el ling (grü′əl ing) *Informal.* exhausting, very tiring. *adj.*

gul ly (gul′ē), small ravine; ditch made by running water. *n.*, *pl.* **gullies.**

gum tree, any of several trees yielding a sticky juice called gum. The eucalyptus is one kind of gum tree.

Gully

gur gle (gėr′gəl), 1. flow or run with a bubbling sound: *Water gurgles when it flows over stones.* 2. a bubbling sound. 3. make a bubbling sound: *The baby gurgled happily.* 1, 3 *v.*, **gur gled, gur gling;** 2 *n.*

gym na si um (jim nā′zē əm), a room, building, etc. fitted up for physical exercise or training and for indoor athletic sports. *n.*

hail[1] (hāl), 1. small, roundish pieces of ice coming down from the clouds in a shower; frozen rain. 2. a shower like hail: *A hail of bullets met the soldiers. n.*

hail[2] (hāl), 1. greet; cheer: *The crowd hailed the new President.* 2. a greeting; a cheer. 1 *v.*, 2 *n.*

Ha ji (hä′jē′), *Burmese. n.*

har ness (här′nis), 1. a combination of leather straps, bands, and other pieces used to connect a horse or other animal to a carriage, wagon, etc. 2. something resembling a harness: *parachute harness. n.*

haunch (hônch), 1. the part of the body around the hips. 2. the leg and loin of an animal, used for food: *a haunch of mutton. n.*

heave (hēv), 1. lift with force or effort: *He heaved the heavy box into the wagon.* 2. a heaving; a throw: *a mighty heave.* 1 *v.*, **heaved** or **hove, heav ing;** 2 *n.*

heave to, stop a ship; stop.

hat, āge, cãre, fär; let, bē, tėrm; it, īce; hot, gō, ôrder; oil, out; cup, pūt, rüle, ūse; ch, child; ng, long; th, thin; ŦH, then; zh, measure; ə represents *a* in about, *e* in taken, *i* in April, *o* in lemon, *u* in circus.

herb (ėrb or hėrb), a plant with leaves that are used for medicine, seasoning, or food. Sage, mint, and lavender are herbs. *n.*

hin der (hin′dər), hold back; .be in the way of: *Deep mud hindered travel.* *v.*

hinge (hinj), 1. joint on which a door, gate, etc., moves back and forth. 2. depend: *The success of the picnic hinges on the kind of weather we will have.* 1 *n.*, 2 *v.*, **hinged, hing ing.**

hmit (hmit), *Burmese.* *v.*

hob ble (hob′l), 1. walk awkwardly; limp: *The wounded man hobbled away.* 2. tie the legs together: *hobble a horse to keep it from running away.* 3. rope, strap, etc., used to hobble an animal. 1, 2 *v.*, **hob bled, hob-bling;** 3 *n.*

hold[1] (hōld), 1. grasp and keep; not let go: *Please hold my hat.* 2. a grasp or grip: *The wrestler got a good hold on his opponent.* 3. keep in some place or position: *Hold the paper steady while you draw.* 4. contain: *This theater will hold a thousand people.* 5. have: *Shall we hold a meeting of the club?* 6. keep from acting; keep back: *to hold one's breath.* 1, 3-6 *v.*, **held, hold ing;** 2 *n.*

hold on, *Informal.* keep one's hold.

hold up, 1. keep from falling. 2. show; display. 3. delay.

lay or **take hold of,** seize; grasp.

hold[2] (hōld), the lowest part of a ship's interior. A ship's cargo is carried in its hold. *n.*

homme du nord (om dʏ nôr′ *Cdn. French*), a seasoned fur trader or voyageur who spent his winters in the fur country. *n.*

horde (hôrd), crowd; swarm: *hordes of grasshoppers.* *n.*

ho ri zon (hə rī′zn), the line where earth and sky appear to meet. You cannot see beyond the horizon. *n.*

hor ri fy (hôr′ə fī or hor′ə fī), 1. cause to feel horror. 2. *Informal.* shock very much: *We were horrified by the wreck.* *v.*, **hor ri-fied, hor ri fy ing.**

hor ror (hôr′ər or hor′ər), 1. a shivering, shaking fear and dislike; terror and disgust caused by something frightful or shocking. 2. a very strong dislike; very great disgust: *That girl has a horror of snakes.* *n.*

hov er (huv′ər), 1. stay in or near one place in the air: *The two birds hovered over their nest.* 2. stay in or near one place; wait nearby: *The dogs hovered around the meat truck.* 3. be in an uncertain condition: *hover between life and death.* *v.*

hy e na (hī ē′nə), a wild animal much like a large dog in shape and size. *n.*

-ian, form of **-an,** as in *Bostonian.*

-ic, suffix meaning:
1. of or having to do with, as in *atmospheric.*
2. having the nature of, as in *artistic, heroic.*
3. made by; caused by, as in *volcanic.*
4. like; like that of, as in *antagonistic.*

-ical, suffix meaning:
1. *-ic,* as in *geometrical, hysterical.*
2. *-ic* specialized in meaning, as in *economical.*

-ically, suffix meaning: *-ic* + *-ly.* Instead of *artistic-ly* we write *artistically.*

i den ti fi ca tion (ī den′tə fə kā′shən), an identifying; recognizing as being a certain person or thing; something used to prove what a person or thing is. *n.*

Igraine (i grān′). *n.*

il-, prefix meaning: not, as in *illegal, illogical.* in- becomes il- before *l.*

il le gal (i lē′gəl), not lawful; against the law. *adj.*

im-[1] form of **in-**[1] before *b, m, p,* as in *imbalance, impatient.*

im-[2] form of **in-**[2] before *b, m, p,* as in *imbedded, implant, imperil.*

im press (im pres′), 1. have a strong effect on the mind or feelings of: *Bravery usually impresses us.* 2. make marks by pressing or stamping: *impress wax with a seal.* *v.*

in-[1] prefix meaning: not; the opposite of; the absence of, as in *inattention, inconvenient, inexpensive.*

in-[2] prefix meaning: in; within; into; on; toward, as in *inborn, indoors, inland.*

in cense[1] (in′sens), substance giving off a sweet smell when burned. *n.*

in cense[2] (in sens′), make very angry; fill with rage. *v.*, **in censed, in cens ing.**

In dia (in′dē ə), country in S Asia. *Capital:* New Delhi. *n.*

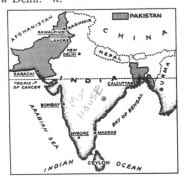

in ject (in jekt′),   force (medicine, etc.) into a tissue, etc.: *to inject penicillin into an arm. v.*

inn (in),   a public house for lodging and caring for travellers. Hotels have largely taken the place of the old inns. *n.*

in sert (in sèrt′ for 1; in′sèrt for 2),   **1.** put in; set in: *to insert a key into a lock.* **2.** something put in or set in: *The picture section in the Sunday newspaper was an insert.* 1 *v.*, 2 *n.*

in su late (in′sə lāt),   protect from losing heat or electricity: *Wires are insulated by a covering of rubber. v.*, **in su lat ed, in su lat ing.**

in tact (in takt′),   with no part missing; uninjured; whole. *adj.*

in tel li gence (in tel′ə jəns),   **1.** ability to learn and know; understanding: *A dog has more intelligence than many other animals.* **2.** knowledge; news; information: *The general had secret intelligence of the plans of the enemy.* **3.** getting or distributing information, especially secret information. **4.** group engaged in obtaining secret information. *n.*

in tel li gent (in tel′ə jənt),   having or showing intelligence; able to learn and know; quick at learning: *Elephants are intelligent. adj.*

in te ri or (in tēr′ē ər),   **1.** inside; inner surface or part: *The interior of the house was beautifully decorated.* **2.** part of a region or country away from the coast or border. *n.*

in tri cate (in′trə kit),   with many twists and turns; perplexing, entangled, or complicated. *adj.*

in vig or ate (in vig′ər āt),   give vigor to. *v.*, **in vig or at ed, in vig or at ing.**

io dine (ī′ə dīn),   a substance used in medicine, etc. Iodine is put on cuts and wounds to kill disease germs and prevent infection. *n.*

-ion,   suffix meaning:
1. act of _____ing, as in *investigation, nomination.*
2. condition or state of being _____ed, as in *adoption, fascination.*
3. result of _____ing, as in *abbreviation.*

ir-,   prefix meaning: not; the opposite of; the absence of, as in *irregular, irresistible.* in- becomes ir- before *r.*

iso bar (ī′sə bär),   on a weather map, a line connecting places which have the same average atmospheric pressure. *n.*

Ita la (ē tä′lä),   *Italian. n.*

-ity,   suffix meaning: condition or quality of being, as in *humidity, activity.*

Iz mir (iz′mir),   seaport in W Turkey. *n.* Also, **Smyrna.**

jack (jak),   jackfruit. *n.*

jack al (jak′əl or jak′ôl),   **1.** a wild dog of Asia and Africa. In many parts of Asia, a jackal is considered to be clever and sly. **2.** person who is clever and sly. *n.*

Jackal (about 15 in. high at the shoulder)

jack fruit (jak′früt′),   **1.** the jack (tree), widely cultivated in tropical regions. **2.** its fruit. *n.*

jas mine or **jas min** (jas′mən or jaz′mən),   shrub or vine with clusters of fragrant flowers. There are yellow, white, and red jasmines. *n.* Also, **jessamine.**

Je ru sa lem (jə rü′sə ləm),   a famous city of E Palestine, and the capital of Israel. *n.*

jes sa mine (jes′ə min),   jasmine. *n.*

Kan dy (kän′dē),   city in central Ceylon, famous for its Buddhist temples. *n.*

Ka ren (kə rän′),   **1.** a member of a people living in S and SE Burma, not related in culture to the native Burmese. **2.** any of various languages of these people spoken in the different districts where they live. *n.*

kelp   (kelp), a large, tough, brown seaweed. *n.*

Kelp

Ket Kay (ket kā),   *Burmese. n.*

kite (kīt),   **1.** a light wooden frame covered with paper or cloth. Kites are flown in the air on the end of a long string. **2.** a hawk with long, pointed wings. *n.*

knot (not),   **1.** a tying together of parts of ropes, strings, etc., to fasten them together: *a square knot, a slip knot.* **2.** to tie in a knot. **3.** a measure of speed; one nautical

---

hat, āge, cãre, fär;   let, bē, tèrm;   it, īce;   hot, gō, ôrder;   oil, out;   cup, pùt, rüle, ūse; ch, child;   ng, long;   th, thin;   ₮H, then;   zh, measure;   ə represents *a* in about, *e* in taken, *i* in April, *o* in lemon, *u* in circus.

mile (6080.27 ft.) per hour: *Our ship's speed is eighteen knots.* 1, 3 *n.,* 2 *v.,* **knot ted, knot ting.**

ko a la (kō ä′lə), a furry gray mammal of Australia. *n.*

kook a bur ra (kŭk′ə bèr′ə or kŭk′ə-bèr′ə), a bird of Australia and New Guinea. *n.*

kraal (kräl), 1. village of South African natives, protected by a fence. 2. a pen for cattle or sheep; stockade. *n.*

kra ken (krä′kən or krā′kən), a mythical sea monster said to appear off the coast of Norway. *n.*

lab o ra to ry (lab′ə rə tô′rē or lab′rə tô′-rē), place where scientific work is done or scientific investigations are made: *a chemical laboratory, a police laboratory. n., pl.* **lab o-ra to ries.**

lag (lag), 1. move too slowly; fall behind: *In the last part of the cross-country race, some of the runners began to lag.* 2. amount by which a person or thing lags: *a time lag of fifteen seconds.* 1 *v.,* **lagged, lag ging;** 2 *n.*

lah (lä), *Burmese. v.*

lap (lap), a part of any course travelled. *n.*

lar va (lär′və), the early form of an insect. A caterpillar is the larva of a butterfly or moth. *n., pl.* **lar vae.**

lash¹ (lash), 1. the part of a whip that is not the handle. 2. strike with a whip. 3. hit: *The wild horse lashed out at the cowboy with its hoofs.* 4. eyelash. 1, 4 *n.,* 2, 3 *v.*

lash² (lash), tie or fasten with a rope, cord, etc.: *The boys lashed logs together to make a raft. v.*

la va (lä′və), 1. melted rock flowing from a volcano. 2. rock formed by the cooling of this melted rock. *n*

le gal (lē′gəl), 1. of law: *legal knowledge.* 2. of lawyers: *legal advice.* 3. lawful. *adj.*

Le nor mand (lə nôr mäN′), *French. n.*

Le vas sor (lə vä sôr′), **Emile** (ā mēl′), *French. n.*

lift-web (lift′web′), *British.* one of several special straps by which a parachutist's harness is attached to the parachute. The American term for such a strap is *riser. n.*

lin en (lin′ən), 1. cloth or thread made from the flax plant. 2. articles made of linen or some substitute. Tablecloths and sheets are called linen. 3. made of linen: *a linen handkerchief.* 1, 2 *n.,* 3 *adj.*

lin ger (ling′gər), stay on; go slowly, as if unwilling to leave: *Daylight lingers long in the summertime. v.*

link (lingk), 1. one ring or loop of a chain. 2. join as a link does; unite or connect. 1 *n.,* 2 *v.*

link net, one of the layers in an Apollo suit. It holds the suit in shape and keeps it from ballooning.

liv er y (liv′ər ē), 1. any uniform provided for servants, or adopted by a group or profession: *a butler's livery.* 2. the feeding, care, etc., of horses for pay; the hiring out of horses and carriages. *n., pl.* **liv er ies.**

livery stable, stable engaged in the livery business.

lob ster (lob′stər), a sea animal. Lobsters are used for food. Their shells turn a bright red when boiled. *n.*

Lobster (about 1 ft. long, including claws)

lo cal (lō′kəl), 1. of a place; having to do with a certain place or places: *the local newspaper, local gossip.* 2. making all, or almost all, stops: *a local train.* 3. branch or chapter of a labor union. 1, 2 *adj.,* 3 *n.*

lo co (lō′kō), *Slang.* crazy. *adj.*

lo co mo tive (lō′kə mō′tiv), 1. a railroad engine. 2. any engine that goes from place to place on its own power. *n.*

log ic (loj′ik), 1. the science of proof. 2. reason; sound sense. *n.*

log i cal (loj′ə kəl), 1. having something to do with logic. 2. reasonable. *adj.*

loom¹ (lüm), machine for weaving cloth. *n.*

loom² (lüm), appear dimly or vaguely; appear as large or dangerous: *A large iceberg loomed through the thick gray fog. v.*

loss (lôs), a losing or being lost: *The loss of a pencil is not serious. n.*

at a loss, puzzled; uncertain; in difficulty.

Lt., Lieutenant.

lurk (lèrk), stay about without arousing attention; wait out of sight; be hidden. *v.*

-ly, suffix meaning:

1. in a _____ way or manner, as in *anxiously, sternly.*

2. in, to, or from a direction, as in *westerly.*

3. like a _____, as in *manly.*

4. like that of a _____, as in *sisterly.*

5. of each or every _____, as in *daily.*

mael strom (māl′strəm), **1.** any great or violent whirlpool. **2.** The **Maelstrom** is a dangerous whirlpool off the northwestern coast of Norway. *n.*

mag nif i cent (mag nif′ə sənt), grand; splendid: *a magnificent palace. adj.*

ma hout (mə hout′), keeper and driver of an elephant. *n.*

Maj da Koom (mäj′dä′ kùm), *Burmese. n.*

make shift (māk′shift′), **1.** something used for a time instead of the right thing; a temporary substitute: *Construction workers used wooden boxes as a makeshift for chairs at lunchtime.* **2.** used as a temporary substitute: *a makeshift stretcher consisting of two broom handles and a blanket.* 1 *n.,* 2 *adj.*

mam mal (mam′əl), an animal that gives milk to its young. Human beings, horses, dogs, rats, and whales are all mammals. *n.*

man i fest (man′ə fest), apparent to the eye or to the mind; plain; clear. *adj.*

mar gin (mär′jən), **1.** edge; border: *the margin of a lake.* **2.** the blank space around the writing or printing on a page. *n.*

ma rine (mə rēn′), **1.** of the sea; found in the sea: *Whales are marine animals.* **2.** soldier formerly serving only at sea, now also participating in land and air action. 1 *adj.,* 2 *n.*

mass-pro duce (mas′prə dūs′ or mas′-prə düs′), make goods in large quantities by machinery. *v.*

me di ae val (mē′dē ē′vəl or med′ē ē′vəl), medieval. *adj.*

me di e val (mē′dē ē′vəl or med′ē ē′vəl), belonging to or having to do with the Middle Ages (the years from about 500 A.D. to about 1450 A.D.). *adj.* Also, **mediaeval.**

med i tate (med′ə tāt), **1.** think quietly; reflect: *A Buddhist monk is supposed to meditate for long periods of time.* **2.** think about; consider; plan; intend: *The major was meditating an attack on the enemy position. v.,* **med i tat ed, med i tat ing.**

-ment, suffix meaning:
1. act or fact of ____ing, as in *agreement, measurement.*
2. state of being ____ed, as in *amusement.*
3. means or instrument for ____ing, as in *attachment.*

me phi tis (mi fī′tis), a foul or nasty smell. *n.*

Me phi tis (mi fī′tis), a genus of mammals that includes some North American skunks. *n.*

mer chant (mèr′chənt), **1.** person who buys and sells: *Some merchants do business mostly with foreign countries.* **2.** trading; having to do with trade: *merchant ship.* 1 *n.,* 2 *adj.*

Mir i mi chi (mēr′ə mi shē′), a river and a bay in New Brunswick.

mite[1] (mīt), a very tiny animal that lives in foods, on plants, or on other animals. *n.*

mite[2] (mīt), **1.** anything very small: *Each kindergarten child contributed his mite to charity.* **2.** *Informal.* little; a bit: *That pork roast is a mite undercooked.* 1 *n.,* 2 *adv.*

mor tar (môr′tər), a mixture of lime, sand, and water, for holding bricks or stones together. *n.*

Morte d'Ar thur (môrt′ där′thər), means *Death of Arthur* in French. Many of the King Arthur stories were in the French language in Sir Thomas Malory's time. Malory told these stories in English.

Mos cow (mos′kou or mos′kō), city in the central part of Russia and capital of the Soviet Union. *n.*

Mos lem (moz′ləm or mos′ləm), **1.** a follower of Mohammed; believer in the religion founded by him. **2.** of Mohammed or the religion founded by him. 1 *n., pl.* **Mos lems** or **Moslem;** 2 *adj.* Also, **Muslim, Muslim.**

mosque (mosk), a Moslem place of worship. *n.*

Mosque

Mount Roy al (mount roi′əl), *English* for *French* **Mont Royal** (mōN roi al′). Name given by Cartier to the mountain on which the Indian village of Hochelaga was located and from which the name of the city of Montreal is derived.

Mus lem or **Mus lim** (muz′ləm or mus′-ləm), Moslem. *n., adj.*

mus te line (mus′tə lin′ or mus′tə lin), belonging to a group of related animals which includes weasels, skunks, etc. *adj.*

---

hat, āge, cãre, fär; let, bē, tèrm; it, īce; hot, gō, ôrder; oil, out; cup, pùt, rüle, ūse; ch, child; ng, long; th, thin; ŦH, then; zh, measure; ə represents *a* in about, *e* in taken, *i* in April, *o* in lemon, *u* in circus.

NASA (nas′ə), National Aeronautics and Space Administration of the United States. *n.*

nat (nät), in Burma, one of a class of spirits. *n.*

nav i ga tor (nav′ə gā tər), a person skilled in the art of steering or managing a ship or aircraft. *n.*

neigh (nā), **1.** sound that a horse makes. **2.** make this sound. 1 *n.*, 2 *v.*

new fan gled (nū′fang′gəld or nü′fang′-gəld), lately come into fashion; of a new kind. *adj.*

New ton (nūt′ən or nüt′ən), Isaac (ī′ zək), 1642-1727, English scientist and mathematician. *n.*

noo dle[1] (nü′dəl), a mixture of flour and water, or flour and eggs, like macaroni, but made in flat strips. *n.*

noo dle[2] (nü′dəl), a stupid or foolish creature; a simpleton. *n.*

nymph (nimf), **1.** one of the lesser Greek and Roman goddesses of nature, who lived in seas, rivers, springs, hills, woods, or trees. **2.** insect in the stage of development between larva and adult insect. It has no wings. *n.*

ob scure (əb skūr′), **1.** not easily discovered; hidden. **2.** hide from view; dim; darken. 1 *adj.*, 2 *v.* **ob scured, ob scur ing.**

ob sta cle (ob′stə kəl), something that stands in the way or stops progress; hindrance. *n.*

of fend (ə fend′), **1.** pain; displease; hurt the feelings of; make angry: *Rude behavior offends me.* **2.** sin; do wrong: *In what way have I offended?* *v.*

of fice (ôf′is or of′is), **1.** place in which the work of a position is done; room or rooms for clerical work: *His office is on the second floor.* **2.** position, especially in the public service: *The President holds the highest public office in the United States.* *n.*

of fi cer (ôf′ə sər or of′ə sər), **1.** person who commands others in an army or navy. **2.** person who holds a public, church, or government office: *a police officer, a health officer.* *n.*

of fi cial (ə fish′əl), **1.** person who holds a public position or who is in charge of some public work or duty: *government officials; officials of a sports contest.* **2.** of or having to do with an office: *official duties.* 1 *n.*, 2 *adj.*

Omar (ō′mär), *Arabic.* *n.*

Oo Yan (ü yän), *Burmese.* *n.*

op er ate (op′ər āt), **1.** run; keep working: *The machinery operates night and day.* **2.** perform an operation: *The doctor operated on the man.* *v.*, op er at ed, op er at ing.

op er a tion (op′ər ā′shən), **1.** working; the way a thing works: *operation of a machine.* **2.** something done to the body, usually with instruments, to improve health. **3.** military mission or action or plan, usually with a code name added: *Operation Sea Lion was the name of a German plan to invade England during World War II.*

opos sum (ə pos′əm), a small mammal that lives mostly in trees, common in the S United States, also found in S Ontario; possum. *n.*

Opossum
(total length 33 in.)

or bit (ôr′bit), **1.** the path of the earth or of any one of the planets about the sun. **2.** the path of any heavenly body about another heavenly body. *n.*

Orbit of the earth (E)
around the sun. Arrows
show direction.

-ous, suffix meaning: having; full of, as in *dangerous, joyous.*

ox y gen (ok′sə jən), a gas without color or odor that forms about one fifth of the air. *n.*

pad[1] (pad), **1.** a soft mass used for comfort, protection, or stuffing; cushion: *a pad for a baby carriage.* **2.** fill with something soft; stuff: *pad a chair.* **3.** one of the cushionlike parts on the bottom side of the feet of dogs, foxes, and some other animals. **4.** cloth soaked with ink to use with a rubber stamp. **5.** launching pad. 1, 3-5 *n.*, 2 *v.*, **pad ded, pad ding.**

pad[2] (pad), **1.** walk; tramp; trudge. **2.** walk or trot softly. *v.*, **pad ded, pad ding.**

pa go da (pə gō′də), temple with many stories forming a tower. *n.*

pan ic (pan′ik), **1.** unreasoning fear; a fear spreading through a multitude of people so that they lose control of themselves: *When the theatre caught fire, panic spread through the audience.* **2.** *Slang.* make

Pagoda

(an audience, etc.) laugh: *The comedian panicked the crowd.* **3.** go into a state of panic; become panicky: *Though many were killed by falling bombs, the people of London didn't panic.* 1 *n.*, 2, 3 *v.*, **pan icked, pan ick ing.**

pan to mime (pan′tə mīm),   **1.** a play without words, in which the actors express themselves by making motions with their hands, arms, etc. **2.** express by making motions with the hands, arms, etc.   1 *n.*, 2 *v.*, **pan to mimed, pan to mim ing.**

par a pet (par′ə pet),   **1.** a low wall or mound of stone, earth, etc., to protect soldiers. **2.** a low wall at the edge of a balcony, roof, bridge, etc. *n.*

Parapet of a fort

par ty (pär′tē),   **1.** a group of people doing something together: *a hunting party, a party of mountain climbers.* **2.** a gathering for pleasure: *birthday party.* *n.*, *pl.* **par ties.**

pass (pas),   **1.** go by; move past: *We passed a big truck.* **2.** move on: *The days pass quickly.* **3.** be successful in (an examination, etc.): *Jim passed Latin.* **4.** hand around; hand from one to another: *Joe passed the football.* **5.** transferring of the ball, etc., as in football: *a forward pass.* **6.** spend: *pass the time.* **7.** narrow road; path: *a pass across the mountains.* 1-4, 6 *v.*, **passed, passed** or **past, pass ing;** 5, 7 *n.*

Pas teur (pas tèr′; *French* päs tœr′), **Louis,** 1822-1895, French chemist who invented a way of preventing hydrophobia and of keeping milk from spoiling. *n.*

pas teur i za tion (pas′chər ə zā′shən), process of pasteurizing. *n.*

pas teur ize (pas′chər īz),   heat (milk, etc.) hot enough and long enough to destroy germs. *v.*, **pas teur ized, pas teur iz ing.**

Pei ping (pā′ping′ or bā′ping′), Peking. *n.*

Pe king (pē′king′), city in NE China, the capital of China. *n.* See **China** for map.

pelf (pelf),   money or riches. *n.*

per ish (per′ish),   die; be destroyed: *Many flowers perish in the cold.* *v.*

perk (pèrk),   **1.** move, lift the head, or act in a quick and lively way. **2.** make trim

or smart: *She is all perked out in her Sunday clothes.* *v.*

perk up, brighten up; become lively and energetic. *v.*

per son nel (pèr′sə nel′), persons employed in any work, business, or service. *n.*

pil lar (pil′ər),   **1.** a slender upright support; column. Pillars are usually made of stone, wood, or

Pillars

metal and are used as supports or ornaments for a building. **2.** anything slender and upright like a pillar. *n.*

plan et (plan′it),   one of the heavenly bodies that move around the sun. Mercury, Venus, the earth, Mars, Jupiter, Saturn, Uranus, Neptune, and Pluto are planets. *n.*

plat y pus (plat′ə pəs),   duckbill. *n.*, *pl.* **plat y pus es, plat y pi** (-pī)

pluck (pluk), **1.** pick; pull off: *to pluck flowers.* **2.** pull off the feathers or hair from. **3.** courage: *to show pluck in a difficult or dangerous situation.* 1, 2 *v.*, 3 *n.*

por cu pine (pôr′-kyə pīn),   an animal covered with spines or quills. *n.*

Porcupine (about 3 ft. long, including the tail)

por tage (pôr′tij; *French* pôr tazh′),   **1.** a carrying of boats, canoes, provisions, etc. overland from one stretch of water to another. **2.** carry canoes, etc. from one stretch of water to another. **3.** a place where such a carrying takes place.   1, 3 *n.*, 2 *v.*, **por taged, por tag ing.**

Port Su dan (sü dan′ or sü dän′),   seaport in NE Sudan, a country of NE Africa. See **Red Sea** for map.

pouch (pouch),   **1.** bag or sack: *a postman's pouch.* **2.** a baglike fold of skin. A kangaroo carries its young in a pouch.   *n.*

power plant,   powerhouse; building containing boilers, engines, etc., for producing power.

pres ent[1] (prez′ənt),   **1.** at hand; not absent: *Every member of the class was present.* **2.** at this time; being or occurring now: *present conditions, present prices.* *adj.*

---

hat, āge, cāre, fär; let, bē, tèrm; it, īce; hot, gō, ôrder; oil, out; cup, pút, rüle, ūse; ch, child; ng, long; th, thin; ŦH, then; zh, measure;   ə represents *a* in about, *e* in taken, *i* in April, *o* in lemon, *u* in circus.

pre sent[2] (pri zent′ for 1, 3, 4; prez′ənt for 2), **1.** give: *They presented flowers to their teacher.* **Present with** sometimes means give to: *Our class presented the school with a gift.* **2.** gift; something given: *a Christmas present.* **3.** introduce; make acquainted: **4.** bring before the public: *Our class presented a play.* 1, 3, 4 *v.*, 2 *n.*

pres ent ly (prez′ənt lē), soon. *adv.*

pres sure (presh′ər), **1.** the continued action of a weight or force: *air pressure.* **2.** a compelling force or influence: *Pressure was brought to bear on John.* **3.** put pressure on: *He tried to pressure me into buying.* 1, 2 *n.*, 3 *v.*, **pres sured, pres sur ing.**

pres sur ize (presh′ər īz), keep the atmospheric pressure inside the cabin of an airplane at a normal level in spite of the altitude. *v.*, **pres sur ized, pres sur iz ing.**

prick le (prik′əl), **1.** a small sharp point; thorn. **2.** feel a prickly or smarting sensation; tingle; smart: *Her skin prickled when she saw the big snake.* 1 *n.*, 2 *v.*, **prick led, prick ling.**

pro (prō), *Informal.* a professional, especially a professional athlete. *n.*

pro ce dure (prə sē′jər), way of proceeding; method of doing things. *n.*

pro ceed (prə sēd′), **1.** go on after having stopped; move forward: *We proceeded slowly through the tunnel.* **2.** carry on any activity: *He proceeded to light his pipe. v.*

proc ess (pros′es or prō′ses), **1.** set of actions or changes in a special order: *the process of making cloth from wool.* **2.** treat or prepare by some special method: *This cloth has been processed to make it waterproof.* 1 *n.*, 2 *v.*

prop[1] (prop), hold up by placing a support under or against: *His chin was propped on his hands. v.*, **propped, prop ping.**

prop[2] (prop), *Informal.* an object, such as a weapon or chair, used in a play. *n.*

pro pel (prə pel′), drive forward: *Some boats are propelled by oars, some by wind, some by diesel engines. v.*, **pro pelled, pro pel ling.**

prop er ty (prop′ər tē), **1.** thing or things owned: *Kindly do not take that umbrella, sir; it is my property.* **2.** piece of land or real estate. *n.*, *pl.* **prop er ties.**

properties, furniture, weapons, etc. (everything except scenery and clothes), used in staging a play.

pro vide (prə vīd′), **1.** take care for the future: *to provide for your old age.* **2.** supply; furnish: *Sheep provide us with wool. v.*, **pro vid ed, pro vid ing.**

pro vi sion (prə vizh′ən), **1.** statement making a condition: *Our library has a provision that hands must be clean before books are taken out.* **2.** act of providing; preparation: *He made provision for his children's education.* **3.** supply with provisions. 1, 2 *n.*, 3 *v.*

provisions, a supply of food and drinks.

pub lic i ty (pub lis′ə tē), public notice: *Actors and actresses usually want publicity. n.*

quar ter back (kwôr′tər bak′), in football, the player whose position is immediately behind the centre of the line of scrimmage. *n.*

ra bies (rā′bēz), the disease a mad dog has; hydrophobia. *n.*

ra di a tion (rā dē ā′shən), **1.** the act or process of giving out light, heat, or other radiant energy. **2.** the energy radiated. *n.*

ra di o-ac tive (rā′dē ō ak′tiv), giving off radiant energy in the form of alpha, beta, or gamma rays by the breaking up of atoms. *adj.*

R.A.F. Royal Air Force (of Great Britain).

Ran goon (rang gün′), capital and chief port of Burma, in the S part. *n.*

Rat wat ti (rät wät′tē). *n.*

ra vine (rə vēn′), a long, deep, narrow valley worn by running water. *n.*

re-, prefix meaning:
1. again; once more, as in *rejoin, retrain, rewax.*
2. back, as in *repay, replace.*

rear[1] (rir), **1.** the back part: *the rear of the house.* **2.** at the back, in the back: *rear door.* 1 *n.*, 2 *adj.*

rear[2] (rir), **1.** make grow; help to grow; bring up: *to rear children.* **2.** of an animal, rise on the hind legs: *My horse reared when it saw the rattlesnake. v.*

rea son (rē′zən), **1.** cause; motive; explanation: *What is the reason for your behavior?* **2.** think things out: *If you reason carefully, you are sure to solve more of your problems.* **3.** consider; discuss; argue: *Try to reason with him instead of just shouting.* 1 *n.*, 2, 3 *v.*

Red Sea, a narrow sea between Arabia and Africa. See the map in the next column.

Red Sea

reef[1] (rēf),　a narrow ridge of rocks or sand or coral at or near the surface of the water: *The ship was wrecked on a hidden reef.*　*n.*

reef[2] (rēf),　reduce the size of (a sail) by rolling or folding up a part of it.　*v.*

re main (ri mān′),　1. continue in a place; stay: *to remain after school.* 2. last; keep on: *The memory of loved ones remains long after they are gone.* 3. be left: *How much time remains before the game is over?*　*v.*

remains, 1. what is left. 2. a dead body.

re pel lent (ri pel′ənt),　anything that repels or forces back.　*n.*

re pose (ri pōz′),　1. rest; sleep: *a night's repose.* 2. lie at rest: *to repose on the sofa.* 1 *n.*, 2 *v.*, **re posed, re pos ing**

re sist (ri zist′),　act against; strive against; oppose: *A healthy body resists disease.*　*v.*

re sist ance (ri zis′təns),　1. opposition: *Our players didn't offer much resistance to the visiting team.* 2. people who organize and fight for their freedom when their country is occupied or controlled by another country: *the French resistance in World War II.*　*n.*

res o lu tion (rez′ə lü′shən),　1. thing decided on; thing determined: *a New Year's resolution.* 2. act of resolving.　*n.*

re solve (ri zolv′),　1. make up one's mind; determine; decide: *He resolved to do better work in the future.* 2. firmness in carrying out a purpose; determination: *Washington was a man of great resolve.* 3. answer and explain; solve: *His letter resolved all our doubts.* 4. decide by vote: *It was resolved that our school should have a lunchroom.* 1, 3, 4 *v.*, **re solved, re solv ing;** 2 *n.*

re sort (ri zôrt′),　1. go; go often: *Many people resort to the beaches in hot weather.* 2. place people go to: *There are many summer resorts in the mountains.* 3. turn for help: *Many people resort to fans and air conditioners in very hot weather.* 1, 3 *v.*, 2 *n.*

rhythm (riŦH′əm),　movement with a regular repetition of a beat, accent, or the like: *the rhythm of music, the rhythm of one's heartbeats.*　*n.*

rhyth mic (riŦH′mik),　having rhythm; of rhythm; having to do with rhythm.　*adj.*

rig id (rij′id),　1. stiff; firm; not bending: *a rigid support.* 2. strict: *Our club has few rigid rules.*　*adj.*

roan (rōn),　1. yellowish- or reddish-brown sprinkled with gray or white. 2. a roan horse. 1 *adj.*, 2 *n.*

Rou quay rol (rü kā rōl′),　**Be noît** (bə nwä′),　*French.*　*n.*

route (rüt or rout),　1. way to go; road: *Are you driving by the northern route?* 2. send by a certain route; direct: *The policeman routed the traffic down a side street because of the accident.* 3. a selected territory to be covered: *a delivery route.* 1, 3 *n.*, 2 *v.*, **rout ed, rout ing.**

rub ble (rub′əl),　rough broken stones, bricks, etc.　*n.*

Ruf fec (rY fek′),　town in W France.　*n.*

ruf fi an (ruf′ē ən or ruf′yən),　a rough, brutal, or cruel person; bully; rowdy.　*n.*

rug ged (rug′id),　1. rough; uneven: *rugged rocks.* 2. strong; vigorous; sturdy: *Pioneers were rugged people.* 3. difficult; making for a severe test of ability: *Retaking that position from the enemy is going to be rugged.*　*adj.*

Ruhr (rúr),　1. river in W Germany. 2. rich mining and industrial region along this river.　*n.*

sa cred (sā′krid),　1. belonging to or dedicated to God or a god; holy: *In most of India the cow is a sacred animal.* 2. that must not be violated or disregarded: *a sacred promise.*　*adj.*

sa li va (sə lī′və),　the liquid produced by glands in the mouth.　*n.*

---

hat, āge, cãre, fär;　let, bē, tėrm;　it, īce;　hot, gō, ôrder;　oil, out;　cup, pút, rüle, ūse; ch, child;　ng, long;　th, thin;　ŦH, then;　zh, measure;　ə represents *a* in about, *e* in taken, *i* in April, *o* in lemon, *u* in circus.

salve (sav or säv), **1.** a soft, greasy substance put on wounds and sores; healing ointment. **2.** soothe; smooth over: *to salve someone's feelings.* 1 *n.*, 2 *v.*, **salved, salv ing.**

sap (sap), **1.** the life-giving juice of a plant. Sap does for trees what blood does for us. **2.** *Slang.* a silly, stupid person; fool. *n.*

sat el lite (sat′əl īt), **1.** a small planet that revolves around a larger planet. **2.** a sphere or other object launched into an orbit around the earth. **3.** country that is supposedly independent but actually under the control of a more powerful country. *n.*

scamp (skamp), rascal; rogue; worthless person. *n.*

scent (sent), **1.** a smell: *the scent of roses.* **2.** to smell: *The dog scented a rabbit.* **3.** perfume: *She used too much scent.* 1, 3 *n.*, 2 *v.*

Schi a pa rel li (skyä′pä rel′lē), **Gio van ni** (jō vän′nē), 1835-1910, Italian astronomer. *n.*

scho las tic (skə las′tik), of or relating to schools, scholars, or education. *adj.*

sci ence (sī′əns), **1.** knowledge of facts and laws arranged in an orderly system. **2.** branch of such knowledge. Biology, chemistry, and astronomy are sciences. **3.** skill; technique: *the science of boxing. n.*

sci en tif ic (sī′ən tif′ik), **1.** using the facts and laws of science: *a scientific experiment.* **2.** of or having to do with science: *scientific instruments. adj.*

sci en tist (sī′ən tist), person who is trained in, or is familiar with, science. *n.*

scorn (skôrn), **1.** look down upon; despise. **2.** a feeling that a person, animal, or act is mean or low; contempt: *We feel scorn for a traitor.* 1 *v.*, 2 *n.*

scraw ny (skrô′nē), *Informal.* lean; thin; skinny: *Turkeys have scrawny necks. adj.*, **scraw ni er, scraw ni est.**

scur ry (skėr′ē), run quickly; scamper; hurry: *We could hear the mice scurry about in the walls. v.*, **scur ried, scur ry ing.**

sea far ing (sē′fār′ing), going, travelling, or working on the sea: *Sailors are seafaring men. adj.*

sen ate (sen′it), a governing or lawmaking assembly. *n.*

sen sa tion (sen sā′shən), **1.** action of the senses; power to see, hear, feel, taste, smell, etc.: *the sensation of smell.* **2.** strong or excited feeling: *The announcement of war caused a sensation. n.*

sen sa tion al (sen sā′shən əl), **1.** arousing strong or excited feeling. **2.** of the senses; having to do with sensation. *adj.*

sergeant-at-arms or **sergeant at arms,** officer who keeps order in a legislature, law court, etc. *n., pl.* **ser geants-at arms** or **ser geants at arms.**

sham rock (sham′rok), a bright-green leaf composed of three parts. The shamrock is the national emblem of Ireland. *n.*

Shan (shän or shan), **1.** a member of certain tribes of SE Asia, especially in the Shan state of Burma. **2.** the language of this group. **3.** a state of Burma. *n.*

Shamrock

Si am (sī am′), country in SE Asia. *Capital:* Bangkok. The official name of Siam is **Thailand.** *n.* See **Burma** for map.

sil i cate (sil′ə kit or sil′ə kāt), a compound containing silicon with oxygen and an alkali. *n.*

sim plic i ty (sim plis′ə tē), **1.** the state of being simple. **2.** plainness. *n.*

sire (sīr), **1.** the male parent: *The sire of that race horse was a champion.* **2.** be the father of: *My German shepherd dog sired a litter of beautiful puppies.* **3.** title of respect used formerly to a great noble and now to a king. 1, 3 *n.*, 2 *v.*, **sired, sir ing.**

slith er (sliᴛн′ər), **1.** slide down or along a surface, especially unsteadily; go with a sliding motion. **2.** a slithering movement; a slide. 1 *v.*, 2 *n.*

slo gan (slō′gən), word or phrase used by a business, club, political party, etc., to advertise its purpose; motto: *"Service with a smile" was the store's slogan. n.*

smol der (smōl′dər), **1.** burn and smoke without flame: *The campfire smoldered for hours after the blaze died down.* **2.** a slow, smoky burning without flame; smoldering fire. **3.** show feeling that is held back: *His enemy's eyes smoldered.* 1, 3 *v.*, 2 *n.* Also, **smoulder.**

smoul der (smōl′dər), smolder. *v., n.*

Smyr na (smėr′nə), seaport in W Turkey. *n.* Also, **Izmir.**

snipe (snīp), **1.** a marsh bird with a long bill. **2.** shoot at soldiers as a sportsman shoots at game; shoot from under cover. 1 *n.*, *pl.* **snipes** or **snipe;** 2 *v.*, **sniped, snip ing.**

sol der (sod′ər), **1.** metal that can be melted and used for joining or mending. **2.** fasten with solder; mend with solder. 1 *n.*, 2 *v.*

Sol o mon (sol′ə mən), a king of Israel in the tenth century B.C. *n.*

soothe (süŦH), **1.** quiet; calm; comfort: *The mother soothed the child.* **2.** make less painful: *Heat soothes some aches.* *v.*, **soothed, sooth ing.**

sort (sôrt), **1.** kind; class: *What sort of work does he do?* **2.** arrange by kinds or classes; arrange in order: *Sort these cards according to their colors.* 1 *n.*, 2 *v.*

out of sorts, ill, cross, or uncomfortable.

spe cies (spē′shēz), a group of animals or plants that have certain permanent characteristics in common; distinct sort or kind: *A lion is a species of cat.* *n.*, *pl.* **spe cies.**

spec i men (spes′ə mən), one of a group or class taken to show what the others are like; a single part, thing, etc. regarded as an example of its kind. *n.*

spell[1] (spel), **1.** write or say the letters of (a word) in order: *Some words are easy to spell.* **2.** mean: *Delay spells danger.* *v.*, **spelled** or **spelt, spell ing.**

spell[2] (spel), **1.** word or set of words having magic power: *The wicked witch muttered a spell, turning the princess into stone.* **2.** the influence of a word or set of words supposed to have magical powers: *They were under the spell of the wizard.* *n.*

spell[3] (spel), **1.** period of work or duty: *The sailor's spell at the wheel was four hours.* **2.** period or time of anything: *a spell of hot weather.* **3.** *Informal.* work in place of (another) for a while: *spell another person at rowing a boat.* 1, 2 *n.*, 3 *v.*, **spelled, spell ing.**

spell er (spel′ər), **1.** person who spells words. **2.** book for teaching spelling. *n.*

spelling bee, a spelling contest.

spi nal (spī′nəl), of the spine or backbone. The **spinal column** is the backbone. The **spinal cord** is a cord of nerve tissue in the spinal column. *adj.*

spine (spīn), **1.** the backbone. **2.** a thorn or something like it. A cactus has spines; so has a porcupine. *n.*

squall[1] (skwôl), sudden violent gust of wind, often with rain, snow, or sleet. *n.*

squall[2] (skwôl), **1.** cry out loudly; scream violently: *The baby squalled.* **2.** loud, harsh cry: *a baby's angry squall.* 1 *v.*, 2 *n.*

square (skwär), **1.** anything having this shape □, or nearly this shape: *The marching band formed a square.* **2.** having this shape: *a square block of concrete.* **3.** of a given distance on each side of a square: *A room ten feet square measures ten feet on each side.* **4.** open space in a city or town, bounded by streets: *village square.* **5.** straightforward; direct. **6.** solid and strong. 1, 4 *n.*, 2, 3, 5, 6 *adj.*, **squar er, squar est.**

square mile, a measure of area which is equal to a square measuring one mile on each side.

St., 1. Street. **2.** Saint.

stall (stôl), **1.** place in a stable for one animal. **2.** small place for selling things: *At the market, different kinds of foods were sold in different stalls.* **3.** a compartment or booth for taking a shower. **4.** put or keep in a stall: *The horses were safely stalled.* **5.** stop against one's wish: *He stalled the engine of his automobile.* 1-3 *n.*, 4, 5 *v.*

stam pede (stam pēd′), **1.** a sudden scattering or headlong flight of a frightened herd of animals. **2.** scatter or flee in a stampede: *The horses stampeded.* **3.** cause to stampede: *A gunshot stampeded the cattle.* 1 *n.*, 2, 3 *v.* **stam ped ed, stam ped ing.**

star board (stär′bərd or stär′bôrd), the right side of a ship, when facing forward. *n.*

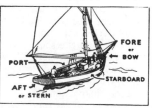

star tle (stär′təl), surprise; frighten suddenly. *v.* **star tled, star tling.**

stave (stāv), **1.** one of the curved pieces of wood which form the sides of a barrel, tub, etc. **2.** stick or staff. *n.*

stealth (stelth), secret or sly action. *n.*

stealthy (stel′thē), done by stealth. *adj.*, **stealth i er, stealth i est.**

stern[1] (stèrn), severe; strict; harsh: *He was stern with his children.* *adj.*

stern[2] (stèrn), the hind part of a ship or boat. *n.* See **starboard** for diagram.

hat, āge, cãre, fär; let, bē, tèrm; it, īce; hot, gō, ôrder; oil, out; cup, put, rüle, ūse; ch, child; ng, long; th, thin; ŦH, then; zh, measure; ə represents *a* in about, *e* in taken, *i* in April, *o* in lemon, *u* in circus.

sti fle (stī′fəl), **1.** stop the breath of; smother: *The smoke stifled the firemen.* **2.** stop; keep back: *to stifle a yawn.* *v.,* **sti fled, sti fling.**

sti fling (stī′fling), that stifles; suffocating. *adj.*

stray (strā), **1.** wander; roam: *Our dog has strayed off somewhere.* **2.** wandering; lost: *a stray cat.* **3.** wanderer; lost animal. **4.** scattered; here and there: *There were a few stray huts along the beach.* 1 *v.,* 2, 4 *adj.,* 3 *n.*

St. Ste phen (stē′vən), an early Christian saint. **St. Stephen's Day** is celebrated on December 26.

stun (stun), **1.** make senseless; knock unconscious: *The champion stunned his opponent.* **2.** daze; bewilder; shock: *She was stunned by the news of her friend's death.* *v.,* **stunned, stun ning.**

sub-, prefix meaning:
1. under; below, as in *subway, sub-zero.*
2. near; nearly, as in *subarctic.*
3. slightly; somewhat, as in *subacid.*
4. of less importance, as in *subcommittee.*

Su ez (sü′əz or sü ez′), **1.** city in NE Egypt, at the S end of the Suez Canal. **2. Isthmus of,** the narrow strip of land between Asia and Africa. It is a part of Egypt. *n.* See **Red Sea** for map.

Suez Canal, canal across the Isthmus of Suez, connecting the Mediterranean and Red seas. See **Red Sea** for map.

surf (sèrf), the waves or swell of the sea breaking on the shore. *n.*

sur vey (sər vā′ for 1, 3; sèr′vā or sər vā′ for 2, 4), **1.** look over; examine: *The buyers surveyed the goods offered for sale.* **2.** examination; inspection: *We were pleased with our first survey of the house.* **3.** measure for size, shape, position, boundaries, etc.: *Land is surveyed before it is divided into house lots.* **4.** a careful measurement: *A survey showed that the northern boundary was not correct.* 1, 3 *v.,* 2, 4 *n., pl.* **sur veys.**

sus pect (səs pekt′ for 1-3; sus′pekt for 4), **1.** imagine to be so; think likely: *The mouse suspected danger and did not touch the cheese.* **2.** believe guilty, false, bad, etc., without proof: *The policeman suspected the thief of lying.* **3.** be suspicious. **4.** person suspected: *The police have arrested a suspect in connection with the robbery.* 1-3 *v.,* 4 *n.*

sus pi cion (səs pish′ən), **1.** suspecting; the state of mind of one who suspects: *to regard somebody with suspicion.* **2.** very small amount: *a suspicion of rust on a rifle.* *n.*

sus pi cious (səs pish′əs), **1.** causing suspicion. **2.** suspecting; feeling suspicion. *adj.*

tah (tä), *Burmese.* *v.*

tail gate, at the rear of a truck, a board or gate that is let down or removed.

tal on (tal′ən), claw of a bird of prey; claw. *n.*

tan (tan), **1.** make (a hide) into leather by soaking in a special liquid. **2.** yellowish brown: *tan shoes.* **3.** make or become brown by exposure to sun and air: *Sun and wind tanned the sailor's face.* **4.** the change in a person's skin caused by being in the sun and air: *to get a tan at the beach.* 1, 3 *v.,* **tanned, tan ning,** 2 *adj.,* 4 *n.*

tan ner (tan′ər), person whose work is tanning hides. *n.*

tat too (ta tü′), **1.** a signal on a bugle, drum, etc., calling soldiers or sailors to their quarters at night. **2.** series of raps, taps, etc.: *The hail beat a tattoo on the windowpane.* *n., pl.* **tat toos.**

tea (tē), **1.** a common drink. **2.** the dried and prepared leaves of a shrub from which this drink is made. **3.** *especially British.* a meal in the late afternoon or early evening, at which tea is commonly served. *n.*

teak (tēk), **1.** a large tree of SE Asia with a hard, yellowish-brown wood. **2.** the wood of this tree. *n.*

tem ple[1] (tem′pl), a building used for the service or worship of a god or gods: *Many ancient Greek temples are still standing.* *n.*

tem ple[2] (tem′pl), the flattened part on either side of the forehead. *n.*

tend[1] (tend), be apt; incline (to): *Fruit tends to decay. Homes tend to use more electricity.* *v.*

tend[2] (tend), take care of; look after: *A nurse tends the sick.* *v.*

ter mi nal (tèr′mə nl), **1.** at the end; forming the end. A terminal bud grows at the end of a stem. **2.** either end of a railroad, trucking line, or air line. 1 *adj.,* 2 *n.*

the a tre or **the a ter** (thē′ə tər), place where plays are acted; place where motion pictures are shown.

the at ri cal (thē at′rə kəl), of or having to do with the theatre or actors. *a dj.*
theatricals, stage performances, especially cially as given by amateurs.

the o ry (thē′ə rē), explanation; explanation based on thought; explanation based on observation and reasoning: *There were several theories about the way in which the fire started.* *n., pl.* **the o ries.**

thick et (thik′it), shrubs, bushes, or small trees growing close together. *n.*

throng (thrông), **1.** a crowd; a multitude. **2.** to crowd; fill with a crowd: *People thronged the theatre to see the famous actress.* 1 *n.,* 2 *v.*

Ti bet (ti bet′), a country in central Asia, now under Chinese control. *n.*

til ler (til′ər), **1.** bar or handle used to turn the rudder in steering a boat. **2.** bar used for steering an early model of automobile. *n.*

tim ber (tim′bər), **1.** wood for building and making things. **2.** large piece of wood used in building. Beams and rafters are timbers. **3.** growing trees; forests: *Half of his land is covered with timber.* **4.** cover, support, or furnish with timber: *to timber a roof.* 1-3 *n.,* 4 *v.*

tin der box (tin′dər boks′), **1.** box for holding material used to start a fire. **2.** object or place that can catch fire easily. *n.*

tink er (tingk′ər), **1.** man who mends pots, pans, etc. **2.** work or repair in an unskilled way: *He likes to tinker with gadgets.* 1 *n.,* 2 *v.*

to ken (tō′kən), **1.** a mark or sign (of something): *Black is a token of mourning.* **2.** piece of metal used in place of money: *bus token. n.*

Tours (túr), city in W France. *n.*

trade mark (trād′märk′), **1.** a mark, picture, name, or letters used by a manufacturer, merchant, etc., to distinguish the goods or services he sells from the goods or services of others. **2.** to label with a trademark: *Every baseball glove that our company offers for sale is trademarked.* 1 *n.,* 2 *v.*

tra di tion (trə dish′ən), the handing down of beliefs, opinions, customs, stories, etc., from parents to children. *n.*

tra di tion al (trə dish′ən əl), according to tradition; customary: *Turkey is a traditional Thanksgiving dish. adj.*

tra di tion al ly (trə dish′ən əl ē), according to tradition; customarily: *We traditionally eat turkey on Thanksgiving. adv.*

trans mis sion (trans mish′ən or tranz-mish′en), **1.** a sending over; passing on; passing along; letting through. **2.** the passage through space or radio waves from the transmitting station to the receiving station. *n.*

tread (tred), **1.** walk; step; set the foot down: *Don't tread on the flowers.* **2.** act or sound of treading: *the tread of marching feet.* **3.** the part of a wheel or tire that touches the ground. 1 *v.,* **trod, trod den** or **trod, tread ing;** 2, 3 *n.*

tread water, keep oneself from sinking by moving the feet up and down.

tri fle (trī′fəl), **1.** thing having little value or importance: *He purchased the island from the Indians for beads and other trifles.* **2.** small amount; little bit. **3.** play or toy (with): *He trifled with his pencil and pen.* 1, 2 *n.,* 3 *v.,* **tri fled, tri fling.**

trot line
(trot′līn′),
in fishing, a
long line to
which bait-
ed hooks are
attached at
different places. *n.*

Trotline

trum pet (trum′pit), **1.** a musical wind instrument that has a powerful tone. **2.** blow a trumpet. **3.** make a sound like a trumpet: *The elephant trumpeted.* 1 *n.,* 2, 3 *v.*

tur ret (tėr′it), **1.** a small tower, often on the corner of a building. **2.** cockpit in a military plane, usually enclosed by plastic material and sometimes containing movable guns. *n.*

Ul fi us (ul′fē əs). *n.*

Ulm (úlm), street in Paris. *n.*

un-, prefix meaning:
1. not, as in *undimmed, untended.*
2. do the opposite of, as in *unfasten.*

un prec e dent ed (un pres′ə den′tid or un prē′sə den′tid), never done before; never known before; having no precedent. *adj.*

ur gen cy (ėr′jən sē), urgent character; urgent quality. *n., pl.* **ur gen cies.**

ur gent (ėr′jənt), demanding immediate action or attention: *an urgent message. adj.*

Uther (ū′thər). *n.*

---

hat, āge, cãre, fär; let, bē, tėrm; it, īce; hot, gō, ôrder; oil, out; cup, pút, rüle, ūse; ch, child; ng, long; th, thin; ᴛн, then; zh, measure; ə represents *a* in about, *e* in taken, *i* in April, *o* in lemon, *u* in circus.

vac cine (vak′sēn or vak′sin), a preparation of disease germs, or the like, which is used to prevent a particular disease: *Polio vaccine is used to prevent polio.* *n.*

Val dez (val′dēz or val dēz′), seaport in S Alaska. *n.*

ven ture (ven′chər), **1.** a risky or daring undertaking: *He lost a fortune in a business venture.* **2.** expose to risk or danger: *Men venture their lives in war.* **3.** dare: *No one ventured to interrupt the speaker.* **4.** dare to come or go: *He ventured onto the thin ice and fell through.* 1 *n.*, 2-4 *v.*, **ven tured, ven tur ing.**

vig or (vig′ər), active strength or force; healthy energy or power. *n.*

vi rus (vi′rəs), any of a group of substances, probably living, that cause disease in man or animals. *n.*

Vlad i vos tok (vlad′ə vos tok′ or vlad′-ə vos′tok), seaport on Sea of Japan in SE Soviet Union. *n.*

Vos khod (vəs Hôd′), *Russian.* *n.*

vo ya geur (voi′ə zhėr′; *French,* vwä yä-zhœr′), **1.** a boatman, especially a French Canadian, in the service of the early fur-trading companies. **2.** a boatman or woodsman of the Canadian forests, esp. in the North. *n.*

wah (wä), *Burmese.* exclamation used to express excitement, pride, disagreement, disapproval, etc. *interj.*

wal low (wol′ō), **1.** roll about: *The pigs wallowed in the mud.* **2.** place where an animal wallows. 1 *v.*, 2 *n.*

Water buffalo

water buffalo, the common buffalo of Asia and the Philippines.

weap on (wep′ən), any instrument used in fighting; means of attack or defence. Swords, spears, arrows, clubs, guns, etc., are weapons. *n.*

wea sel (wē′zəl), a small animal with a long slender body, that feeds on rats, mice, birds and their eggs, etc. *n.*

Weasel (6 to 8 in. long, without the tail)

weave (wēv), **1.** form (threads or strips) into a thing or fabric. People weave thread into cloth, straw into hats, and reeds into baskets. **2.** method or pattern of weaving: *a coarse weave, a fine weave.* 1 *v.*, **wove** or *(Rare)* **weaved, wo ven** or **wove, weav ing;** 2 *n.*

weav er bird (wēv′ər bėrd′), a bird of Asia, Africa, and Australia, that weaves its nest. *n.*

weird (wird), mysterious; wild; strange. *adj.*

Wen ces las (wen′səs lôs), 903?-935, Duke and patron saint of Bohemia. *n.*

wil low (wil′ō), **1.** tree or shrub with tough, slender branches and narrow leaves. The branches of most willows bend easily. **2.** made of willow. 1 *n.*, 2 *adj.*

wince (wins), draw back suddenly; flinch slightly: *The boy winced at the sight of the dentist's drill.* *v.*, **winced, winc ing.**

Weeping willow

wind[1] (wind), **1.** air in motion: *a strong wind.* **2.** breath; power of breathing: *A long-distance runner needs good wind.* *n.*

wind[2] (wīnd), **1.** move this way and that: *a path that winds through the woods.* **2.** twist or turn around something: *to wind a bandage around a finger.* **3.** make (some machine) go by turning some part of it: *to wind a clock.* *v.*, **wound, wind ing.**

wind ward (wind′wərd), **1.** toward the wind. **2.** the side toward the wind. 1 *adv.*, 2 *n.*

wist ful (wist′fəl), longing; yearning: *A child stood looking with wistful eyes at the toys in the window.* *adj.*

with er (wiᴛʜ′ər), **1.** make or become dry and lifeless; shrivel: *Flowers wither after they are cut.* **2.** cause to feel ashamed or confused: *She withered him with a look.* *v.*

World War, 1. World War I lasted from 1914 to 1918. Great Britain, France, Russia, the United States, and their allies were on one side; Germany, Austria-Hungary, and their allies were on the other side. **2. World War II** lasted from 1939 to 1945. Great Britain, the United States, the Soviet Union, and their allies were on one side; Germany, Italy, Japan, and their allies were on the other side.

wor ship (wèr'ship), **1.** great honor and respect for God or a god. **2.** pay great honor and respect to God or a god. **3.** great love and admiration: *hero worship.* **4.** have great love and admiration for: *She worships her older brother.* 1, 3 *n.*, 2, 4 *v.*, **wor shiped, wor ship ing** or *especially British*, **worshipped, wor ship ping.**

wound[1] (wünd), **1.** a hurt or injury caused by cutting, stabbing, shooting, etc.: *a knife wound.* **2.** injure by cutting, stabbing, shooting, etc.; hurt. 1 *n.*, 2 *v.*

wound[2] (wound). See wind[2]. *She wound the string into a ball. It is wound too loosely. past and past participle of* wind[2]. *v.*

yearn (yèrn),   feel a longing or desire; desire earnestly: *He yearns for home.* *v.*

yes ter year (yes'tər yēr'),   *Archaic* or *Poetic.* last year; some year before this.

yo kel (yō'kl),   a country fellow. *n.*

ze ro (zir'ō), **1.** naught; 0: *There are three zeros in 40,006.* **2.** temperature that registers zero on the scale of a thermometer. **3.** zero hour. *n., pl.* **ze ros** or **ze roes.**

zero hour,   time set for beginning an attack, etc.

zo ol o gy (zō ol'ə jē),   the science of animals; the study of animals and animal life. *n.*

---

hat, āge, cāre, fär;   let, bē, tèrm;   it, īce;   hot, gō, ôrder;   oil, out;   cup, pùt, rüle, ūse; ch, child;   ng, long;   th, thin;   ₮H, then;   zh, measure;   ə represents *a* in about, *e* in taken, *i* in April, *o* in lemon, *u* in circus.

About This Book

Open Highways, Book Six, is designed to give the children who read it extra help in improving their reading competence. Because of the gradually increasing reading difficulty and the systematic reteaching of basic skills, pupils should conclude the book with feelings of success and satisfaction.

The name *Open Highways* is significant. All barriers to steady progress have been removed along this highway to reading enjoyment and competence. Once a girl or a boy is on the way, the going will be so easy and the distance covered so great that the child can make up lost time and perhaps overtake classmates following a parallel route.

A *Guidebook,* a *Think-and-Do Book,* and a *Reading Test* accompany *Open Highways,* Book Six. The *Guidebook* suggests procedures for reteaching, reviewing, and reinforcing basic skills according to individual and group needs. The *Think-and-Do Book* provides for inventory, diagnosis, practice, and evaluation of these basic skills. At the halfway point the *Think-and-Do Book* contains an informal test that will aid in evaluating progress. The *Reading Test* measures how well children have mastered the skills emphasized in The Open Highways Program for grade six.

Ease and speed along the open highway to reading are promoted through the high interest and widely varied nature of the selections in Book Six, as well as the method of organizing these materials. Selections in *Open Highways,* Book Six, are grouped in sections rather than units arranged around themes as are the materials in *Cavalcades,* The New Basic Reader for sixth grade. Each of the first five sections of *Open Highways,* Book Six, includes many areas of interest. Topics change often and dramatically. If a truck roadeo and the special vocabulary of truck drivers have little appeal to some boys and girls, perhaps the next topic—sports, particularly football—will arouse enthusiasm. If Australian holiday customs and animals seem less than fascinating, perhaps achievements in space or knights in armor may be of greater interest. Aircraft of World War II may excite some children more or less than hunting wild game with Frank Buck.

The selections in each of the first five sections of *Open Highways,* Book Six, vary in length, and have tucked among them jokes and cartoons for sheer enjoyment and for sharing with friends. Now and again

478

readers will find directions for making something—a recipe for fudge, foolproof and strictly noncook, for example. The selections also vary in form—newspaper articles, comic-strip presentations, a folk song with music, a short play, poems both funny and serious, photographic essays. And of course there are stories—stories that dip into history, adventure in Canada and abroad, and favorites such as "The Case of the Sensational Scent," reprinted from Robert McCloskey's *Home Price*.

Here and there in *Open Highways*, Book Six, the reader will find headnotes that give needed background information and that set purposes for reading, questions to be answered and discussed, and lists of books to read. Best of all, the reader will find as he progresses through the book that he is becoming a more critical thinker and reader at the same time that he is accumulating a stock of anecdotes and information that almost anyone would like to have. How many people know, for example, that the first auto race of all time was run in France, from Paris to Bordeaux, in 1895 and that the winning car had a tiller instead of a steering wheel?

Open Highways, Book Six, ends with the reprint of a complete book, *Burma Boy*. While enjoying this adventure in the Burmese jungle, girls and boys will apply major skills reviewed or retaught during the reading of the first five sections of the book.

Through the appeal, range, and diversity of its contents, through its systematic reteaching of reading skills, including use of a dictionary, and through reorienting of attitudes, The Open Highways Program encourages discouraged readers. By giving them a new lease on reading, the program frees them for an education that is not of necessity substandard, and opens for them the variegated world of newspapers, magazines, and books.

Acknowledgments

Grateful acknowledgment is hereby given for the right to adapt and use the following copyright material:

"A Roadeo! What's That?" adapted from "A Truck Roadeo." Published in *Trucks and Things You'll Want to Know about Them* by the American Trucking Association.

"Truck Drivers' Dictionary" reprinted from "Trucking Terms." Published in *Truck Drivers' Dictionary* by the American Trucking Association.

"Adventures of Thomas O'Toole" adapted from "O'Toole Discovers America" by D. R. Kearns in *Trailblazers for Juniors*, copyright 1956 by W. L. Jenkins. Published by the Westminster Press. Although an extensive search has been made, the editors of this book have been unable to locate D. R. Kearns, author and copyright owner of "O'Toole Discovers America."

"The King and the Cats" retold by Nancy Ford. Reprinted by special permission from the estate of the author and *Jack and Jill.* © 1956 The Curtis Publishing Company.

"Louis Pasteur" adapted from *Louis Pasteur, Scientist* with the co-operation of the Metropolitan Life Insurance Company.

"A Spear for Omar" by Heddy Rado. Published in *Story Parade* by Story Parade, Inc. Adapted and reprinted by permission of the author.

"Code of Signals for Football Officials" is based on information and diagrams in *The Official Playing Rules for Canadian Football, 1969*, published by the Canadian Football League.

"An Interview with Russ Jackson" was prepared with the kind co-operation of Mr. Russ Jackson.

"The Voyageurs." The author of "The Voyageurs" and of "The Great Canadian Canoe Race" is indebted to *The Voyageur* by Grace Lee Nute as a source of reference. (Reprint edition, copyright, 1955 by the Minnesota Historical Society, Saint Paul.)

"En roulant ma boule." The English translation by Edith Fowke of this French Canadian folk song appears in *Folk Songs of Canada* by Edith Fowke and Richard Johnston published by Waterloo Music Company, Ltd.

The illustrations in this book are by:

Phoebe Moore (cover); Bill Carr (pp. 8-13); Carl Carter, Jr. (pp. 14-16); Ken Crabtree (pp. 17-18); Richard E. Loehle (pp. 19-30, 302-312); Leo Rich (pp. 113-114); Steve Karall (pp. 46-47, 61-62, 182, 193-194); Bill Chambers (pp. 48-51); Dick Wiley (pp. 52-60); Rod Ruth (pp. 63-69, 167-169, 357-375); Justin Wager (pp. 70-75); Lynn Hutchinson (pp. 95-97, 242-253); Charles A. McBarron (pp. 314-319); Bob Brunton (pp. 98-104); Chuck Kessler (pp. 105-112); Wendell Kling (pp. 115-124); George Suyeoka (pp. 125-129, 376-377); Al Stine (pp. 138-145); Shannon Stirnweis (pp. 150-165); Merle Smith (pp. 174-182); Jack Wallen (pp. 195-209); Fernando Dias Da Silva (pp. 212-221); Harley Shelton (pp. 222-224, 297, 313); Jack Smith (pp. 226-241); Jean Galt (pp. 254-255); Ted Carr (pp. 277-278); Larry Fredericks (pp. 279-289); Stan Fleming (pp. 320-327); Parviz Sadighian (pp. 338-349).

The photographs for "Something to Sing About" (pp. 242-253) are by Freeman Patterson.

Reader

Open Highways 6

copy 11